●●●POWER ENGINEERING

Third Class

Part B1

Edition 2.0

2015

PanGlobal
TRAINING SYSTEMS

Published by PanGlobal Training Systems Ltd.
Publisher of Power Engineering Training Systems Courseware

The material in this series is aligned with Third Class Syllabus, dated January 2014.
For more info visit http://www.sopeec.org/Syllabus/SyllabusThirdClass.pdf

Address all inquiries to:
PanGlobal Training Systems
1301 – 16 Ave. NW, Calgary, AB, Canada. T2M 0L4

This curriculum is approved by the SOPEEC, Standardization of Power Engineering Examinations Committee and ACI, Canadian Association of Chief Inspectors as meeting the standard for preparation for the National Third Class Syllabus.

This curriculum is endorsed by the Canadian Institute of Power Engineers (IPE).

Cover image courtesy of TransAlta Corporation. The image is a section of the 575-megawatt (MW) gas-fired facility at Transalta's Sarnia Regional Cogeneration Plant, located in Sarnia, Ontario.

We would like to acknowledge all Power Engineering Instructors who contributed to Edition 2.0 of the 3rd Class with special thanks to the Power Engineering instructors of SAIT, NAIT & BCIT for their formal reviews.

LEGAL NOTICE

Printed by Data Group
Third Class - Part B1
Edition 2.0, February 2015
ISBN13: 978-1-926900-00-1

For information on this and other products visit our website located at **www.powerengineering.org**
Any technical or editorial errors may also be reported on our website by using our electronic Corrections Submissions Form or faxing suggested corrections to 1-403-284-8863.

1301 16th Ave. NW
Calgary, Alberta
T2M 0L4

Third Class
Part B1
Edition 2.0

Table of Contents

CHAPTER 1

Watertube Boiler Designs

LEARNING OUTCOME

When you complete this chapter you should be able to:

Describe common designs, configurations and circulation patterns for modern bent-tube watertube boilers and steam generators and explain how boilers are rated.

LEARNING OBJECTIVES

Here is what you should be able to do when you complete each objective:

1. Explain the difference between packaged, shop assembled, and field-erected watertube boilers. Explain how boilers are rated.

2. Explain the process of water circulation in a watertube boiler and the factors that influence circulation.

3. Identify examples of and describe the A, O, and D design configurations and explain the water and gas circulation patterns for each. Define integral furnace.

4. Define a steam-generating unit, identify oil and gas-fired units, and explain the components, heating surfaces, and flow patterns through a typical unit. State typical temperatures throughout the unit.

5. Differentiate between critical and super-critical boilers.

6. Explain the purpose and advantage of forced circulation and describe the flow through a typical controlled circulation boiler.

7. Explain the purpose and design of a once-through boiler.

OBJECTIVE 1

Explain the difference between packaged, shop assembled, and field-erected watertube boilers. Explain how boilers are rated.

PACKAGED WATERTUBE BOILER

A packaged watertube boiler is assembled in a factory and leaves the factory as a complete package. It is shipped complete with fuel burning equipment, mechanical draft equipment, and automatic controls and accessories. These units have water-cooled furnaces and the air for combustion is supplied under pressure from a forced draft fan. A steel casing covers the outside of the boiler and furnace and prevents combustion gas leakage into the boiler room. A simple skid-type steel foundation is included and the boiler is bottom-supported.

Capacities range from 2300 kg to over 65 000 kg of steam per hour and operating pressures usually range up to 1700 kPa although in some cases may be over 6200 kPa.

Figure 1 shows a cutaway view of a two-drum packaged water tube boiler. The water-cooled furnace construction and the compact design of the unit with its steel clad exterior are clearly shown.

Figure 1	Two-Drum Packaged Boiler

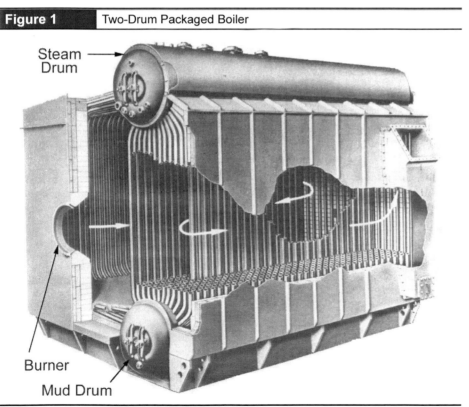

The main advantage of the packaged boiler is its low cost. The manufacturing costs are lower as the entire boiler is built and assembled in the factory rather than in the field. Shipping costs are lower if the boiler is sent as a unit rather than in parts. Because the packaged boiler is shipped by truck or rail car, the width and height are somewhat standard for any particular design of boiler. Boiler length can be changed to create different capacities. Figure 2 shows a 100 000 kg/h packaged boiler.

Figure 2 B&W Shop Assembled Boiler

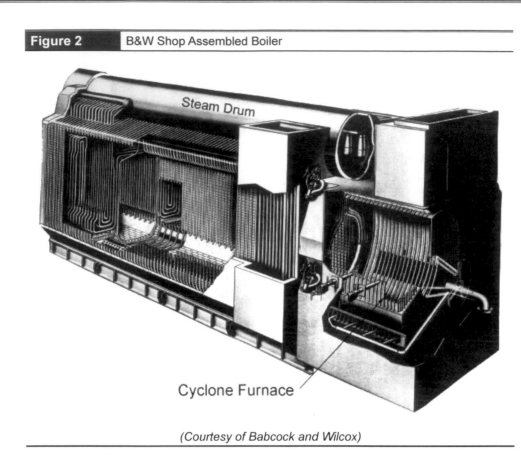

(Courtesy of Babcock and Wilcox)

Shop Assembled Watertube Boiler

"Shop-assembled" could easily be confused with "packaged". The difference is mainly in the size and the amount of shop assembly that occurs. A simple distinction is that a shop-assembled boiler cannot be ordered "off the shelf"; they are generally assembled to the exact specifications provided by the purchaser.

Shop-assembled units are generally larger and cannot necessarily be shipped from the assembly shop as a single unit. However, the larger, main sections of the boiler are assembled in the shop. The steam generating section is fully assembled, with all tube/drum/header connections complete. The refractory and outer casings may or may not be installed. Burner and draft equipment, including exhaust stack, may be constructed as separate assemblies. External controls and devices will usually be installed later.

The various sections are usually shipped separately to the purchaser's site, where final assembly occurs. Site construction time is limited to this final assembly, plus any refractory, casing, control, or auxiliary attachments. Testing and approval of the boiler than occurs on site.

Field Erected Watertube Boilers

Boilers too large for transport to the site in one piece must be field erected. Large sections of water wall, superheaters and economizers may be constructed in the manufacturer's plant and then shipped to the site for assembly.

This on-site assembly will include erecting all the support structures, hanging the drums and headers in place, and attaching all tube sections by welding, rolling, etc. Burners, air and exhaust ductwork, internal and external refractory and insulation, and outer casings must be installed. Steam drum internals are installed after all tubes have been attached. All external auxiliaries, such as draft fans, air heaters, safety devices, and controls are then attached. Finally, on-site testing, approvals and commissioning are done.

Most field erected boilers have outputs of 150 000 kg/h or more. However, there are some applications where a smaller field-erected boiler is the best solution. Figure 3 is an example of a smaller field-erected watertube boiler.

Arrows on the main body of the sketch show the gas path through the unit. The cross-flow design provides maximum heat absorption and virtual uniformity of temperature and flow of combustion gas across the width of the heating surface. Arrows to the bottom right show air inlet to a duct under the furnace floor tubes. This construction permits less overall unit height than is attainable in units using overhead air ducts. Capacities range up to 163 000 kg/h steam at 6550 kPa and 480°C. Fuel for this model of boiler can be natural gas or oil. However, other field erected boilers may be designed for other fuels, including coal, biomass, etc.

Figure 3	Field Erected C-E Watertube Boiler
	C-E VU 60 Boiler Fired by C-E Type R Horizontal Burners

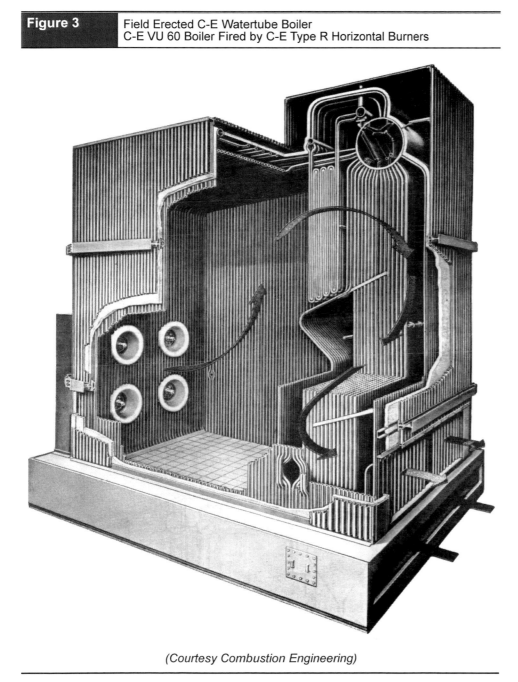

(Courtesy Combustion Engineering)

Boiler Ratings

Regulations made under various provincial legislative acts specify for three different methods for calculating the output or rating of a boiler:

1. One square metre of heating surface equals 10 kilowatts. Heating surface is the total area of all surfaces through which heat is transferred from the furnace or combustion gases to the water. The heating surface of a boiler must be determined by computing the area of the surface involved in square metres and where a computation is to be made of a curved surface, the surface having the greater radius shall be taken.

2. Where electric power is used as the heating source, the boiler rating shall be the maximum kilowatt rating of the heating element.

3. Where neither of the above methods is applicable, an hourly boiler output of 36 megajoules is equivalent to 10 kilowatts.

Steam Capacity

The steam capacity of a boiler is expressed in kilograms of steam per hour. This is not a true measure of the thermal energy supplied by the boiler because other factors, such as steam quality, steam temperature, and feedwater temperature must be considered.

Steam generator capacities are described in terms of maximum continuous steam output, in kg/h, at design steam temperature and pressure. Where the boiler provides its entire steam supply to an electric generating unit (i.e., to a steam turbine driving a generator) the output of the boiler is often expressed in terms of the power output of the generator (for example a 300 megawatt boiler).

OBJECTIVE 2

Explain the process of water circulation in a watertube boiler and the factors that influence circulation.

CIRCULATION IN WATERTUBE BOILERS

In order for the water to obtain heat from the heating surfaces of the tubes, there must be sufficient and positive circulation of water within the tubes. Circulation in a boiler refers to the flow of water through the boiler tubes. In a watertube boiler circulation is directed through definite paths by arranging the tubes to form circuits. The tubes are divided into two categories: downcomers and risers as shown in Figure 4.

The downcomers are located in the relatively cooler sections of the boiler, removed from the furnace. The risers are located in the hottest zones of the boiler, exposed directly to radiant heat of the furnace or to the very hot combustion gases from the furnace.

The water within the downcomers is at or slightly below saturation temperature and is much denser than the steam-water mixture within the riser tubes. Positive flow or circulation is produced as the denser water falls in the downcomers and pushes the less dense water and steam upwards in the risers.

Figure 4	Circulation in Watertube Boilers

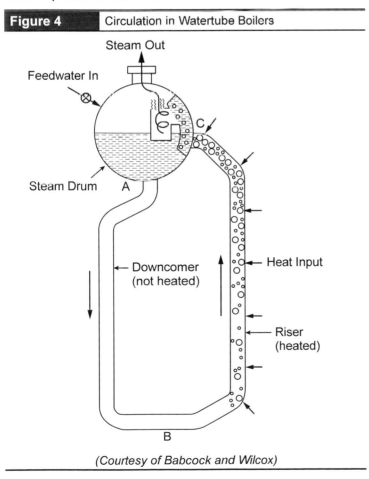

(Courtesy of Babcock and Wilcox)

Figure 5 is a simplification of the circulation flows in a typical boiler. Most downcomers run vertically between the steam drum and the mud drum. Water flows from the mud drum to the bottom of the wall sections. The flow then proceeds up the walls where the tubes are exposed to the high temperatures of the furnace and steam bubbles are created in the water. The flow goes back to the steam drum, where the steam separating equipment is located.

The steam separating equipment separates the steam from the steam/water mixture. The steam then exits the steam drum via the tubes coming off the top of the drum. These tubes lead to the superheater section or to the steam outlet header, depending on the boiler design. The water is routed back to the downcomers for another pass through the heated sections of the boiler.

Figure 5	Circulation in a Watertube Package Boiler

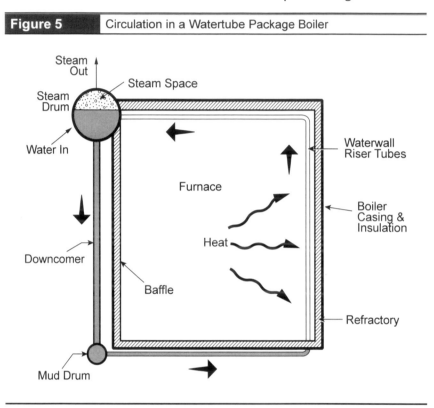

Factors that Influence Natural Circulation

There are several factors that influence the natural circulation (circulation not aided by a pump) in a watertube boiler. These are:

1. The height of the steam drum above the bottom drum or header. The greater the height of the steam drum the greater the difference in mass between the risers and downcomers. The greater difference in mass results in a larger differential pressure and increased flow, or circulation.

2. The amount of heat applied to the tube. The hotter the tube becomes, the more steam bubbles are formed, creating more mass differential and thus more circulation.

3. The operating pressure of the boiler. As boiler pressures increase, the density of the steam increases. There is then less difference between the density of the water in the downcomers and the density of the steam water mixture in the risers. Therefore, as the operating pressure increases, the natural circulation decreases. Natural circulation boilers are limited to pressures below 21 000 kPa.

4. The cleanliness of the tubes. Dirty heating surfaces on either the fireside or the steamside will reduce heat transfer. This results in less steam being produced in the riser tubes and, therefore, circulation is reduced. The deposits also physically restrict the flow of water.

OBJECTIVE 3

Identify examples of and describe the A, D, and O design configurations and explain the water and gas circulation patterns for each. Define integral furnace.

A-TYPE BOILER

Most boilers follow one of the structural configurations shown in Figures 6, 7 and 8. The A-type has two small lower drums or headers. The upper drum is larger to permit separation of water and steam. Most steam production occurs in the central furnace wall tubes.

A three-drum, A-type, packaged boiler is shown in Figure 6.

The steam drum is centered above the two mud drums, forming an "A" shape. Bent tubes running from the upper steam drum to the two lower mud drums form the furnace enclosure. Burner, draft fan, control panel and other accessories are mounted on the boiler front.

Figure 6	A-Type Boiler

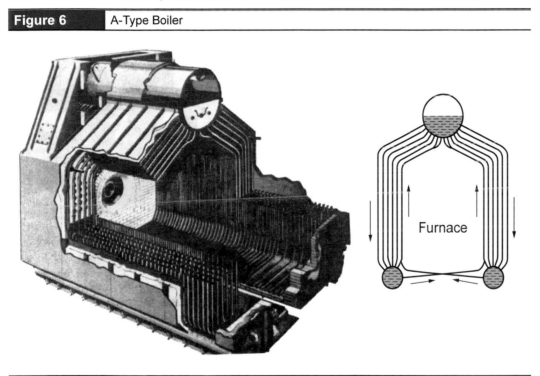

D-Type Boiler

The D-type boiler, as shown in Figure 7 has two drums. Bent tubes on one side of the boiler generating bank of tubes form a water-cooled furnace. This forms the "D", which encloses the furnace. In this figure, the burner or burners are located at one end of the furnace section, firing parallel to the drums. In other D-type configurations the burner(s) may be located in the side wall (ie. the curved side of the "D"), firing perpendicular to the drums. In either case, the burner wall is also covered with tubes and the tubes are bent around the burner opening. The back wall, or target wall, usually has refractory with some tubes for cooling.

The more active steaming tubes become risers and enter the drum near the water line. Superheaters and economizers can be added to the D-type radiant or convection zone with relative ease.

Figure 7	D-Type Boiler

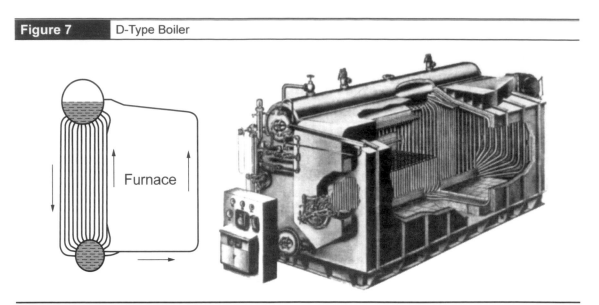

O-Type Boiler

The O-type boiler has an upper and a lower drum. The tubes connecting these two drums are arranged in an "O" shape which surrounds a water-cooled furnace. The O-type, as seen in Figure 8, has a symmetrical design but exposes the least tube surface to radiant heat.

Figure 8	O-Type Boiler

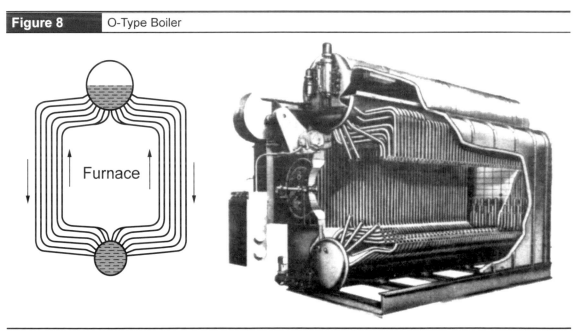

Manufacturers tend to standardize package boiler designs with regard to the outside dimensions of width and height and to vary the length according to the required boiler output rating. This is largely determined by the size limitations imposed on rail or road transportation.

Circulation

In each of the three designs, steam bubbles form in the hottest tubes and rise to the steam drum, where the steam is separated out of the water and steam mixture. Circulation is maintained by water returning to the mud drum through the cooler tubes. The hotter tubes, risers, are the ones in the radiant area of the furnace and the hottest areas of the generating bank of tubes.

The flue gas flow through these units is not always the same. Typically the burners are on one end of the furnace. The combustion gases reach the other end of the furnace and are directed back through the generating bank of tubes, toward the burner end of the boiler. The flue gas is partially cooled at this point before entering the economizer to heat the incoming feed water. This is a two pass of flue gas design. Often more than two passes can be used.

Figure 9 shows the flue gas path of a packaged boiler. The flow path in this design is a cross flow design. The gases make three passes across the width of the boiler. In the furnace they provide radiant heat for the waterwall tubes. From the furnace they first reach the screen tubes, which absorb most of the remaining radiant heat and "screen" the superheater tubes. The gas passes through the superheater bank of tubes, and then is directed by baffles to make two passes through the generating tubes before exiting the boiler.

Figure 9	Flue Gas Flow Through an Integral Furnace D-Type Boiler

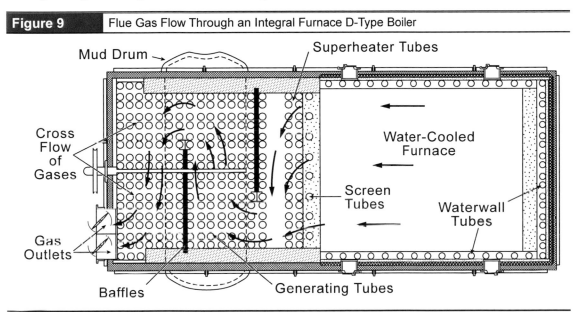

Since these types of boilers (A, D, and O) have furnaces cooled by watertubes that line the furnace walls, they are also referred to as "integral furnace" boilers. That is, the furnace wall tubes are an integral part of the boiler circulation circuit.

OBJECTIVE 4

Define a steam generating unit, identify oil and gas-fired units, and explain the components, heating surfaces, and flow patterns through a typical unit. State typical temperatures throughout the unit.

STEAM GENERATING UNITS

A steam generating unit consists of several elements, all of which contribute to the production of steam, usually at high temperature and high pressure, which is generally used to supply large turbines. The elements of a typical steam generator include the boiler, superheater, reheater, economizer, air heater, fuel equipment, draft fans, and (in solid fuel units) ash removal equipment.

- The **boiler** itself consists of the sections where water is converted into steam. Therefore, the term "boiler" is often used to describe the entire generating unit.

- The temperature of steam from the boiler section is increased above the saturation point by the addition of sensible heat in the **superheater** section. When superheated steam is used to drive a large turbine the plant efficiency is higher and there is a reduction in the amount of steam condensing in the lower pressure stages of the turbine.

- In many larger units there is a heating section called a **reheater** in which steam that has passed through a steam turbine (or part way through the turbine), where it has cooled considerably, is brought back to the reheater and heated back to its original superheated temperature.

- Feed-water entering the boiler section first passes through the **economizer** section where it is heated by the combustion gases leaving the boiler. In this way some of the heat that would otherwise pass out the stack is recovered. Normally the feed-water is heated to within 20°C of the boiler water temperature. A temperature of 280-300°C would be normal for a drum temperature of 320°C.

- Combustion air for the burners is preheated to 350°C in the **air preheater** section by combustion gases leaving the economizer section. In this way more heat is recovered from the gases before they reach the stack. The heated air improves combustion efficiency. Where pulverized coal is the most economical fuel to use, coal pulverizers are included as part of the **fuel-burning equipment**.

- Generally two types of **draft fans** are used. A forced draft fan supplies air to the air preheater. The preheated air (350°C) for combustion goes to the coal pulverizers and to the burners. An induced draft fan exhausts the combustion gases (170°C) from the air heater to the stack. Ash from the combustion of the coal accumulates in the hopper at the bottom of the furnace. Removal of the ash from the unit often involves the use of pneumatic or hydraulic equipment.

Figure 10 shows the arrangement of one steam-generating unit.

Steam is produced from water in the furnace wall tubes and is separated from the water in the steam drum. The temperature of the saturated steam is the saturation temperature for the operating pressure of the steam generator.

The saturated steam passes from the steam drum to the primary convection superheater and then to the radiant superheater. The temperature of the steam is progressively increased in both of these sections to a typical, final temperature (for large units) of +/- 538°C.

The air for combustion is preheated in the air heater before going to the burners.

Notice, this particular unit does not have a reheater.

Figure 10   Arrangement of Steam Generating Unit

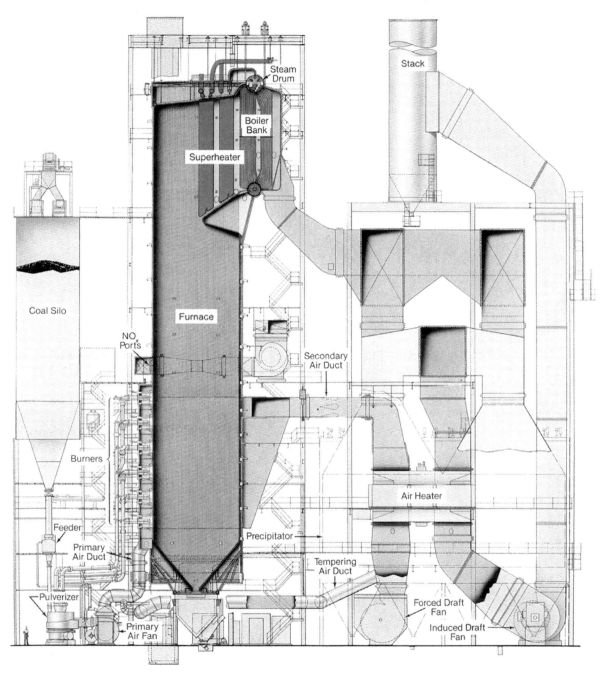

(Courtesy of Babcock and Wilcox)

Figure 11 shows another steam generator design, this one fired on pulverized coal with steam capacity of 136 000 kg per hour or higher.

It has a reheater and two superheater sections. Steam from the drum goes to the primary (convection) superheater first and then to the secondary (radiant) superheater.

The superheated steam then passes to the high-pressure stages of a turbine. As the steam expands through the turbine stages its temperature and pressure drops. After passing through a certain number of stages the steam is returned to the **reheater section** of the steam generator. In the reheater section, the temperature of the steam is raised to approximately the original superheat temperature (+/-538°C). The steam then leaves the reheater and goes back to the remaining stages of the turbine.

The path of the combustion gases in Figure 11 is indicated by arrows showing the travel through furnace, secondary superheater, reheater, primary superheater, economizer, air heater and finally to the induced draft fan, which discharges to the stack. The air from the forced draft fan passes through the air heater to the burners.

Figure 11	Pulverized Coal-Fired Steam Generator

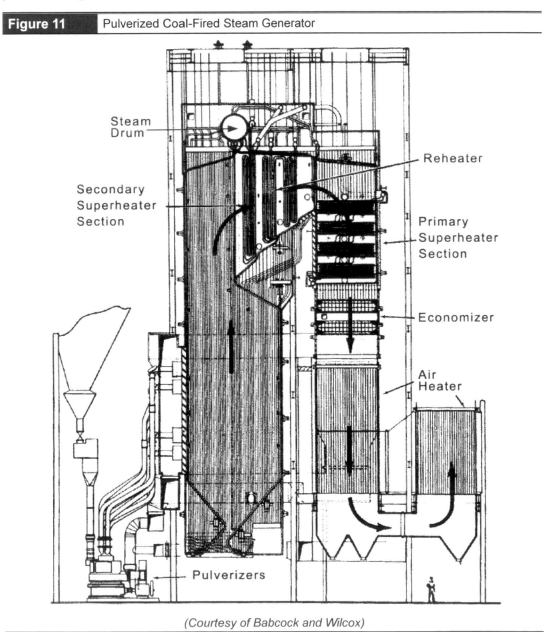

(Courtesy of Babcock and Wilcox)

Figure 12 shows a steam generator that is designed to burn either oil or natural gas, with steam capacity of 450 000 kg per hour. Steam pressure is 12 700 kPa and the steam is superheated to 538°C and reheated to 538°C.

This unit has primary and secondary superheaters, with an attemperator between them. The attemperator injects water into the steam to control the steam temperature. There are also two stages of reheater.

Figure 12	Gas or Oil-Fired Steam Generator

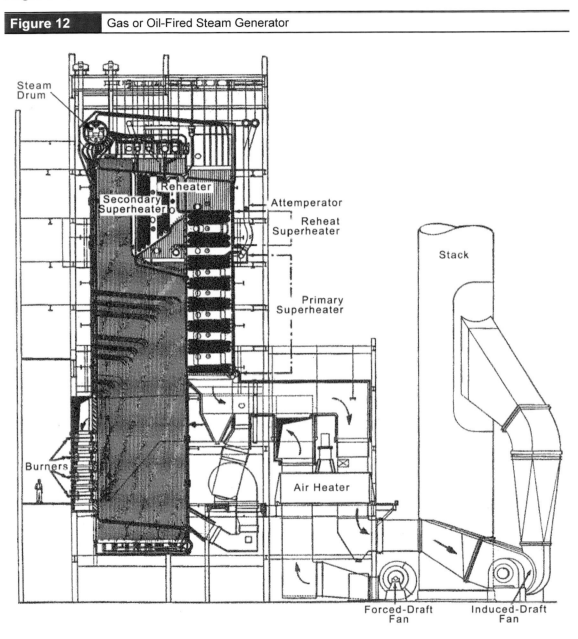

(Courtesy of Babcock and Wilcox)

Steam generators are constructed for practically any capacity. Some of the higher capacity units produce over 3 000 000 kg of steam per hour at 17 900 kPa, superheated to 538°C and reheated to 538°C. The overall height of the larger units may be in excess of 61 metres.

A stoker-fired steam generator is illustrated in Figure 13.

Capacity of this unit is 136 000 kg of steam per hour at 8960 kPa and superheated to 513°C. A reheater is not included in this unit.

Figure 13	Stoker-Fired Steam Generator

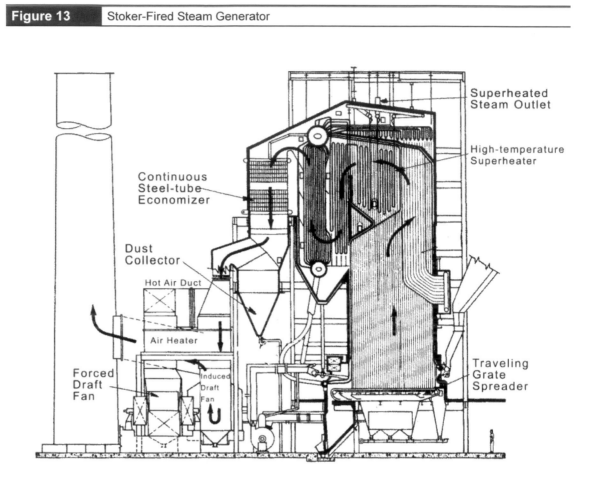

(Courtesy of Babcock and Wilcox)

Steam Generator Temperature Profile

The following list of temperatures is typical for a coal fired steam generator that supplies superheated steam at 11 274 kPa to a steam turbine that drives a 300 MW power generator. The flows, along with corresponding temperatures, are illustrated in the schematic in Figure 14. Temperatures do vary between units, so those given only represent a typical temperature profile through one steam generator.

Gas temperatures:

Furnace temperature	1650°C
Flue gas exit furnace	1100°C
Flue gas exit superheaters	600°C
Flue gas exit economizer	380°C
Flue gas exit air heater	170°C (to stack)

Water and Steam Temperatures:

Water inlet economizer	254°C (depends on number of stages of feedwater preheat)
Water exit economizer	280°C
Boiler drum	320°C (saturation temperature for 11 274 kPa)
Steam temperature	538°C
Reheat temperature	538°C

Figure 14   Temperatures for a Coal Fired Steam Generator

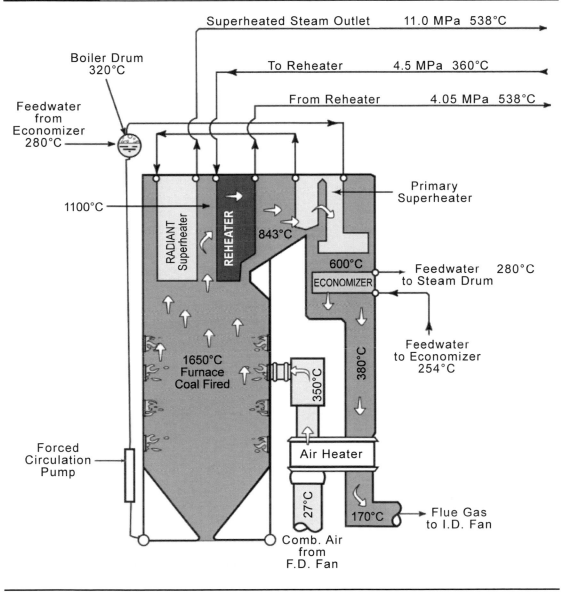

OBJECTIVE 5

Differentiate between critical and super-critical boilers.

CRITICAL PRESSURE

Natural circulation in a boiler depends upon the difference in the density of a column of water and the density of a column containing a steam/water mixture. The difference in density produces the circulation head. At low pressures, the difference in densities is large, so circulation is relatively easy to maintain.

The difference in density between water and saturated steam becomes progressively less with increased pressure and becomes zero at the critical pressure of 22 090 kPa.

Figure 15 shows a graph of density vs. pressure, also showing the density differential between water and steam at all pressures. Above the critical pressure, the densities of water and steam are the same. This means a boiler operating at the critical pressure cannot have natural circulation and pumps must be used to provide forced circulation.

Figure 15	Pressure-Density Curve for Water and Steam

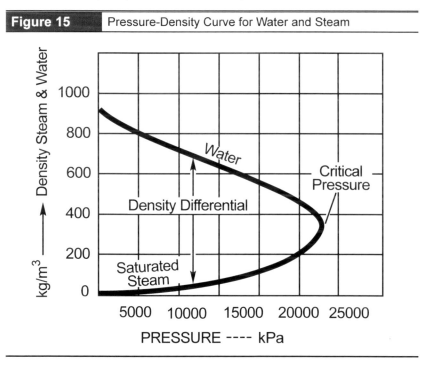

Steam generators operating above critical pressure are said to be **super-critical** and steam generators operating below critical pressure are classed as **sub-critical**.

The boiler in Figure 16 is a super-critical boiler, built by B&W. Being a once-through, forced circulation boiler, it has no steam drum. The other major components of this boiler are physically similar to those of a natural circulation boiler.

Figure 16 Super-Critical Boiler

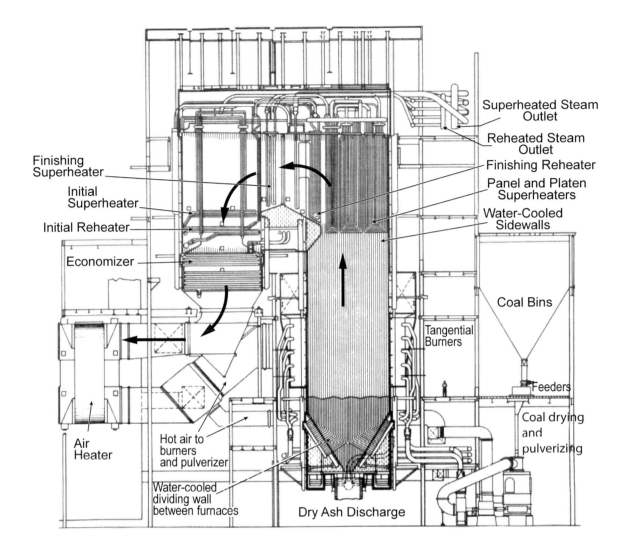

(Courtesy of Babcock and Wilcox)

OBJECTIVE 6

Explain the purpose and advantage of forced circulation and describe the flow through a typical controlled circulation boiler.

FORCED CIRCULATION BOILERS

Boilers designed to operate at high pressures, particularly those with intricate tube paths must be designed with great care in order to ensure good natural circulation. Alternatively they may employ a pump (or pumps) in the boiler water circulation path to provide forced circulation. Figure 17 shows how a pump can be used to aid circulation.

Figure 17	Forced Circulation Boiler Schematic

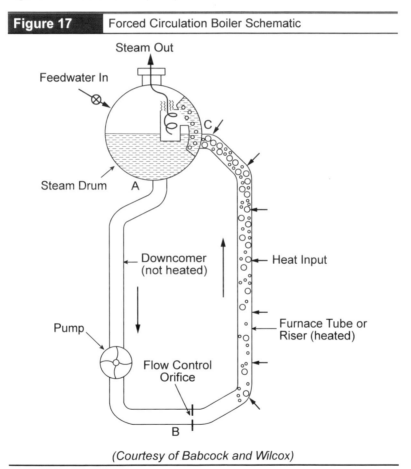

(Courtesy of Babcock and Wilcox)

The advantage of forced circulation is a positive flow in all tubes. This ensures that no tubes become overheated from lack of internal water flow. Further, by fitting orifices or nozzles of varying sizes at tube inlets, the flow in the tubes can be regulated.

The disadvantages are increased equipment cost for pumps, piping, etc. and an increase in maintenance and operating costs. One particular difficulty is in effectively sealing the glands of the circulating pump to prevent leakage to atmosphere.

Forced circulation becomes advantageous at pressures of about 12 500 to 13 800 kPa and higher and is absolutely necessary for boilers operating at or above the critical steam pressure of 22 090 kPa (22.09 MPa).

Forced circulation boilers can be divided into two general classes:

1. "Controlled circulation" or "recirculating" boilers

2. Once-through boilers (see Objective 7)

CONTROLLED CIRCULATION BOILERS

Figure 18 shows the basic components of a controlled circulation boiler.

Feedwater is brought into the boiler drum through an economizer section. In the economizer the boiler feed-water is preheated to very close to the saturation temperature of the boiler water. Once in the boiler drum the water flows through the downcomers to the circulation pumps.

From here it is pumped to an inlet header which distributes it to the steam generating tubes. Orifices in the inlet header control the amount of water fed to each steam generating circuit.

The steam/water mixture produced in the radiant and convection sections of steam generating tubes discharges into the steam drum. Separating equipment removes the free water from the mixture and the saturated steam then flows through a superheater section where its temperature is increased. It then leaves the steam generator via superheated steam outlet.

| Figure 18 | Controlled Circulation Steam Generator Schematic |

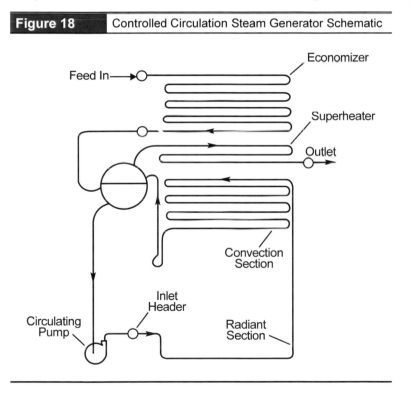

Figure 19 shows a controlled circulation steam generator in more detail, with final steam conditions of 18 100 kPa and 540°C, and reheat steam temperature of 540°C. The unit is coal fired with Raymond bowl mill pulverizers and has tilting tangential burners for superheat temperature control.

The supply of water to the waterwalls begins with the steam drum. The water travels downwards, through the downcomers, to the boiler circulating pumps. The circulating pumps discharge into headers, which have flow distribution orifices. From there the water flows upward, through the waterwalls in which heat transfer produces steam. The steam and water mixture is collected in a series of headers, above the furnace roof, and is directed through connecting tubes to the steam drum. In the steam drum the water is separated from the steam and enters the downcomers, while the steam leaves the top of the drum and goes to the superheater.

Figure 19	Controlled Circulation Boiler Schematic

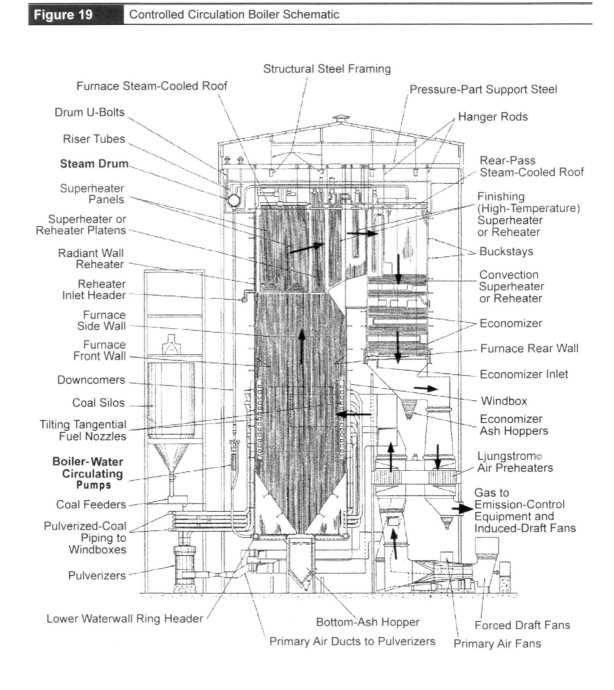

(Courtesy of Alstom Power)

OBJECTIVE 7

Explain the purpose and design of a once-through boiler.

ONCE-THROUGH BOILERS

Once-through boilers use forced circulation. The feedwater is forced through one continuous circuit in the boiler and the various heat transfers and the change of state (water to steam) take place during this continuous flow path. There is no steam drum and, therefore, no re-circulation of water.

Figure 20 shows the arrangement of a once-through boiler. Notice, there are no drums.

The feedwater is heated and then evaporated and superheated during one passage through the unit.

- The feed pump supplies water to the economizer inlet and, after passing through the economizer, the heated water flows to the furnace wall tubes, which are in the radiant zone. Approximately 85% of the water is evaporated in this 'radiant evaporator' section.

- Then the steam/water mixture passes to the final evaporator section where it is completely converted to steam. This final evaporator section is located in a zone of lower flue gas temperature.

- The steam leaving the evaporator section flows to a convection superheater section and, finally, through a radiant superheater section to the steam outlet.

Figure 20	Once-Through Boiler Schematic

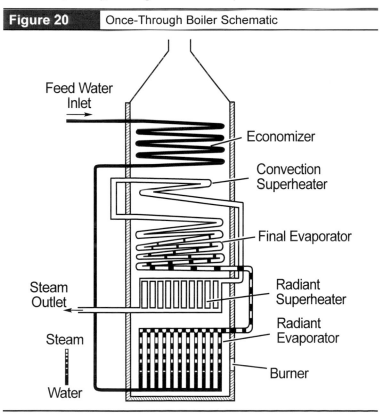

Figure 21 shows a Babcock and Wilcox universal pressure, once-through boiler, designed for both pulverized coal and oil firing.

Steam conditions are 16 500 kPa at 538°C with one reheat to 538°C. The capacity of the unit is 1 197 000 kg/h at which the maximum capability of the unit approaches 400 MW.

The single furnace is approximately 15 metres wide, with firing through both front and rear walls. This design requires no steam drum or circulating pumps.

| Figure 21 | B & W Universal Pressure (Once-Through) Boiler |

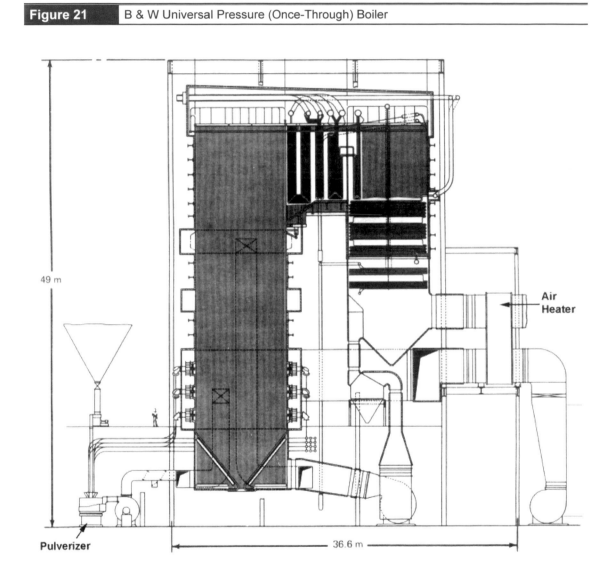

(Courtesy of Babcock and Wilcox)

CHAPTER 1 - QUESTIONS

1. Illustrate by means of simple sketches the following watertube boiler designs: D-type, A-type, and O-type.

2. List the advantages of the packaged type boiler.

3. List the typical elements of a steam generating unit and explain the purpose of each element.

4. Define the term "integral furnace" and list any advantages to be obtained by using this type of construction.

5. Explain the difference between shop assembled boilers and packaged boilers

6. Explain the difference between field erected and shop-assembled boilers.

7. Describe forced water circulation and discuss its necessity in very high pressure boilers, its advantages and disadvantages.

8. Explain, with the aid of a sketch, natural water circulation in a steam boiler. What factors influence natural circulation?

9. What are the three different methods of calculating the output or rating of a boiler?

ANSWERS: All answers are found within the content of the chapter.

Special Boiler Designs

LEARNING OUTCOME

When you complete this chapter you should be able to:

Describe the designs, components, firing methods, and operating considerations for some special boilers used in industry.

LEARNING OBJECTIVES

Here is what you should be able to do when you complete each objective:

1. Describe typical designs, components and operating strategies for once-through, steam flood boilers.

2. Describe typical designs, components and operating strategies for Fluidized Bed boilers.

3. Describe typical designs, components and operating strategies for Heat Recovery Steam Generators.

4. Describe typical designs, components and operating strategies for Black Liquor Recovery boilers used in pulp mills.

5. Describe typical designs, components and operating strategies for Refuse boilers used in waste disposal.

6. Describe typical designs, components and operating strategies for waste heat, biomass boilers.

OBJECTIVE 1

Describe typical designs, components and operating strategies for once-through, steam flood boilers.

STEAM FLOODING

A particular application of the once-through boiler design is the steam-flooding boiler. This is a boiler used for flooding oil wells with steam in order to increase the oil recovery.

Steam injection increases the recovery of oil from wells that have been partially depleted. The operation is particularly suited to the recovery of high viscosity (heavy) crude oils. Using steam allows the maximum amount of heat to be put into the well with a minimum amount of injected fluid. This minimizes the amount of fluid that must be pumped out later. The amount of oil recovered is proportional to the temperature achieved at the bottom of the well. The optimum temperature is 178°C (the saturation temperature of 950 kPa steam), which is more easily reached with a supply of high-temperature steam.

Steam Flooding Boilers

These boilers are often described as oilfield heaters because they are specifically designed to provide steam and/or hot water for oil recovery operations. They are forced circulation boilers with a single pass, once-through coil. The boiler has no steam drum, which simplifies controls. The produced steam is injected into the well with no steam/water separation.

Steam flood boilers are designed to produce steam that is 75 to 80% dryness, depending upon the solids concentration in the feedwater. To keep the salts in the boiler water dissolved and avoid deposits on the tubes, the steam produced should contain 20 to 25% moisture. When steam is produced, the salts stay dissolved in the water portion of the wet steam.

Outputs from these boilers range from 5 million kJ/h to 50 million kJ/h in standard sizes and up to 125 million kJ/h in special cases. Working pressures are up to 20 000 kPa. In smaller sizes, the boilers are skid or truck mounted for mobility. Larger units are usually built on a chassis or frame, which makes the boiler easier to move.

Figure 1 shows an external view of a packaged steam flooding boiler.

Figure 1	Packaged Steam Flood Boiler, External View

Figure 2 shows a similar, trailer-mounted boiler, complete with water-treating equipment. These boilers incorporate feedwater treatment since water must be treated for hardness and oxygen removal to ensure trouble-free operation. Feedwater with a relatively high percentage of solids can be handled provided the solids have been converted to soluble form.

Figure 2	Trailer-Mounted Steam Flood Boiler

Figure 3 is a simple schematic of the flows through a steam flood boiler. The flow is described after the figure.

Figure 3	Steam Flood Boiler Flows

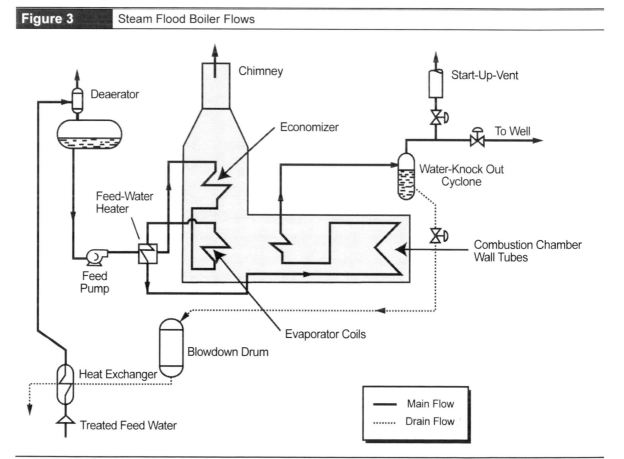

- Pretreated water is sent to the **deaerator** for oxygen and carbon dioxide removal.
- The **feedwater pump** takes water from the deaerator and pumps it through a **feedwater heater** to the boiler.
- It is heated further in the **economizer** by heat exchange with the flue gases.
- The water then passes through the **evaporator coils**, located at the back of the furnace, where a majority of the water is evaporated into steam.

- The steam/water mixture passes back through the feedwater heater and then into the **radiant coils** in the furnace proper, which produces further steam.

- The steam exits the boiler and flows through a **cyclone separator** for removal of the free water.

- The **start-up vent** is used to vent steam until the required steam temperature is reached. The vent also allows the boiler to remain in operation if the flow to the wells is shut off. The boiler must have a flow of water and steam through it at all times to prevent overheating of the tubes.

Figure 4 shows the internal construction of the steam flood boiler.

The combustion chamber is enclosed by tubes, in the form of membrane walls. This makes the combustion chamber gas tight and self-supporting. No refractory is required. Each section of the boiler is constructed so that the boiler is completely drainable. The boiler is compact and provides maximum heat transfer surface.

Figure 4	Steam Flood Boiler Tubing Layout

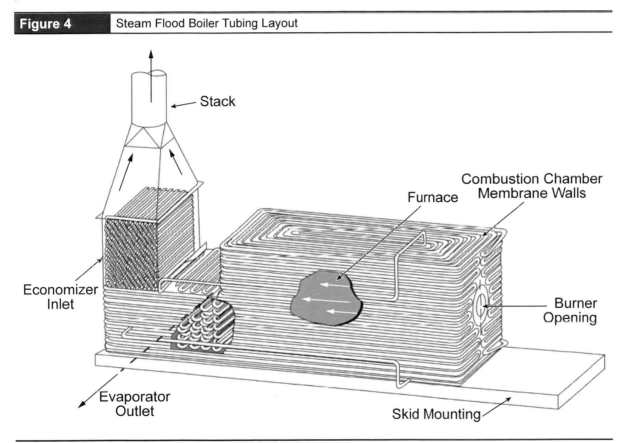

OBJECTIVE 2

Describe typical designs, components and operating strategies for Fluidized Bed boilers.

FLUIDIZED BED COMBUSTION

One method of burning coal is called fluidized bed combustion. In this design there is a series of modules, each containing a bed of inert granular material, such as ashes or crushed rocks, and enclosed by heating surfaces (water tubes). Crushed coal from 1.6 mm to 6 mm is injected into the bed using injection air.

Figure 5 shows a very simplified schematic of the arrangement.

Figure 5	Simplified Fluidized Bed Boiler

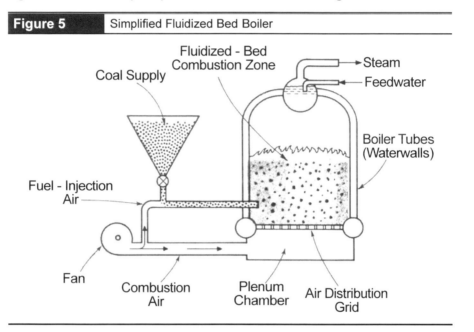

Combustion air is introduced beneath the bed and is blown up through the entire bed. The combustion air lifts the inert bed and the crushed coal off the supporting grid and the bed becomes loose and "floating" (ie. it appears fluidized). An external burner provides initial ignition. The turbulent fluidized bed is itself in direct contact with a large area of the module's heating surface, giving direct heat transfer. The heating surfaces above the bed receive heat by radiation from the bed and by convection from the hot combustion gases.

The advantages of this method of combustion are:

1. Less costly boilers because of efficient heat transfer and elimination of pulverizing equipment

2. A reduction in SO_2 emissions. Crushed limestone can be used in the bed to combine with the sulphur in the fuel and reduce the SO_2 produced in the flue gases.

3. Low-grade fuels can be burned in an environmentally acceptable manner. This ability results from the turbulent mixing that occurs in the fuel beds and which promotes good combustion.

4. Ability to burn several, different fuels, such as biomass, wood products, coke (petcoke), industrial waste products, and even tires

5. Different fuels can be burned together, such as mixed grades of coal or coal mixed with other fuels

6. Less NO_X due to lower combustion temperatures

7. More thorough combustion, due to the recycle of ash, and unburned fuel

Figure 6(a) shows combustion in a shallow, fluidized bed. Volatile matter (VM) rises above the bed and mixes with the air during combustion. A limited amount of air is supplied to the shallow bed design to limit combustion and bed temperature.

Figure 6(b) shows a deep bed design with in-bed combustion plus volatile matter combusting above the bed. More air is fed to the deep bed design. Evaporator tubes within the bed control bed temperature by providing in-bed cooling.

Figure 6	Fluidized Bed Combustion

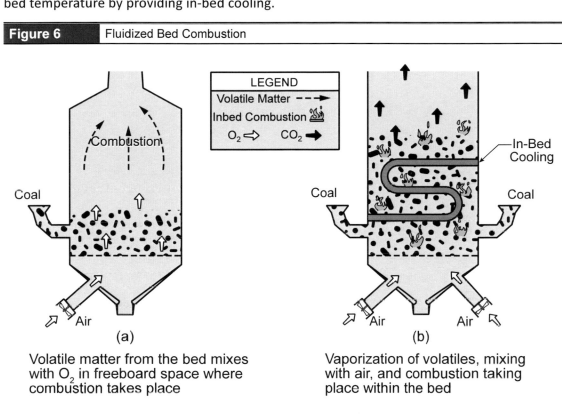

(a)
Volatile matter from the bed mixes with O_2 in freeboard space where combustion takes place

(b)
Vaporization of volatiles, mixing with air, and combustion taking place within the bed

Combustion can occur at lower temperatures, ranging from 800°C to 900°C, rather than normal combustion temperatures of 1600°C to 1900°C for pulverized coal and oil firing. The ability to burn material at the lower temperatures is an important feature of fluidized beds. It makes it possible to burn low quality fuels. Also, the lower combustion temperatures result in less NO_X (nitrogen oxides) emissions.

Because of the low operating temperatures, an inexpensive material, such as $CaCO_3$ (lime), can be added to the bed. It acts as an absorbant to remove SO_2 (sulphur dioxide) from the flue gases. SO_2 emissions can thus be reduced by up to 80%.

There are two types of fluidized bed boilers. They are the:

- Bubbling fluidized bed (BFB)
- Circulating fluidized bed CFB)

Bubbling Fluidized Bed Boilers (BFB)

Figure 7 shows a bubbling fluidized bed boiler.

- The solid particles in the bed are kept in suspension by an upward flow of air and combustion gases.

- The bed is in a fluid-like state and has a distinct level that can be easily seen, with air and combustion gases "bubbling" from the surface.

- The mixing of air and fuel leads to complete combustion of the fuel with bed temperature between 815°C and 875°C.

- Depending on which type of fuel is being burned, extra in-bed heat transfer surface may be added to maintain a lower bed temperature. This heat transfer surface consists of tube banks, submerged in the bed, with water flowing through them. A drawback to this is the subjection of the tube bundles to high erosion rates.

- For coal fired BFB boilers, the solids in the flue gas are recovered and routed back to the fluidized bed. The separation takes place downstream of the economizer, using cyclones separators.

- Material can be removed from the bed during operation, via the bed drain tube, to control the bed level.

The bubbling fluidized bed design is simpler and has a lower cost than the circulating fluid bed design.

Figure 7	Fluidized Bed Boiler Module

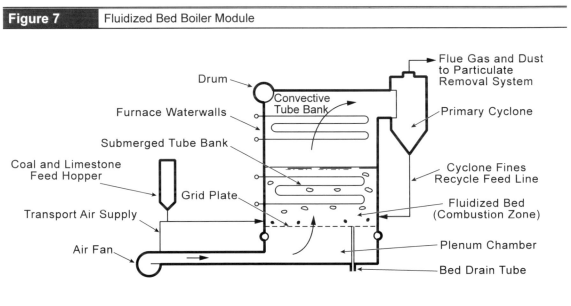

Reproduced with permission of ALSTOM Power Inc., Windsor, CT, from Combustion: Fossil Power Systems (copyright 1981)

Figure 8 illustrates the circulation flows through a typical BFB boiler. The dark arrows represent solids and the white arrows represent flue gas.

- Hot recycle flows from the cyclone directly back to the fluidized bed.
- Cold recycle flows from the cyclone, through the external heat exchanger, then to the bed.
- In this design, secondary combustion is also introduced above the bed, to promote complete combustion.
- The dense bed has a drain to control the bed level.

Figure 8 Fluidized Bed Boiler Gas Flows - BFB

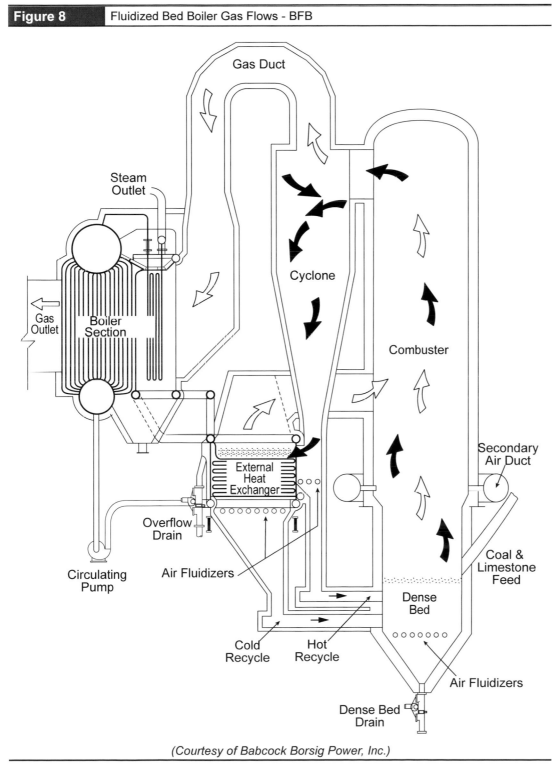

(Courtesy of Babcock Borsig Power, Inc.)

Figure 9 shows a smaller, industrial bubbling bed boiler design.

This design has no in-bed tube bundle. A large quantity of the solids from the bed is recycled internally around the furnace. Collection devices, such as cyclones, collect particles in the flue gases. The solids collected are recycled back to the bed.

Figure 9	Industrial Bubbling Bed Boiler

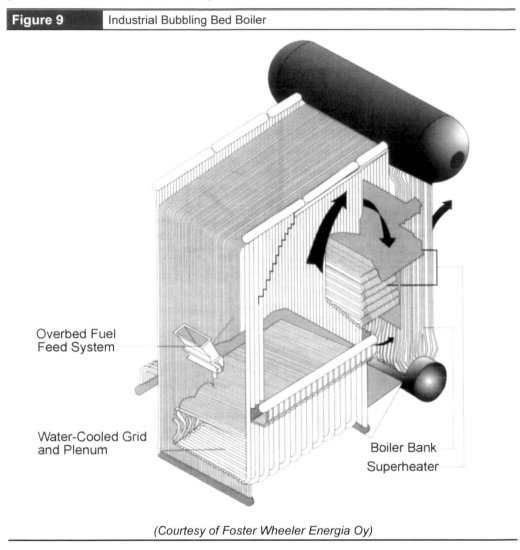

(Courtesy of Foster Wheeler Energia Oy)

Circulating Fluidized Bed Boilers (CFB)

The CFB boiler provides more fluidizing air to the bed than in a BFB boiler. As a result, a distinct bed level may not be observed. Fluidizing air causes the fuel and bed material to rise and circulate within the combustion area of the furnace. From there it goes to the hot cyclone collector where solids are collected and returned to the bed. This continuous circulation of solids provides longer fuel residence time, which results in very efficient combustion.

Ashes are removed from the bottom of the combustion area. Since there is no distinct bed level in a CFB boiler, the density of the bed is controlled, rather than the depth (as in a BFB boiler). The density is controlled by the amount of ash removal.

Figure 10 shows the flows through a CFB boiler.

- Coal and limestone are added to the fluid bed in the main furnace.
- The flue gases leave the main furnace and pass through a cyclone, where most of the heavier particles are removed.
- The gases then pass through superheater and economizer sections before entering the mechanical dust collectors.
- A secondary or smaller fluid bed supplies heat to an evaporator coil in this design. This secondary fluid bed burns unburned fuel drained from the primary cyclone and main economizer sections of the furnace.
- One primary and two secondary air blowers supply the required combustion air.
- Boiler feed from the main economizer passes through the evaporator coils before entering the steam drum.

Figure 10	Fluidized Bed Boiler Module

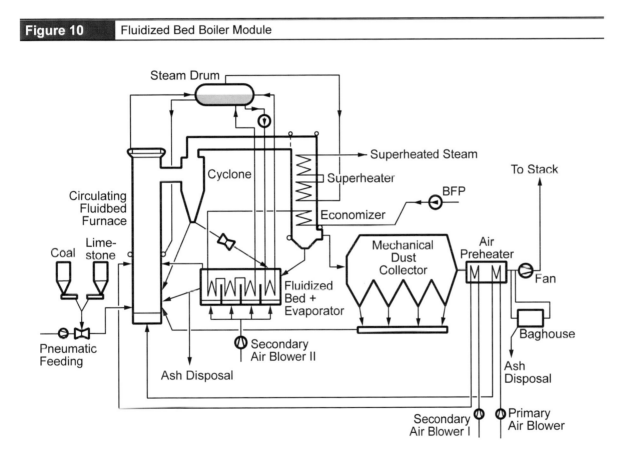

Reproduced with permission of ALSTOM Power Inc., Windsor, CT, from Combustion:
Fossil Power Systems (copyright 1981)

Figure 11 shows a 314 MW CFB boiler. It is similar layout to Figure 10, except there is no secondary fluidized bed.

Figure 11	Circulating Fluidized Bed Boiler, 314 MW Size

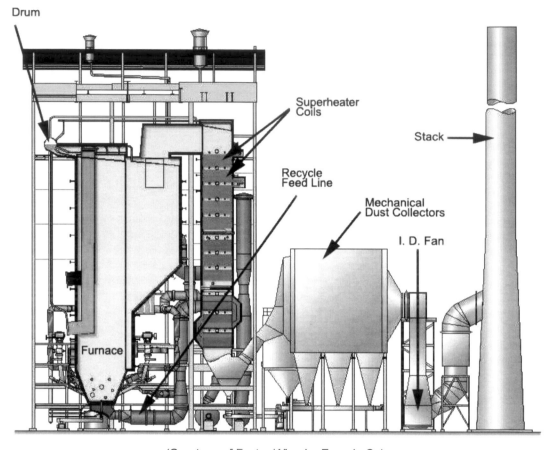

(Courtesy of Foster Wheeler Energia Oy)

Describe typical designs, components and operating strategies for Heat Recovery Steam Generators.

STEAM GENERATION BY HEAT RECOVERY

A popular and practical method of generating steam is to use waste energy from a process or from the exhaust of a heat engine. This reduces the use of high cost fuels, uses heat that would otherwise be wasted from a process, and has definite environmental benefits, reducing overall emissions. Overall cycle and system efficiencies can be greatly increased. For example, in power generation the waste heat from a gas turbine can produce steam to supply a steam turbine. Such combined cycles may produce cycle efficiency of 50% or more.

Combined Cycle Power Generation

A simple combined cycle power generation system may consist of a single gas turbine generator, a heat recovery steam generator (HRSG) and a single steam turbine-generator with condenser and auxiliary systems. Figures 12 and 13 illustrate simple combined cycle arrangements.

More complex configurations are possible, of course. For example, the HRSG may be designed to also supply low-pressure steam for deaeration and feedwater heating. This steam usage can be thought of as equivalent to the extraction steam used for feedwater heating in conventional steam plant cycles.

Figure 12	Combined Cycle Power Generation

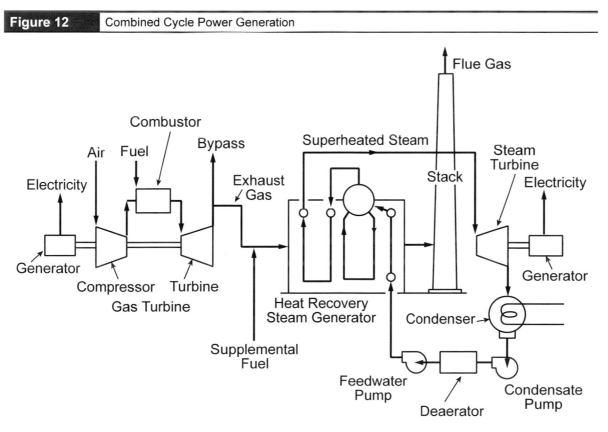

(Courtesy of Babcock and Wilcox)

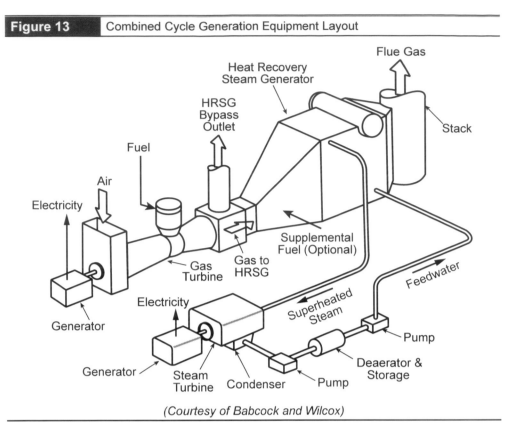

Figure 13 | Combined Cycle Generation Equipment Layout

(Courtesy of Babcock and Wilcox)

Cogeneration

Cogeneration, by one definition, is the simultaneous generation and use of two forms of energy from one fuel source. There are several cogeneration designs, but Figure 14 illustrates one, using a gas turbine and a steam turbine. Fuel is burned in the gas turbine, which turns the generator and also exhausts heat to a HRSG. The HRSG produces steam, which supplies a steam turbine plus heating steam for a process. The total energy utilization of such systems can approach 80%.

Figure 14 | Cogeneration Cycle

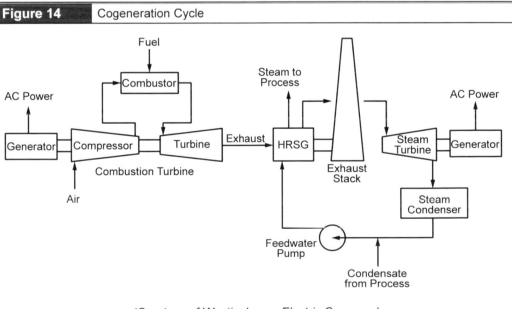

(Courtesy of Westinghouse Electric Company)

HEAT RECOVERY STEAM GENERATORS

The heat recovery steam generator (HRSG) is often referred to as a waste heat recovery boiler (WHRB) or a turbine exhaust gas boiler (TEG). The main application for these boilers is steam generation using gas turbine exhaust as the heat source.

HRSG designs vary with the application. The gas flow may be horizontal or vertical, depending upon the floor space available. Water circulation may be forced or natural. Most horizontal gas flow HRSG boilers use natural circulation. Some HRSG boilers are of the once-through, forced circulation design.

HRSG's may be unfired (using waste heat only) or they may have auxiliary burners to raise the gas temperature at the inlet of the HRSG coils. The duct burners may be used to increased steam production, control superheater temperatures, or to meet process steam pressure/temperature requirements.

Figure 15 shows a HRSG, which much resembles a small boiler, with an "O-Type" steam generating section (also called an "O-Frame Evaporator). The gas turbine exhaust provides the primary source of heat, but a separate furnace contains auxiliary burners that can supplement the turbine exhaust gases. Heating surfaces include superheater, boiler/evaporator tubes, and an economizer. It is, in effect, a natural circulation boiler with a steam drum and water drum.

Figure 15	HRSG with Auxiliary Firing "O-Frame Evaporator"

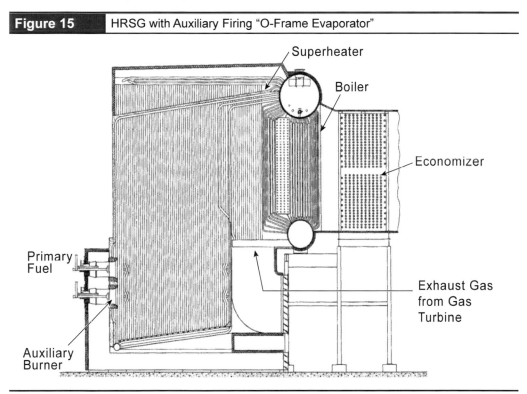

Figure 16 shows another HRSG design, often called a horizontal tube evaporator. The steam generating tubes are mounted horizontally, with headers that distribute water and steam circulation to/from the steam and mud drums. Because the flow of hot gases is vertical through the evaporator banks, this design is referred to as a 'vertical HRSG'.

Notice, there are two exhaust ducts from the gas turbine. There are three sections of tube banks. The hottest gasses pass through the superheater section. This is followed by the evaporator section, and finally the economizer.

Figure 16	Horizontal Tube Evaporator

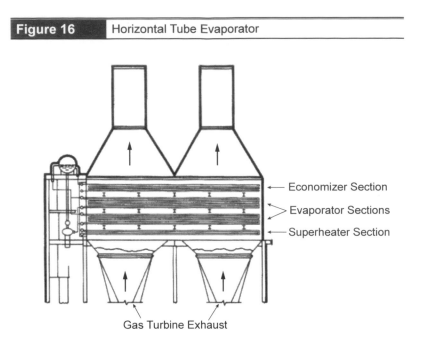

Gas Turbine Exhaust

*Reproduced with permission of ALSTOM Power Inc., Windsor, CT, from
Combustion: Fossil Power Systems (copyright 1981)*

Figure 17 shows a HRSG design with horizontal steam drum, as used in the combined cycles of Figures 12, 13 and 14. This design is called a 'horizontal HRSG' since the gas flows horizontally through the heating sections. Again, there are three heat transfer sections, each one consisting of vertical tube banks and their associated headers. In the order of gas flow they are the superheater, the generating bank (evaporator) and the economizer.

The auxiliary (supplemental) burners, in this case, are called 'duct burners'. The burners are mounted directly in the side of the duct between the gas turbine and the HRSG. There is an exhaust damper to divert the turbine exhaust to atmosphere when the HRSG is out of service or for the purpose of controlling steam production when the HRSG is in service.

Figure 17	Horizontal HRSG for Combined Cycle with I-Frame Evaporator

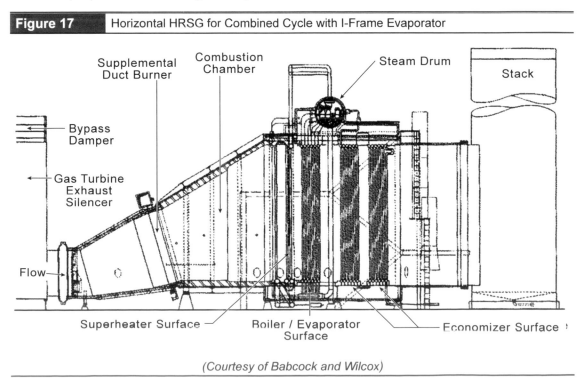

(Courtesy of Babcock and Wilcox)

Figure 18 shows an advanced version of the horizontal HRSG in Figure 18. This design produces steam at three different pressures. Therefore it has a high pressure steam drum (eg. 7000 kPa), intermediate pressure steam drum (eg. 2400 kPa) and a low pressure steam drum (eg. 350 kPa). This arrangement makes maximum use of the gas turbine exhaust heat by providing steam for process heating as well as steam turbine.

Figure 18	3-Drum Horizontal HRSG

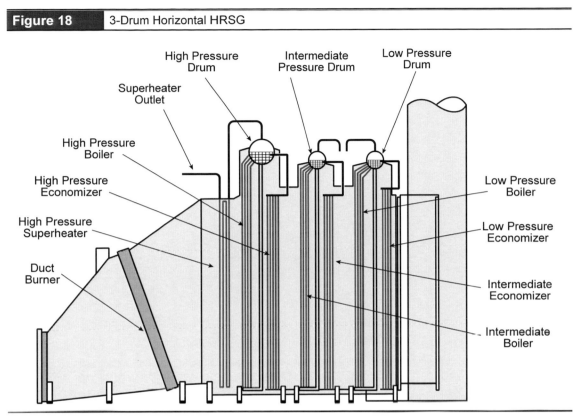

An external view of a HRSG is shown in Figure 19.

Figure 19	External View of Horizontal HRSG

(Courtesy of Babcock and Wilcox)

OBJECTIVE 4

Describe typical designs, components and operating strategies for Black Liquor Recovery boilers used in pulp mills.

INTRODUCTION

In North America, the pulp and paper industry is one of the highest industrial consumers of energy. It is also a leading co-generator of electric power. About half of the steam consumed by this industry is generated from fuels produced during the process, including spent pulping liquor. The heating value of the spent liquor is a reliable fuel source for steam and power production.

The Kraft Process

Most paper production in North America uses the Kraft Process. This process uses sodium sulfate (Na_2SO_4) as a makeup chemical. Figure 20 shows a simple schematic of this process. Each of the numbered sections is explained following the figure.

Figure 20	Kraft Process - Liquor Cycle

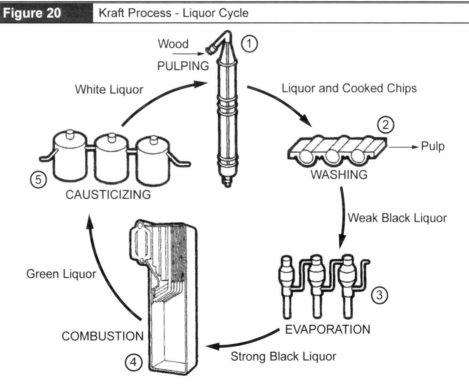

Reproduced with permission of ALSTOM Power Inc., Windsor, CT, from Combustion: Fossil Power Systems (copyright 1981)

1. The process begins with wood chips being fed into the **digester**, in a process called **pulping**. Here the chips are cooked, under pressure, in a steam heated aqueous solution of sodium hydroxide (NaOH) and sodium sulfide (Na_2S). The solution is known as **white liquor** or cooking liquor.

2. After cooking, the pulp is separated or **washed** from the liquor. After washing, the liquor is called **weak black liquor**. It contains 13% to 17% solids.

3. The weak black liquor is then concentrated in **evaporators** to produce **strong black liquor**, which is used for fuel. Steam is normally used as the heat source for the evaporators, although older systems used hot flue gases from the boiler.

4. The **recovery boiler** burns the organic material in the black liquor. Non-combustible, inorganic material collects on the furnace floor. This material, called smelt, is discharged for reclamation of chemicals. It is dissolved in a weak chemical wash to form **green liquor**.

5. In **causticizing**, the green liquor has caustic chemicals (such as lime) added to form **white liquor**. The white liquor is fed into the digester to complete the cycle.

Black Liquor Combustion

Black liquor combustion occurs in the **recovery boiler**. Combustion air is usually supplied at three elevations in a recovery boiler furnace, called primary, secondary, and tertiary. This allows for optimization of the combustion in three furnace zones. The lower furnace is the reducing zone, the middle furnace is the drying zone, and the upper furnace is the combustion completion zone.

Black liquor is sprayed into the furnace as coarse droplets, which fall to the floor in a dry, partially combusted state. This forms a char bed, one to two meters deep, which consists of carbon and inorganic sodium chemicals.

The liquor droplets must be large enough to minimize entrainment in the combustion gases, yet small enough to fall to the bed nearly dry. Therefore, the recovery furnace must promote combustion of the black liquor, in parallel with the reduction of sodium compounds. Figure 21 shows a typical black liquor burner nozzle.

Figure 21	Black Liquor Burner

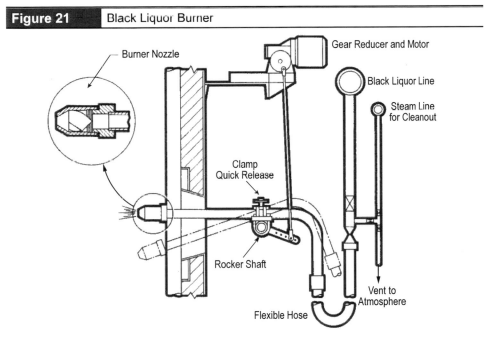

Reproduced with permission of ALSTOM Power Inc., Windsor, CT, from Combustion: Fossil Power Systems (copyright 1981)

The primary function of the recovery boiler is to process black liquor. The boiler can fire auxiliary fuel, which may be natural gas or oil. The auxiliary fuel burners are located at the same level as the secondary air or above. These burners are used to:

- Raise steam during startup
- Sustain a stable ignition while establishing a char bed
- Stabilize conditions during upsets in the black liquor feed
- Produce extra steam as required by the process of for power production
- Burn out the char bed when shutting down

Upper level burners make burning black liquor and auxiliary fuel firing possible without affecting lower furnace conditions.

Figure 22 shows the location of the black liquor nozzles in relation to the smelt bed. Tertiary air is fed above the lower combustion area of the furnace. Completion of burning occurs above the tertiary air inlet.

Figure 22	Black Liquor Burner

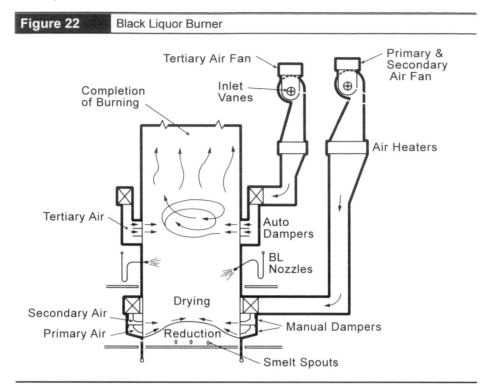

Figure 23 is a more complete view of the flows into and out of a black liquor boiler.

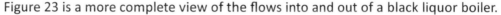

Figure 23	Black Liquor Boiler Flows

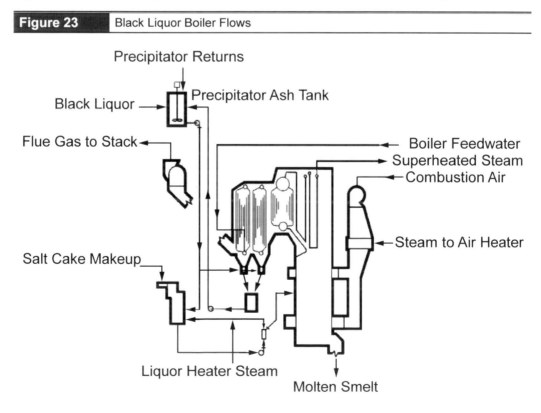

Fig 22 and 23 are Reproduced with permission of ALSTOM Power Inc., Windsor, CT, from
Combustion: Fossil Power Systems (copyright 1981)

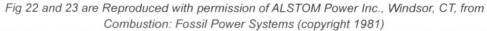

A black liquor recovery boiler is shown in Figure 24.

Note the location of the black liquor nozzles, as well as the primary, secondary, and tertiary air. Also note the black liquor heaters and salt cake mixing tank, located at the burner level.

Figure 24　　Black Liquor Boiler

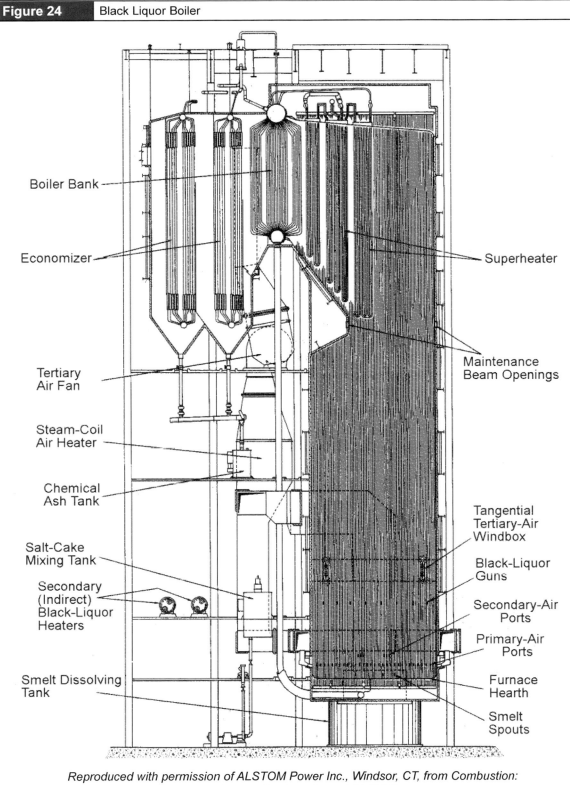

Boiler Bank

Economizer

Superheater

Tertiary Air Fan

Maintenance Beam Openings

Steam-Coil Air Heater

Chemical Ash Tank

Tangential Tertiary-Air Windbox

Salt-Cake Mixing Tank

Black-Liquor Guns

Secondary (Indirect) Black-Liquor Heaters

Secondary-Air Ports

Primary-Air Ports

Smelt Dissolving Tank

Furnace Hearth

Smelt Spouts

Reproduced with permission of ALSTOM Power Inc., Windsor, CT, from Combustion: Fossil Power Systems (copyright 1981)

Safety Hazards when Burning Black Liquor

If water contacts molten smelt, a violent explosion will result. It is not a chemical reaction, but a physical reaction. It is the result of gases expanding very quickly and violently. They produce a shock wave type of reaction. Tube leaks onto the smelt bed will cause a dangerous explosion. Many recovery boilers have an emergency drain system, which very rapidly drains the boiler to just above the furnace floor if a furnace tube leak is detected.

Also, If the black liquor is too weak an explosion can occur. Concentrations above 58% are considered safe for liquor firing. The black liquor furnace is designed with added structural strength in case of explosion.

OBJECTIVE 5

Describe typical designs, components and operating strategies for Refuse boilers used in waste disposal.

REFUSE TO ENERGY

The most common methods of refuse disposal are landfill and incineration. Since landfill sites are becoming less available and less desirable, burning of refuse is gaining wide acceptance. This burning is a good heat source and heat recovery from refuse incinerators is a growing industry. The original, basic incinerators with waste heat recovery have evolved into water-walled boilers with integral stokers. The boilers have become large enough to provide steam for turbine generator sets and commercial power production.

Refuse Burning Techniques

There are two main techniques for burning refuse. They differ in the amount of preparation of the fuel before burning. The first technique, called **mass burning**, uses the fuel as received with little preparation. Only large non-combustible items or bulky items are removed. Trucks dump the refuse directly into pits, as shown in Figure 25. Overhead cranes move the refuse to the feed hoppers which then feed the stoker grates. Combustion occurs on the grates as they move along the bottom of the furnace. Non-combustible material and ash drop into the ash pit or ash extractor at the end of the grate.

Figure 25	Refuse Handling System

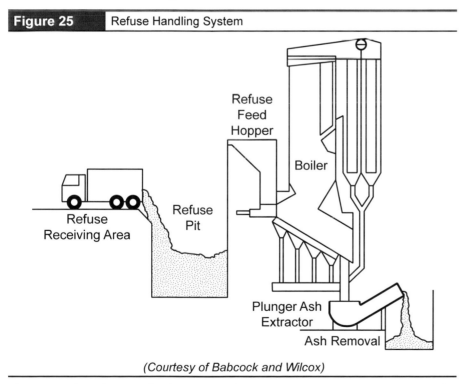

(Courtesy of Babcock and Wilcox)

The second technique for burning refuse involves more preparation before combustion. The refuse is separated, classified, and sorted in various ways, to separate recyclable products. In the fuel preparation schematic, shown in Figure 26, the refuse is screened and shredded. A magnetic separator removes any metallic objects. The prepared fuel is then fed to the boiler, which uses a traveling grate system.

Figure 26	Refuse Preparation System

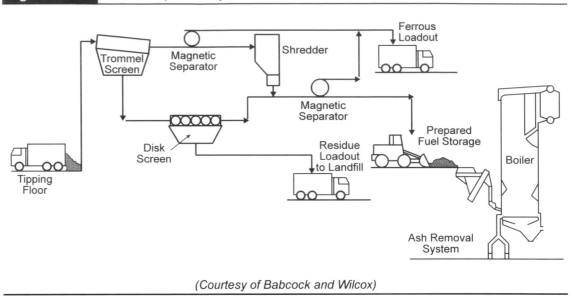

(Courtesy of Babcock and Wilcox)

Refuse Boiler Tube Corrosion

The combustion products from burning municipal waste are very corrosive. In addition to the normal corrosion products of combustion, refuse fired boilers are susceptible to corrosion from chlorides. The chlorides deposit on furnace, superheater, and boiler tubes, causing loss of tube metal. The higher the tube temperature, the greater will be the corrosion rate.

Corrosion of the lower furnace area of a refuse boiler can be severe. All mass-fired refuse boilers have refractory lined lower furnace walls to protect them from corrosion. Figure 27 shows such an arrangement in which the tubes have pin studs welded to them to anchor silicon carbide refractory. The refractory still allows heat transfer from the furnace to the tubes.

Bimetal tubes are another method to prevent corrosion. The carbon steel tubes have an outer layer of Inconel™, which is an alloy of nickel and chromium that resists corrosion.

Figure 27	Tubes with Pin Studs

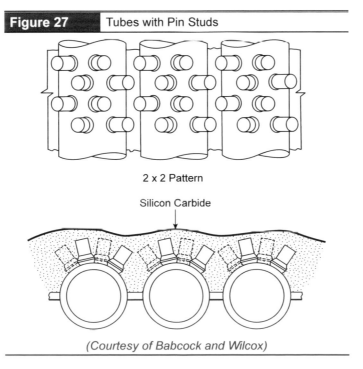

2 x 2 Pattern

Silicon Carbide

(Courtesy of Babcock and Wilcox)

Refuse Firing Installations

Figure 28 shows a mass burning refuse-to-energy plant layout. Refuse trucks dump into a storage pit. Overhead cranes keep the refuse feed hoppers full. Feeders move the refuse to the traveling grate stokers for combustion. The flue gases pass from the boiler to dry scrubbers and a bag-house to remove particulates from the gases, before going to the stack.

Figure 28	Refuse Plant Layout

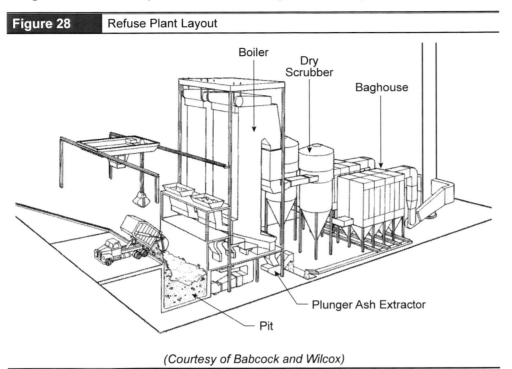

(Courtesy of Babcock and Wilcox)

A typical fuel feeding system, showing combustion airflow locations, is illustrated in Figure 29. Air is fed up under the traveling grate stoker and also above the stoker in over-fire air ducts.

Figure 29	Refuse Fuel Handling System

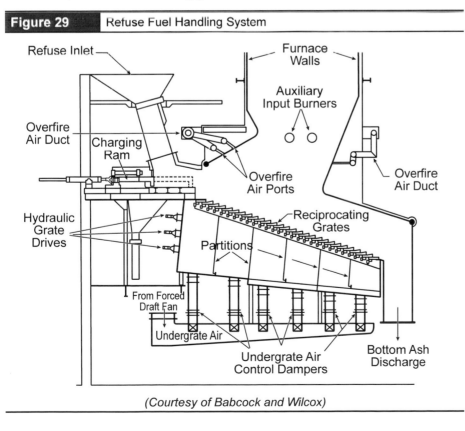

(Courtesy of Babcock and Wilcox)

Figure 30 shows a typical mass-burning boiler. It has a traveling grate stoker and plunger ash extraction. There are auxiliary burners above the stoker area to aid in complete combustion.

Figure 30 | Mass Firing Boiler

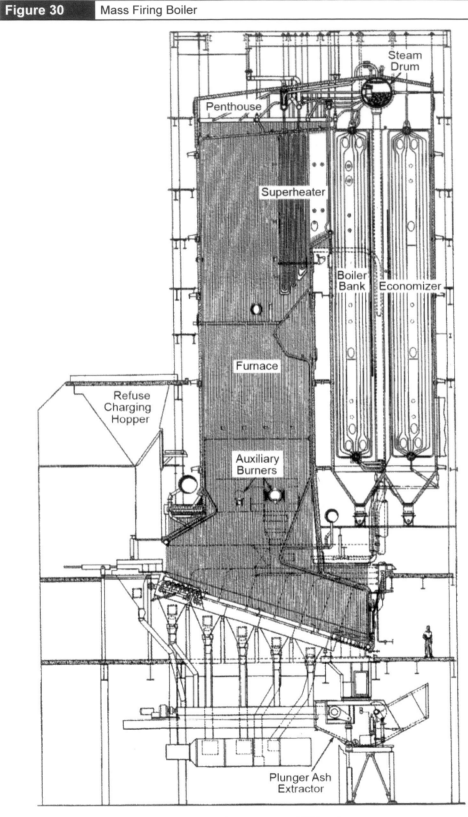

(Courtesy of Babcock and Wilcox)

OBJECTIVE 6

Describe typical designs, components and operating strategies for waste heat, biomass boilers.

BIOMASS

Biomass fuels are biological materials that are derived from recently living substances. Examples include leaves, grasses, bamboo, vine clippings, sugar cane, coffee grounds, rice hulls, wood, bark, sawdust, wood chips, etc. They may include any biodegradable materials that are combustible.

Biomass fuels are most often used in industrial processes where a large supply of energy for heating and drying is required. For example, the production of pulp and paper requires large quantities of mechanical energy and in order to produce a final product, the pulp must be dried, usually using steam. These energy requirements, along with the availability of waste wood products, make firing boilers with wood and biomass products a good choice.

The food processing industry has energy needs that can be supplied by steam, produced in a biomass boiler. These processes are ideal for biomass burning since they usually leave behind waste products, which are easily used as fuel in a boiler. Some examples are coffee grounds, sugar cane fiber, coconut hulls, rice hulls, and shells from nuts.

Utility plants can improve economy by replacing high cost fossil fuels with low cost biomass fuels. Often such a plant is standalone, supplying its own energy and heat requirements, but may also be adjacent to another plant to which it can supply steam.

Biomass may be burned in combination with a fossil fuel, such as coal, natural gas or oil. If coal is burned, there will be a traveling grate, on which the biomass is combined with the coal. When burned with oil or gas, the biomass is fed by a traveling grate while the gas or oil burners are located above the biomass fire.

Biomass Burning Systems

Systems to burn wood and biomass include:

- a separate furnace, called a dutch oven,
- a pinhole grate,
- a traveling grate or
- a vibrating grate arrangement.

Dutch Oven

Figure 31 shows a dutch oven arrangement.

The dutch oven is a refractory walled cell, which is connected to a conventional furnace. Wood or biomass is fed into the top of the dutch oven. It burns in a pile on the oven floor. Air is fed around the sides of the oven, through rows of nozzles in the refractory walls. The walls are often water cooled to prolong the refractory life.

The dutch oven can burn high moisture fuels. Its main disadvantage is the need to reduce firing to clean out the ashes, which is done manually with rakes. The furnace burners are used to supply heat when the dutch ovens are down for cleaning.

Figure 31   Dutch-Oven Fired Boiler

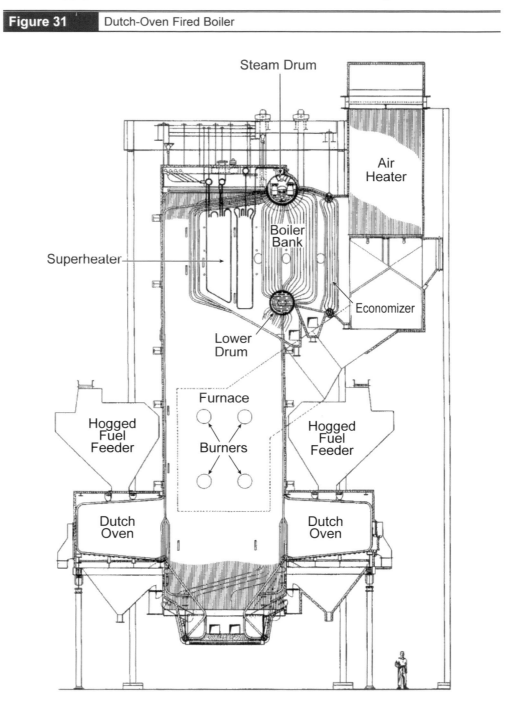

(Courtesy of Babcock and Wilcox)

Pinhole Grate

Figure 32 shows a biomass furnace with a pinhole grate.

This is a water-cooled grate that is clamped to the floor tubes of the furnace. The grates have venturi-type air holes to admit air to the burning material on the grate. This produces a semi-suspension mode of burning. The finer particles burn in suspension, and the heavier fractions accumulate on the floor as ashes. The ashes are removed by raking, either by manual or mechanical means.

The advantage of this system is that little refractory is used and maintenance is low. The main disadvantage involves shutting down or reducing firing to remove the ashes.

Figure 32	Pinhole Grate Stoker

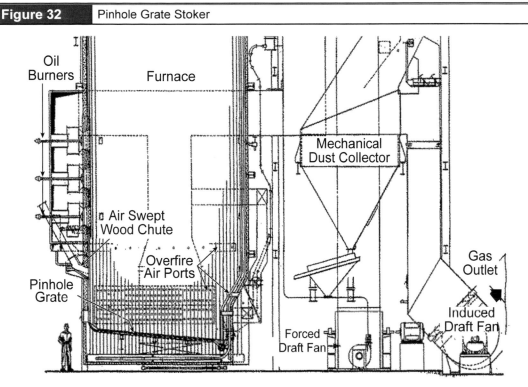

(Courtesy of Babcock and Wilcox)

Travelling Grate

The traveling grate was developed as an improvement on the pinhole grate. It is a moving grate that allows for continuous ash removal. It consists of cast iron grate bars attached to chains. The chains are driven by a slow moving sprocket drive system. There are openings in the grate to feed under-grate air to cool the bars and castings. Usually 60 to 85% of the combustion air is fed from below the grates. The traveling grate system is similar to the traveling grate systems used for firing coal. Problems associated with these types of systems involve high maintenance of the grates and drive system components.

Vibrating Grate

A vibrating grate systems is shown in Figure 33.

Grate bars are attached to a frame that vibrates to remove the ash. The vibration is intermittent and controlled by a timer. The vibrating grate system has lower maintenance costs than the traveling grate system. The vibration also serves to aid combustion by leveling out the bed of burning biomass.

Figure 33	Vibrating Grate Stoker

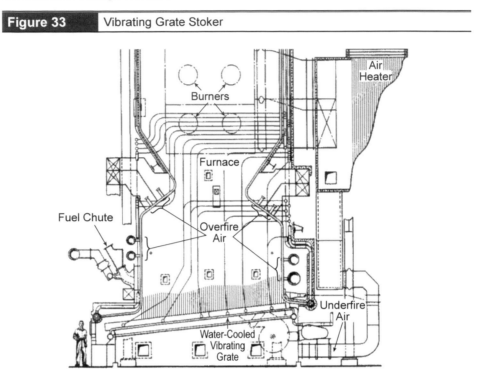

(Courtesy of Babcock and Wilcox)

The vibrating grates may be air-cooled or water-cooled. The water-cooled grates, as shown in Figure 34, allow for high under-fed air temperatures. They are suitable for burning cellulose fuels, including wood. The stationary grate segments, fabricated from heat resistant castings, are supported by the furnace floor tubes, which provide cooling. Maintenance is low since there are no moving parts. The boiler in Figure 35 uses this water-cooled grate arrangement. Water cooled grates are often called 'hydrogrates" and the stoker called a 'hydrograte stoker'.

Figure 34	Water Cooled Grate

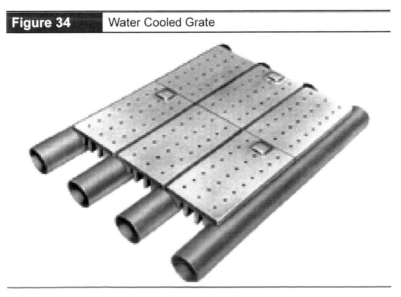

Figure 35	Wood Fired Stirling Boiler

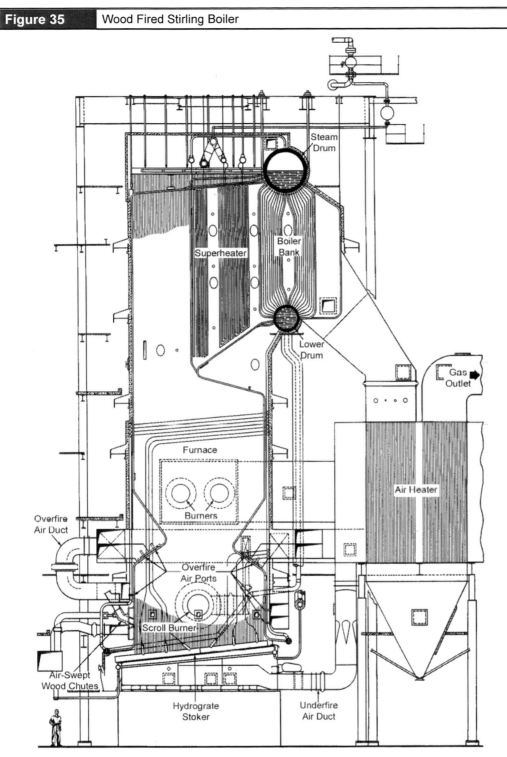

(Courtesy of Babcock and Wilcox)

CHAPTER 2 - QUESTIONS

1. Why is steam injected into oil wells for heating? What is the advantage of using steam instead of hot water?

2. What are the advantages of the fluidized bed method of combustion? Explain the difference between CFB and BFB fluidized bed boilers.

3. What is an HRSG? Explain combined cycle power generation and cogeneration.

4. Describe what black liquor is. Why is air fed to three levels of a typical black liquor recovery boiler? What can cause an explosion in a black liquor boiler furnace?

5. Explain the two techniques used to burn refuse. What causes corrosion of lower furnace tubes in a refuse burning boiler?

6. Briefly describe the following systems used to burn biomass:
   a) Traveling grate system
   b) Pinhole grate system
   c) Vibrating grate system

ANSWERS: All answers are found within the content of the chapter.

Boiler Construction

LEARNING OUTCOME

When you complete this chapter you should be able to:

Explain Code requirements, in general terms, and describe construction and assembly methods for the major components of a large boiler.

LEARNING OBJECTIVES

Here is what you should be able to do when you complete each objective:

1. *Explain top and bottom support and describe the support techniques for various components of a large boiler, including lateral supports for furnace walls. Explain allowances for expansion.*

2. *Explain the purpose, design, locations and installation methods for boiler casing insulation, refractory, and cladding.*

3. *Describe the methods used to fabricate boiler tubes.*

4. *Describe the preparation, fabrication, and testing of boiler drums.*

5. *Describe methods of attaching tubes to drums and headers, including expanding and welding, and explain where each method would be used.*

6. *Explain code requirements/sizes for, and describe the designs and installation of, manholes and handholes, including welded handholes. Explain procedures for removing and installing covers.*

7. *Describe the field assembly of a large boiler or steam generating unit.*

OBJECTIVE 1

Explain top and bottom support and describe the support techniques for various components of a large boiler, including lateral supports for furnace walls. Explain allowances for expansion.

TOP-SUPPORTED BOILERS

Large steam generating units are top-supported by means of steel columns, which require massive foundation piers. The boiler components are held on hangers, which extend from the structural steel to the various components. This allows the pressure parts of the boiler to expand downwards from the main supports at the top.

Figure 1 illustrates the structural steel components of a large steam generator.

Figure 1	Boiler Structural Steel

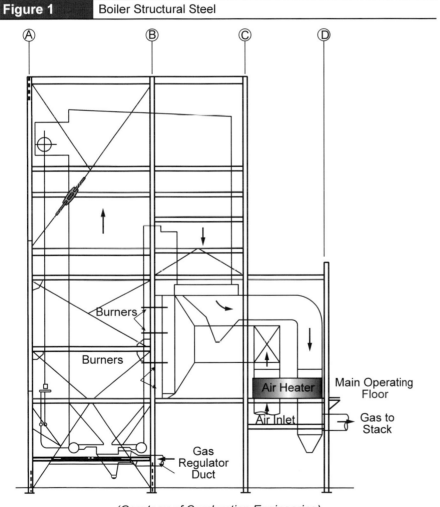

(Courtesy of Combustion Engineering)

When the structural steel is complete, "U" shaped hangers are attached to the structure for support of the main steam drum. Figure 2 shows a steam drum being hoisted into place.

The drum is supported by U-bolts, which permit linear movement (expansion) of the drum with temperature variations. The drum is used as the major anchor point for other boiler components, so accurate location is important.

Figure 2	Lifting Lugs and Tackle for Hoisting Drums

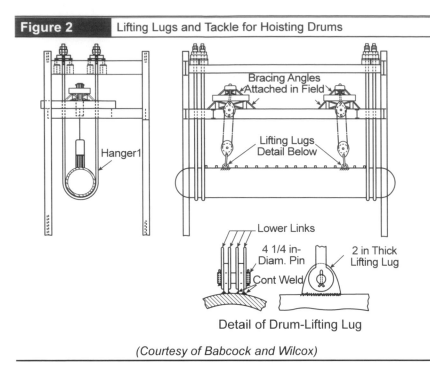

Detail of Drum-Lifting Lug

(Courtesy of Babcock and Wilcox)

With the drum secured in its final position, various components, such as superheater and economizer headers, are positioned in relation to the drum. Superheaters, economizer, and wall tubes are aligned and then welded or expanded to the drums and headers.

The furnace wall tubes are assembled and welded into panels at the manufacturer's facility and then shipped in sections, which are welded into place in the field. Figure 3 shows a furnace wall panel being manufactured in the shop.

Figure 3	Furnace Wall Panel Manufacturing

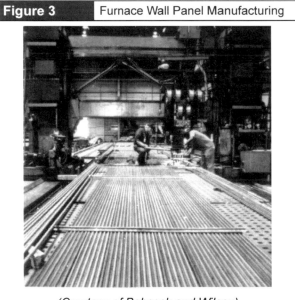

(Courtesy of Babcock and Wilcox)

Figure 4 illustrates the supporting columns and overhead steelwork with the boiler components in place. The concrete foundations upon which the columns are placed are not visible, but the method of supporting the top drum headers and furnace wall tube sections is shown. The method of support for the major components can be seen in Figure 4.

- **Steam drum:** is hung from the top steelwork.
- **Large steam piping and superheaters:** they are hung from the top by large spring hangers.

- **Furnace walls:** tubes are welded into the top headers. They expand downward. The furnace walls also need lateral support. Figure 5 shows a buckstay support system. The buckstays are external beams or trusses, which give the furnace wall additional, lateral support. Figure 5 shows how buckstays are joined at the corners of a furnace. For this type of membrane wall support, the channel bar is welded to the membrane bar between the tubes.

- **Ducts:** supported from the steel beams. Expansion joints must be used, where the ducting is attached to boiler casings, fans, or other auxiliary equipment.

- **Fans:** the fans rest on the concrete foundations. There are expansion provisions in the piping and ducting, which connects the fans to the boiler.

- **Air preheater:** supported from the beams at its side. The air ducts have expansion joints.

Figure 4	Steam Generator Structural Steel and Support Columns

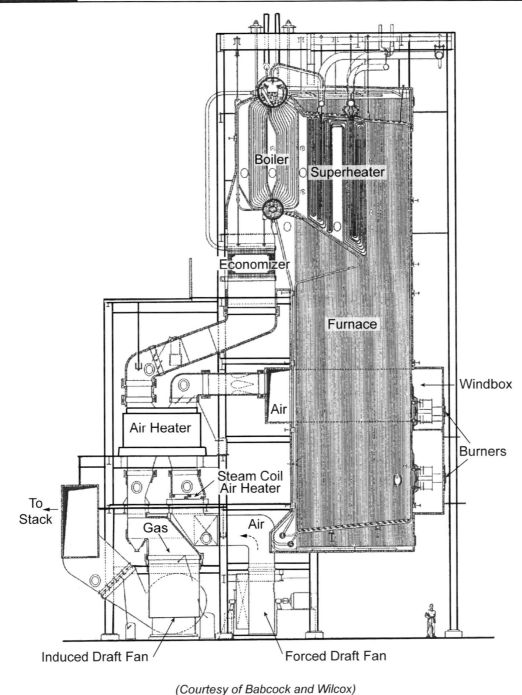

(Courtesy of Babcock and Wilcox)

| **Figure 5** | Tie Bar and Buckstay Arrangement at Corners of Furnace |

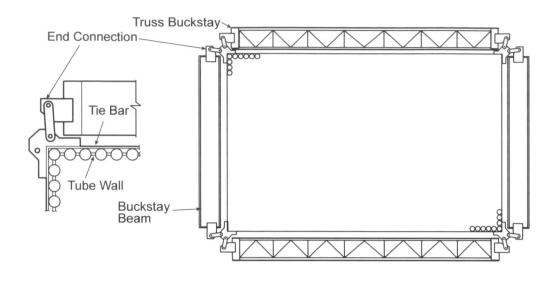

(Courtesy of Babcock and Wilcox)

Bottom-Supported Boiler

The bottom-supported boiler in Figure 6 has concrete drum foundations, which support the bottom drum and bottom headers. The boiler tubes themselves are used to support the top drum. These tubes connecting the two drums are expanded into the tube holes, and then the furnace wall panels are erected and welded into place.

| **Figure 6** | Bottom Supported Boiler |

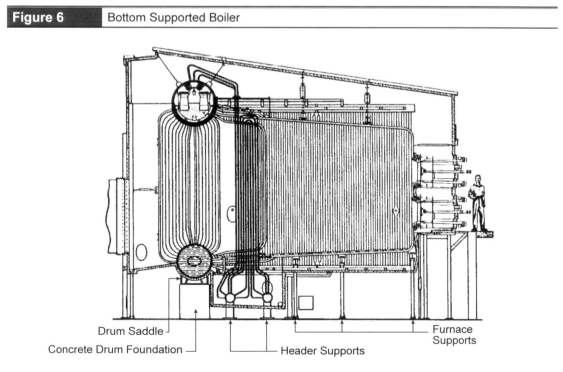

(Courtesy of Babcock and Wilcox)

The bottom drum supports have sliding pads or feet, which allow for expansion. The walls have lateral supports, which attach to the steelwork. All piping and ductwork must have provision for expansion. General expansion in this case is upwards.

OBJECTIVE 2

Explain the purpose, design, locations and installation methods for boiler casing, insulation, refractory, and cladding.

BOILER CASING

'Boiler casing' is the term used to describe the airtight metal casing of a boiler wall. In general, inner and outer boiler casings are used in areas that do not have membrane wall construction. The casings are insulated from the heat of the furnace by a combination of water-wall tubes, refractory and block insulation. It is made of steel plate and will withstand temperatures to 400°C. It also provides support for the refractory. On the outside of the boiler casing is another layer of block or blanket insulation and an outer skin or metal lagging.

Support structure for boiler walls may be welded to the casing, as in Figure 7. Here a beam or channel tie bar is welded to the casing. Another beam, called a buckstay attaches to the tie bar. This is not a rigid connection, but a sliding foot arrangement, allowing for movement.

Figure 7	Boiler Casing

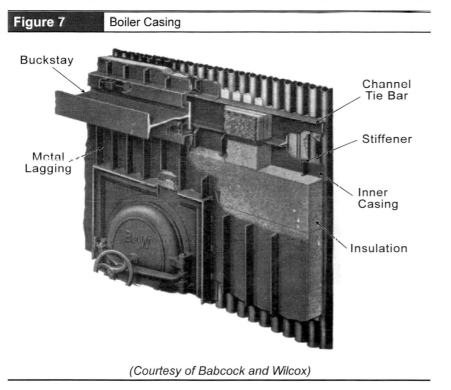

(Courtesy of Babcock and Wilcox)

Insulation

Insulation is used as heat protection for personnel and to stop the loss of heat from the boiler internal sections.

Insulation can be in the form of:

- Mineral wool blanket: made of mineral wool fibers compressed into blanket form. It is used for temperatures to 650°C.
- Mineral wool base block: made of mineral wool fibers and clay, molded under heat and pressure. It is designed to insulate tube walls and casings, and can withstand temperatures up to 1000°C, depending upon the grade. It is used in a layer between a refractory wall and the boiler steel casing, and also between the boiler casing and lagging.

- Calcium silicate block: used on enclosures and piping for temperatures below 650°C.
- High temperature plastic: comes in a moldable cement form and is used to fill gaps in refractory and in block insulation. It has a temperature limit of 1050°C.
- Ceramic fiber: made of high purity fibers, which have a melting point above 1650°C. It is used to make seals for tube enclosures, or in spots where high temperature insulation is specified.

Refractory

Refractory is cement like. It is used to withstand very high temperatures in areas such as burner throats and boiler target walls. The walls often have two layers of castable refractory. One layer, such as 90% alumina castable, will be for extreme heat. The next layer is more of an insulating type of castable, such as insulating castable 1500. There is usually a layer of block insulation between the castable refractory and the steel boiler casing.

The use of membrane or water-cooled walls reduces the use of castable refractories in many watertube boilers. However, A thin layer of castable material may still be applied to membrane wall tubes to protect them from erosion or corrosion.

Castable walls are poured into moulds similar to how cement is poured and can also be troweled in thin layers. Thick walls require a controlled dry-out or curing procedure. The dry-out is used to remove any moisture in a slow and controlled manner. Rapid drying of the castable would result in blistering.

Figure 8 shows the temperature gradient through a furnace wall with layers of firebrick (castable) and block insulation. The castable temperature is nearly as high as the furnace temperature. The main function of the castable is to protect the block insulation from the direct heat of the furnace. The block insulation has a higher insulation value. The outside temperature of the block insulation is 60°C, while the surface contacting the castable is 681°C.

Figure 8	Temperature Gradient Through a Furnace Wall

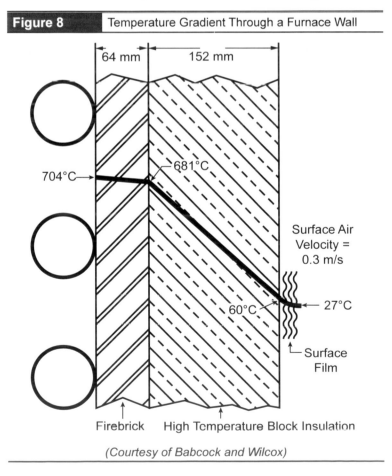

(Courtesy of Babcock and Wilcox)

Lagging

Lagging (also called cladding) is the metal covering that protects the outer surface of the boiler. It is made of light gauge, galvanized steel or aluminum sheets. It can be made water tight for outdoor installations.

Figure 9 shows a membrane wall with metal lagging.

Figure 9	Membrane Wall with Metal Lagging (Cladding)

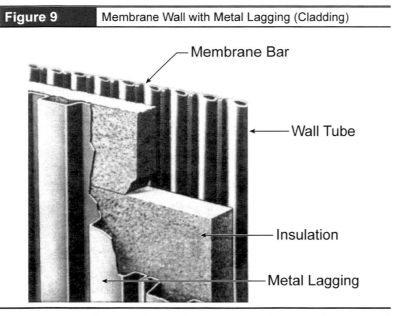

Lagging is usually installed with screws or pins, attaching it to the boiler casing, as shown in Figure 10. The lagging is not used to seal in the flue gases, but acts as an outer skin, protecting the insulation from the elements.

Figure 10	Lagging Installation on Membrane Wall

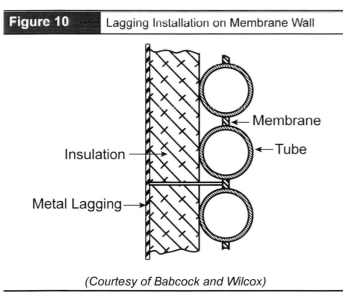

(Courtesy of Babcock and Wilcox)

OBJECTIVE 3

Describe the methods used to fabricate boiler tubes.

WELDED TUBES

Boiler tubes may be seamless or they may be welded. Welded tubes are formed from a flat strip of carbon steel rolled into a tubular form. The edges are then butt welded together. The procedure for the manufacture of Electric-resistance-welded (ERW) tubes is described as follows.

- Flat strips are formed into a tubular shape by rolling. A welding machine, with two electrodes that straddle the tube joint, then welds the tube. The welding current passes between the electrodes, through the tube joint thus producing enough heat to fuse the edges together.

- The tubing is then accurately straightened and cut to the required length in a sizing mill. The tubes are then normalized by heating in a controlled-atmosphere furnace to produce a uniform metallurgical structure throughout.

- During this heat treatment, the tubes receive a rust-retardant oxide finish. As the tubes emerge from the furnace, they are conveyed through rotary straighteners to the cutoff machines.

The final, finishing of welded boiler tubes is done either by **hot-finishing**, or **cold-drawing**, depending on the size, tolerance, and finish desired. The metallurgy of the two is similar; the difference is mainly in surface finish and the permissible tolerance in dimensions. To obtain a fine, smooth and even surface with close tolerances, stainless steel tubing is generally finished by cold drawing only, as shown in Figure 11. The newly formed tube is drawn through a die, which is the exact size of the required outside tube diameter. Inside the tube is a mandrel the size of the required inside diameter.

Figure 11	Drawbench for Producing Cold-Drawn Tubes

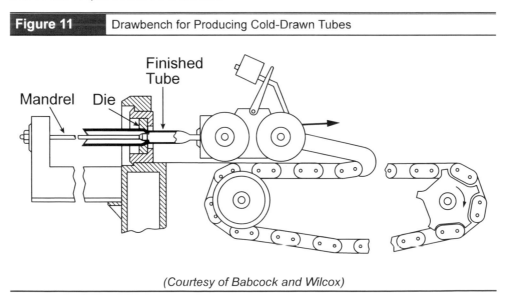

(Courtesy of Babcock and Wilcox)

SEAMLESS TUBES

A seamless tube has no welded joints. The tube is manufactured from a solid, round bar, usually by one of two processes. One process may be called 'piercing' and the other called 'extrusion'.

The piercing method actually has four steps, piercing, rolling, reeling, and finishing. In the first step, piercing, a very hot, solid, round billet of steel is forced over a piercing point bar by conically shaped rolls. The piercing bar produces a hole through the center of the bar as the rollers apply external force at the outside surface. This operation is shown in Figure 12.

Figure 12	Piercing Operation

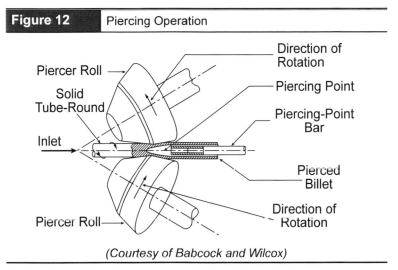

(Courtesy of Babcock and Wilcox)

After piercing, the bar is withdrawn from the inside of the tube and the roughly pierced "hollow" may be reheated in a furnace to the correct temperature for the next step, rolling.

The function of the rolling mill is to lengthen the tube and reduce the wall thickness to the approximate dimensions required. As shown in Figure 13, a ram forces the tube into the grooves of the roller, the rotation of which carries the tube forward over a plug and bar. The metal is squeezed between the groove surface and the plug.

Figure 13	Rolling Operation

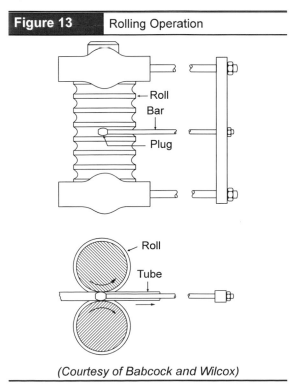

(Courtesy of Babcock and Wilcox)

Figure 14 shows the third step. Immediately after rolling and while the tube is still hot, a reeling machine smooths the outer surface. This is called burnishing. The tube is rounded and expanded in diameter, but the wall thickness remains nearly constant or, depending upon the pressure applied, could be slightly reduced.

Figure 14	Reeling Operation

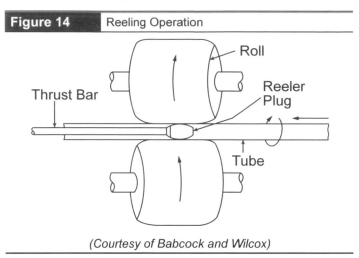

(Courtesy of Babcock and Wilcox)

After reeling, the tube is finished by taking it to the sizing mill to be annealed or heat-treated, straightened, cut to length, hydrostatically tested, and submitted for final inspection.

The extrusion method is illustrated in Figure 15.

A hot, hollow billet is squeezed between a die and mandrel by a ram. The outside diameter of the tube is controlled by the die, and the inside diameter is controlled by the mandrel. A special glass lubricant is used to lubricate the mandrel, billet, and die during the operation. After the hot extrusion process is finished, cold drawing is used to bring the tubes to the desired size.

Figure 15	Extrusion Process

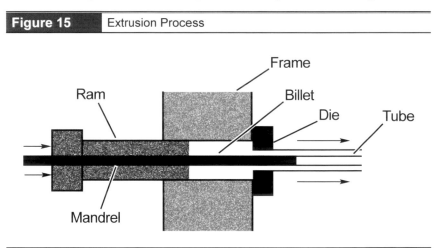

All pressure tubes are subjected to either a hydrostatic pressure test or a nondestructive test over their entire length and periphery as specified in ASME Code, Section I, PW-54 and American Society for Testing and Materials.

Materials used in boiler tube fabrication are specified in ASME Code Section I, PG. 9 and maximum tube size is 127 mm OD as stated in PG. 27.

OBJECTIVE 4

Describe the preparation, fabrication, and testing of boiler drums.

SHELL & DRUM FABRICATION

Boiler shells and drums are fabricated from steel plates, the thickness of which depends upon the pressure they must withstand, the composition of the steel, and the diameter of the finished drum or shell. Plates used in boiler manufacturing range in thickness from 6.4 mm to 250 mm, (ASME Section I, PG-16.3 and PFT 9.1). Guidelines for the selection of the material to be used are given in PG-6.1.

To form a drum or shell of the required diameter, the plates must be rolled to the correct curvature, as shown in Figure 16. If the plate is thin, it may be rolled, without heating, to form a complete cylinder. Thicker plates, however, are often heated first and then formed (pressed) into half-cylindrical sections (see Fig. 17), which are subsequently welded together at the longitudinal seams to form the complete cylinder.

Figure 16	Cold-Rolling Boiler Plate

When short courses (or drum sections) must be used, because of the material dimensions or heat treatment requirements, the plate is rolled into a fully cylindrical course. For large diameter drums, the normal procedure is to press the plate into half-cylinders, in lengths up to about 12 m, and to form a course by welding two half cylinders together longitudinally. The desired drum length is obtained by circumferentially joining courses as required. The automatic submerged-arc welding process is normally used for the longitudinal and circumferential seams in drums.

Drum heads are formed from flat plate by hot pressing with suitable forming dies and then machining the circumferential weld grooves. Circumferential welds are used to join the heads to the drum.

| **Figure 17** | Half Cylinder Section of Thick Drum |

The tube holes are drilled in the drum (see Fig. 18) or flat head and checked for proper size; then any burrs or projections are removed.

Note: ASME Code Section I, PG. 52 states the rules for openings in pressure vessels, and Figures 2, 3, and 4, PG. 52 of the code illustrate these definite patterns.

| **Figure 18** | Drilling Tube Holes In Drum |

Nozzles & Stubs

Nozzles are used to connect the boiler drums to external piping, such as steam outlet line, feedwater inlet, blowdown line, etc. or to fittings, such as safety valves, water columns, etc. The nozzles are generally welded to a pre-drilled (or machined) opening in the drum, following very strict specifications for size of opening, weld design and weld procedures given in ASME Section I.

In locations where it is not possible or practical to attach tubes to drums and headers by expansion of the tube ends, stubs (short sections of tube) are used. The stubs are inserted and welded into the pre-drilled tube holes in the drum or header, again following the strict requirements of the ASME, Section I code. The tubes are then welded to these stubs.

Figure 19 illustrates stubs being attached to a header before the header is stress relieved. After stress relieving, the tubes are welded to the stubs, eliminating the need for welding directly to the header or drum.

Figure 19	Tube Stub Installation in Header

(Courtesy of Babcock and Wilcox)

Welding & Stress Relieving

Prior to and throughout all welding operations a preheat treatment, as specified in the ASME Code Section I, PW-38, may be applied to the weld area to avoid detrimental stress conditions and metallurgical transformations. For some applications, this preheat is maintained after welding until the vessel is stress relieved, or postweld heat-treated.

Postweld heat treatment, often called stress relieving, consists of uniformly heating the welded parts to a temperature sufficient to relieve most of the internal stresses created by the welding heat. The parts are then cooled at a constant rate.

The requirements for postweld heat treatment are contained in paragraph PW 39 in Section I of the ASME Code. Required holding temperatures and times for various materials are listed in this paragraph along with detailed rules and instructions.

- In general, the Code states that, unless specifically excepted, all welded pressure parts of power boilers shall be postweld heat treated at a specified temperature. The welded parts shall be heated slowly to this temperature and held for the required time and then allowed to cool slowly in a still atmosphere to a temperature of 315°C or below.

Various methods of stress relieving are used. At the boiler manufacturers shop the entire boiler drum may be heated, under controlled conditions, in a special stress relieving furnace. In the field, the stress relieving of welded pipe joints may be accomplished using electrical induction coils, which are wrapped around the welded section of the pipe. Another method uses gas burner rings to heat the metal in the welded section.

Figure 20 shows a steam drum with nozzles welded in place, ready for stress relieving. After stress relieving, only the nozzles, not the drum, will be used for welding attachments.

Figure 20	Steam Drum Ready for Stress Relieving

(Courtesy Combustion Engineering Inc.)

It is not permissible, to make any welds directly to the drum after stress relieving. Welds can be made only to nozzles and attachments. If, for any reason, welding must be done to the drum after stress relieving, field stress relieving must be performed afterwards, following the ASME code guidelines.

Inspection & Tests

Before postweld heat treatment, the weld surfaces are smoothed by grinding, then inspected and tested as specified in ASME Code Section I, PW-51, 52, 53, and CSA B51, Section 4.

Radiographic examinations are performed on the longitudinal and circumferential seam welds of a drum, using the X-ray method. The film cassette is positioned on the inner surface of the weld being X-rayed. Figure 21 shows a longitudinal drum being X-rayed.

A final test carried out in the manufacturer's shop is a hydraulic or hydrostatic test (conducted according to the ASME Code Section I, PW-54) at a pressure of 1.5 times the maximum allowable working pressure (MAWP). When the drum has passed the hydrostatic test, it is then considered to be complete and ready for the stress-relieving process.

An internal inspection of a steam drum is being carried out in Figure 22.

Figure 21 | X-Raying of Drum Welds

(Courtesy of Babcock and Wilcox)

Figure 22 | Internal Inspection of Tube Connections

(Courtesy of Babcock and Wilcox)

OBJECTIVE 5

Describe methods of attaching tubes to drums and headers, including expanding and welding, and explain where each method would be used.

TUBE ATTACHMENT

Boiler tubes are attached to drums or sheets by expanding the tube ends into the tube holes, using a special tool, called a tube expander. The expander consists of three rollers, mounted in a cage, which fit inside the tube end. A tapered spindle, called a mandrel, fits between the rollers and when the mandrel is turned, it causes the rollers to rotate and be forced out against the tube wall. This presses the tube tightly outward against the tube hole, which is often grooved to improve the tightness of the joint. The expander also flares the end of the tube.

The position of the expander and mandrel after the tube is expanded and flared is shown in Figure 23. In this case, the tube is being expanded into a flat tubesheet.

Figure 23	Expander and Mandrel

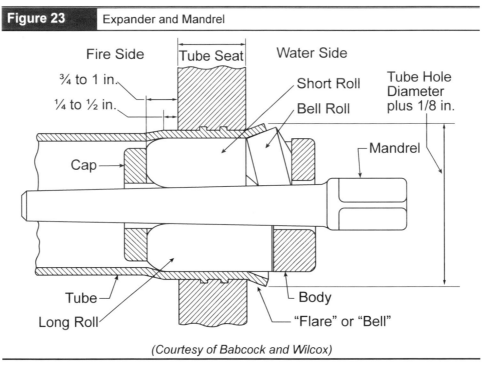

(Courtesy of Babcock and Wilcox)

Figure 24 shows an expander being used inside a boiler drum.

Figure 25 shows a retractive expander being used in a watertube boiler. In this design, the expander is inserted into the tube end to the depth of the tubesheet and then the mandrel is extracted, causing expansion on the way out. The figure shows the mandrel in the starting position and about half way through its extraction.

| Figure 24 | Tube Expander |

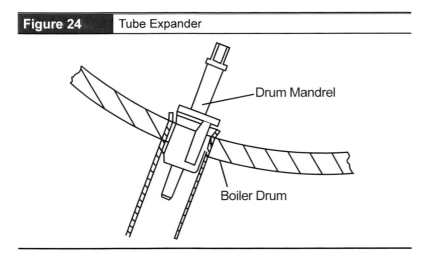

| Figure 25 | Retractive Expander for Watertube Boiler |

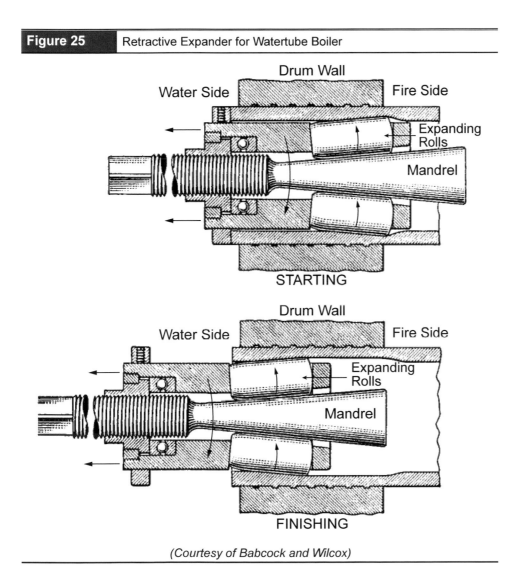

(Courtesy of Babcock and Wilcox)

As explained in Objective 4, boiler tubes are often welded to stubs, which have already been welded to the headers or drum. This method of attachment is often used for superheater, reheater, and waterwall tubes, particularly when joining to relatively small headers.

Figure 26 shows tubes that have been welded to the stubs on a header. It also illustrates how handholes are installed into the header, allowing internal inspection of the header and, occasionally, for back welding the tubes.

Figure 26	Header with Welded Stubs and Tubes

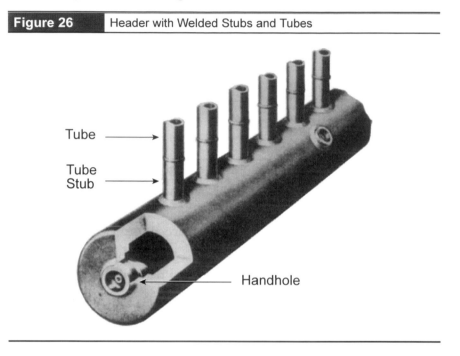

OBJECTIVE 6

Explain code requirements/sizes for, and describe the designs and installation of, manholes and handholes, including welded handholes. Explain procedures for removing and installing covers.

MANHOLES & HANDHOLES

Handholes and manholes are provided in drums and headers to give internal access for cleaning, inspection, and repair during the life of the boiler. Manhole and handhole openings are usually elliptical in shape, but may be circular.

Manholes

The ASME Code Section I, PG-44.1, specifies that the size of an elliptical manhole shall not be less than 300 mm by 400 mm. Circular manholes shall not be less than 380 mm in diameter. Handholes shall have a minimum size of 70 mm by 89 mm with larger sizes being recommended.

When a manhole opening is made in a drum or shell, the area becomes weaker due to the amount of metal removed. Therefore, reinforcement is provided either by forming a flange around the opening or by welding a frame to the shell around the opening.

Figures 27 - 31 are illustrations of various manhole designs.

Figure 27	Bolted Manhole Covers

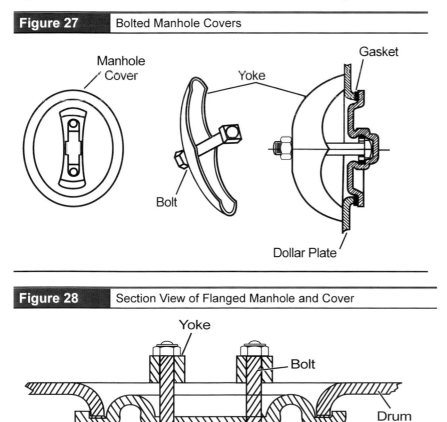

Figure 28	Section View of Flanged Manhole and Cover

| Figure 29 | Solid Flanged Manhole with Cast Steel Cover for Flat Surfaces |

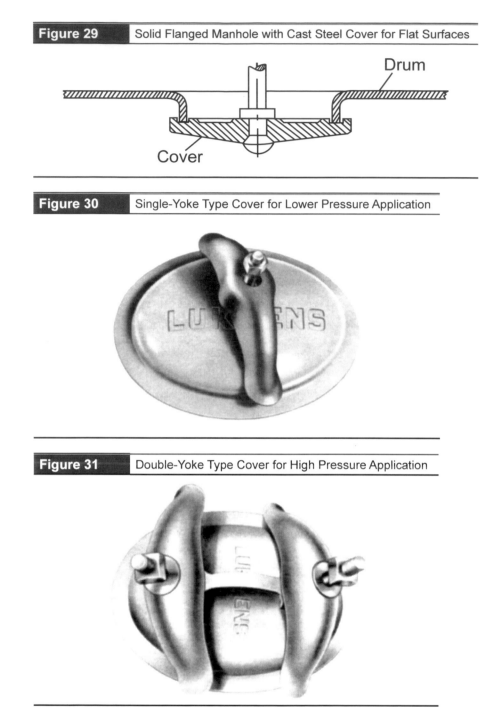

Drum

Cover

| Figure 30 | Single-Yoke Type Cover for Lower Pressure Application |

| Figure 31 | Double-Yoke Type Cover for High Pressure Application |

Manhole Installation

The manhole cover fits against the inside surface of the opening. This means that the elliptical shaped covers can be inserted and removed through the opening, but the circular type must remain in place within the drum. The cover is held in place by bolts and yoke pieces. When the boiler is in operation, the internal pressure within the boiler pushes out against the cover helping to hold the cover in place against the flange.

The gaskets used are the woven type for pressures up to 3450 kPa and the metallic type for higher pressures. Care is taken to center the manhole in the drum opening before it is tightened to manufacturer's specifications. Gaskets are often changed after a hydrostatic test, since the gasket has been compressed beyond normal thickness.

Handholes

When larger openings for maintenance or entry are not needed or possible, such as in headers, a handhole is used. It provides enough access for inspection and cleaning. For pressures up to 8370 kPa and temperatures up to 454°C, handhole covers with gaskets are used and are bolted into place. For higher pressures and temperatures the handhole cover is seal welded into place and mating surfaces are machined so that gaskets are not necessary.

Figure 32 illustrates a gasketed and bolted handhole cover.

Figure 33 shows a welded handhole.

Figure 32	Bolted and Gasketed Handhole Cover

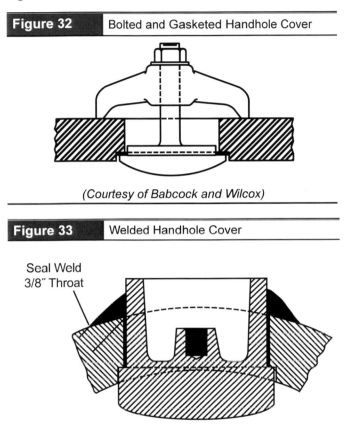

(Courtesy of Babcock and Wilcox)

Figure 33	Welded Handhole Cover

Seal Weld
3/8″ Throat

Handhole Installation & Removal

The bolted handhole cover is oval in shape, allowing it to be inserted through the opening pulled up against the inside of the opening, with the gasket in place. By means of a nut, bolt, and a yoke the cover is then tightened against the inside seat.

A torque of approximately 400 Nm should be applied when tightening the handhole cover and this same torque should be re-applied again after a hydrostatic test of the boiler. When compressed, the gasket must not have a thickness greater than 6 mm, according to the ASME.

Welded handhole covers are circular in shape, allowing them to fit through the opening while tilted by 90 degrees. They can then be turned and the shoulder of the cover fitted onto the machined seat on the inside surface of the header.

Gaskets are not used with welded handhole fittings. Instead the cover has a shoulder with a machined surface, which fits against a similar surface around the inside of the opening. The shoulder provides the mechanical strength of the fitting while a seal weld around the cover on the outside of the header provides the leak tightness.

OBJECTIVE 7

Describe the field assembly of a large boiler or steam generating unit.

FIELD ASSEMBLY

Larger boilers are field assembled, which means they must be built or erected in the field. The components are shipped separately to the customer's facility. A construction crew, under the charge of the manufacturers supervisor, assembling the boiler on site.

Foundations

All foundations must be completed before the structural steel can be installed. Large quantities of concrete are used to complete the foundations, which must support the loads from the boiler and all of the auxiliary equipment. Some parts of the boiler, such as the bottom ash pit may be completed as part of the concrete foundation.

Structural Supports

After the foundations are complete, the structural steel is installed. This structural steel may be part of the building steel or it may be a separate structure. The weight of the structural steel is carried by the foundations. The structural steel carries the weight of the steam drum and the major pressure components. After the steel structure has been put in place and aligned, the major pressure components can be installed.

Pressure Component Installation

The steam drum is usually the first major pressure component placed in the steel structure. The steam drum must be carefully positioned and leveled. The various headers, such as superheater and economizer, are then put into position. Figure 34 shows a steam drum being lifted.

Figure 34	Steam Drum Lift

(Courtesy of Babcock and Wilcox)

Figure 35 shows the drum in final position. Accurate location of the drum is also important, as it is the major anchor point for other boiler components.

Figure 35	Steam Drum in Position

(Courtesy of Babcock and Wilcox)

The superheater, reheater, and economizer are installed as complete modules with the headers attached. Figure 36 shows a superheater module being lifted into place. Superheater, economizer, and wall tubes are aligned and welded or expanded to the drums and headers.

Figure 36	Superheater Module being Lifted

(Courtesy of Combustion Engineering)

Sections of furnace wall tubes are assembled and welded into panels at the manufacturer's shop. These panels are then shipped as sections and welded into place in the field. The furnace wall tubes form a large percentage of the furnace enclosure. Tubes are connected to drums and headers by welding and expanding or by a combination of the two methods. High-pressure connections above 10 MPa are often expanded and seal welded. Another method is to weld the tube to shop attached stubs.

Figure 37 shows two headers with stubs, ready for installation

Figure 37	Header with Stubs, Ready for Installation

(Courtesy of Babcock and Wilcox)

Figure 38 shows a membrane wall panel being lifted into position.

Figure 38	Membrane Wall Panel being Lifted

(Courtesy of Babcock and Wilcox)

After the tubes, drums, headers etc. have been assembled, and before any brick work, refractory or casing has been applied to the boiler, all openings are closed and the boiler is completely filled with water for a hydrostatic test. The test pressure is 1.5 times the maximum allowable working pressure (MAWP). During this test any faulty tube connections will be indicated by leakage. Most of the pressure components have been hydro tested in the shop, but the field welds need to be tested.

The Boiler Inspector carries out an inspection, which normally includes witnessing the hydrostatic test. If the test passes (ie. satisfactory to the Inspector) the refractory and casing can be installed.

Refractory

Large steam generators are constructed mostly of water-cooled tubes, in the form of membrane walls. Little refractory is required. Some refractory is still used in areas such as wall penetrations, door seals, wall box seals, and around burners.

Casing

Boiler casing is used in areas that are not constructed of membrane walls. Inner casing is on the inside of the insulation. It is made of welded steel plates. The purpose of pressure inner casing is to prevent air leakage from the boiler setting. It also serves as a base for the application of insulation and lagging.

Insulation & Lagging

Most of the insulation is applied to the outside of the boiler membrane wall or inner casings. It is typically block or blanket insulation. It must be tight, free of voids, and well anchored. Insulation is also applied to all hot ductwork and piping.

A light gauge metal lagging is installed over the insulation. For outdoor installations, the lagging must be waterproof. The lagging serves as a barrier to protect the insulation from water and physical damage.

Assembly of Auxiliary Equipment

Installing auxiliary equipment is often started as the pressure parts are being installed. Some larger auxiliaries are air heaters, fuel burning equipment, fans, ductwork, and boiler casings. Air heaters must be in position before the larger air ducts can be installed. Coal pulverizers must be installed early to allow installation of coal piping to the boiler.

CHAPTER 3 - QUESTIONS

1. Using simple sketches, explain how the steam drum is supported in bottom-supported and top supported boilers

2. Using a simple sketch, show how metal cladding and insulation are attached to a membrane wall.

3. What are two methods of fabricating boiler tubes? Briefly describe each method.

4. Explain the tests that are performed on a steam drum after welding is complete?

5. Describe the methods for attaching tubes to boiler drums and headers.

6. What is stress relieving? Why is it carried out after the nozzles have been attached to the drum?

7. List the steps in the field assembly of a top-supported steam generator.

8. Describe the installation of a welded handhole cover in a boiler header or drum.

ANSWERS: All answers are found within the content of the chapter.

Boiler Heat Transfer Components

LEARNING OUTCOME

When you complete this chapter you should be able to:

Explain the purpose, location, design and operating conditions for the major heat transfer components of a large watertube boiler or steam generator.

LEARNING OBJECTIVES

Here is what you should be able to do when you complete each objective:

1. Describe baffle designs and locations and explain their significance to boiler heat transfer.

2. Describe the designs of integral furnace sidewall and header arrangements, including tube-and-tile, tangent tube, and membrane.

3. Define primary, secondary, convection, radiation, platen, and pendant as they apply to superheaters. Describe the locations of superheaters within a steam generator and state the operating characteristics of convection and radiant superheaters.

4. Explain the purpose and design of a separately-fired superheater.

5. Explain the purpose and describe the locations of reheaters. Explain the position of and flow through the reheater in relation to the superheaters.

6. Describe designs and locations for integral and separate economizers.

7. Describe the designs, operation, and location of plate, tubular, and rotary regenerative air heaters.

8. Explain operating care and considerations that must be given to the various heat transfer sections of the boiler.

9. Explain a typical water and gas temperature profile through a large steam generating unit.

OBJECTIVE 1

Describe baffle designs and locations and explain their significance to boiler heat transfer.

FURNACE BAFFLES

In order to direct the flow of combustion gas over the tubes in a watertube boiler, it is necessary to use baffles. These baffles are arranged to guide the gas through the furnace to provide the required number of passes through the boiler and ensure maximum exposure to heat transfer surfaces.

Baffles can be placed to cause the gases to flow at right angles to the tube length, in which case they are called cross baffles. When placed to cause the gases to flow parallel to the tubes, they are called longitudinal baffles.

Baffles are usually constructed of refractory material and may be made up of individual bricks or tiles fitted into place around the tubes, or formed in place using castable refractory. Tube walls, where a section of tubes are adjacent to each other, not allowing flow through them, may also be used to form baffles.

Curved or streamlined baffles have the advantage of having no sharp turns to cause eddy currents, increase friction, or form pockets for ash accumulation.

A baffle arrangement in a four-drum boiler is shown in Figure 1, while Figure 2 illustrates an arrangement in a three-drum boiler and Figure 3 shows a two-drum D-type boiler.

Figure 1	Four-Drum Boiler Baffling Arrangement

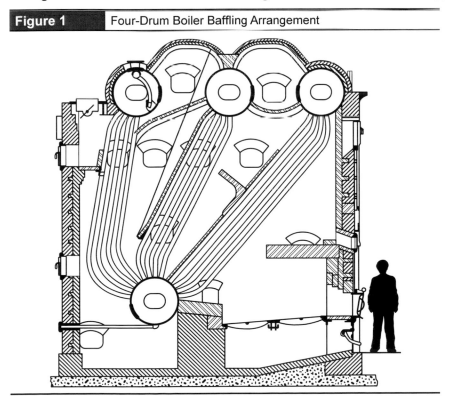

Figure 2	Three-Drum Boiler Baffling Arrangement

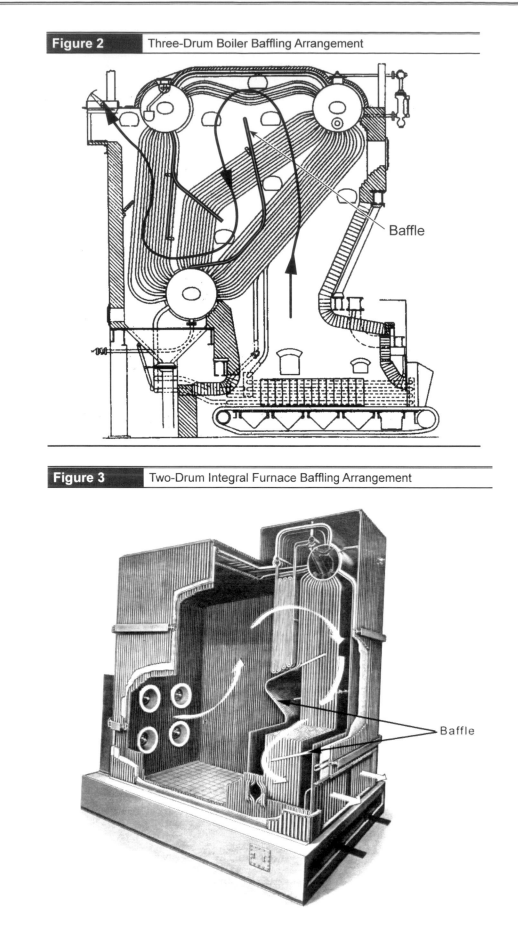

Baffle

Figure 3	Two-Drum Integral Furnace Baffling Arrangement

Baffle

OBJECTIVE 2

Describe the designs of integral furnace sidewall and header arrangements, including tube-and-tile, tangent tube, and membrane.

FURNACE SIDEWALL ARRANGEMENTS

In the watertube boiler, water-cooling of the furnace is achieved by arranging tubes to form all or part of the furnace walls. Various types of construction are used and some of these are illustrated and described.

Figure 4 illustrates a tube and brick wall, consisting of tubes spaced apart and backed by firebrick, which is shaped to fit the contour of the tubes. A thick layer of block insulation, held in place by metal lath, is reinforced with chicken wire. Another layer of thinner block insulation, and a coating of sealing compound, completes the wall. The steel casing on the outside of the block insulation is needed to make this design gas tight.

Figure 4	Screen Tube and Brick Wall

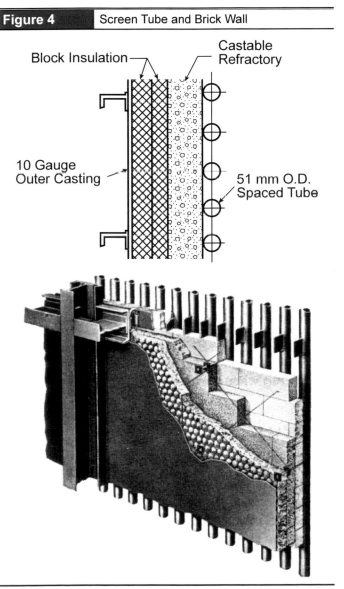

In the wall shown in Figure 5, metal fin bars are welded to adjacent tubes, forming a continuous surface and a pressure-tight wall. Block insulation and an outer steel casing cover the outsides of the welded tubes. This wall is referred to as a welded fin tube wall or a membrane wall. It is very durable and forms a gas tight seal.

Figure 5	Welded Fin Tube (Membrane) Waterwall

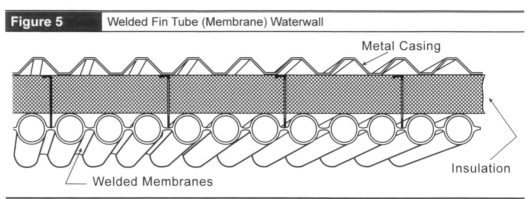

A studded membrane wall is shown in Figure 6. It is lined with refractory material. The refractory and tubes are kept together with cylindrical (pin) studs, welded at short intervals to the tubes along their length. Insulation is applied directly to the tubes and metal lagging is attached to the outside. As the tubes and membranes are welded together, a gas tight seal is formed, requiring no metal seal casing.

Figure 6	Fully Studded Membrane Wall

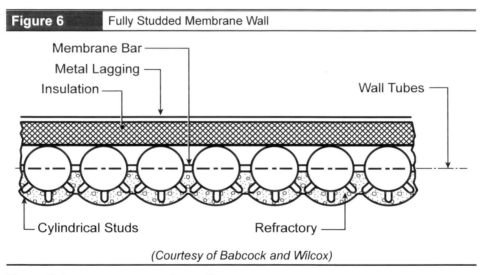

(Courtesy of Babcock and Wilcox)

Figure 7 shows a tangent tube wall.

Here the tubes are side by side and touching each other (tangent) to form a continuous water-cooled envelope around the furnace. The tubes are backed by plastic refractory with an inner steel casing. Block insulation is then applied, and finally an outer casing. The inner steel casing provides the air-tight seal in this design.

Figure 7	Tangent Tube Wall

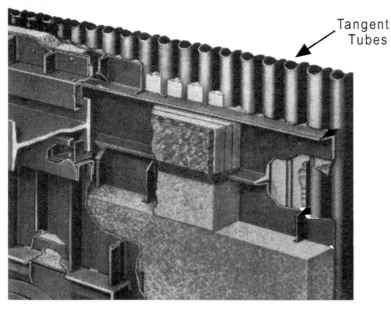

Tangent
Tubes

(Courtesy of Babcock and Wilcox)

Figure 8 shows a flat stud tube wall. In this design, flat plate-type studs are welded to both side of each tube. When the tubes are installed, these studs touch each other and cover the space between the tubes, providing an almost continuous metal surface.

On the outside of the tubes there is an inner casing, a layer of insulation, and an outside casing. The inner casing provides the gas tight seal in this design.

Figure 8	Flat Stud Tube Wall Construction

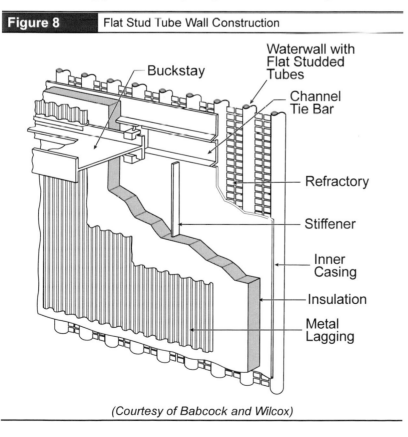

Buckstay

Waterwall with
Flat Studded
Tubes

Channel
Tie Bar

Refractory

Stiffener

Inner
Casing

Insulation

Metal
Lagging

(Courtesy of Babcock and Wilcox)

OBJECTIVE 3

Define primary, secondary, convection, radiation, platen, and pendant as they apply to superheaters. Describe the locations of superheaters within a steam generator and state the operating characteristics of convection and radiant superheaters.

SUPERHEATERS

Steam produced from water in a boiler is at saturation temperature and contains a certain amount of moisture. This steam is termed "wet" or "saturated" steam. If this steam is passed through a superheater, any moisture present will be evaporated and the temperature of the now "dry" or "superheated" steam will be increased. Initially, the superheater will add latent heat and once the steam becomes dry the superheater will begin to add sensible heat to the steam.

Therefore, the purpose of a superheater is to raise the temperature of steam generated in the boiler to above the saturation temperature. Saturated steam is taken from the steam drum, passed through a bank of superheater tubes (located at the furnace outlet), where it is heated to the desired temperature by exchange with hot furnace gases or flue gases

- The increased temperature of the steam means increased energy per kg of steam, which allows the steam to do more work per kg.
- In addition, the increased temperature means the steam will not condense as quickly so the amount of moisture contained in the steam after expanding through a turbine is reduced. This is a great advantage, since moisture in the steam would reduce turbine efficiency and rapidly erode turbine blades.

Superheaters vary in design. A simple superheater has a single stage with only a few loops of tubes. These simple designs are intended to increase the temperature of the steam to compensate for temperature losses in transport lines and to ensure dry steam to a process.

More complex superheaters are designed to increase the temperature of the steam to as high as 540°C, and are used where power generation and steam turbines are involved. These superheaters normally have two stages, primary and secondary, so the steam temperature is increased first in the primary stage and then to its final temperature in the secondary stage.

In some cases, attemperators or desuperheaters are located between superheater stages, allowing steam temperatures to be maintained relatively constant over a wide load range for more efficient power generation. Superheater arrangements vary with boiler design and with the fuel being burned.

A typical two-stage superheater is shown in Figure 9.

| Figure 9 | Boiler with Two-Stage Pendant Superheater |

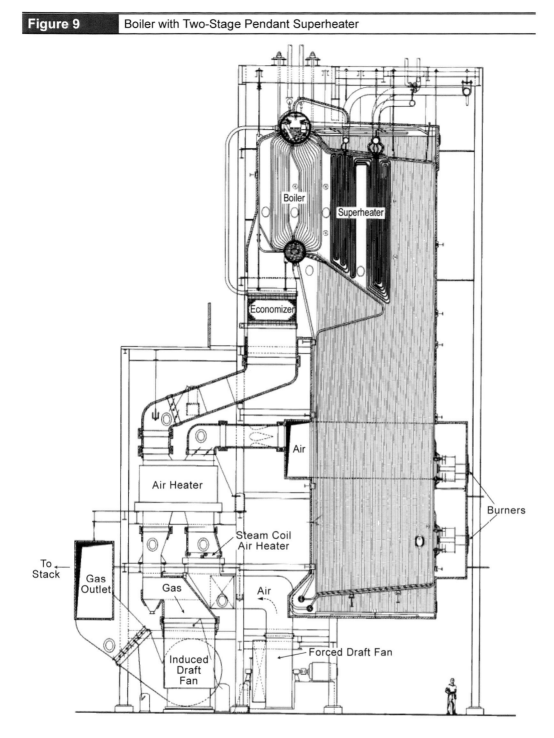

(Courtesy of Babcock and Wilcox)

Some common terms used to classify superheaters are:

- **Pendant type**: In these superheaters, tubes are suspended in a vertical manner. Pendant superheaters are usually of the radiant type at the top of the furnace.

- **Horizontal type**: The tubes run horizontally, normally in a duct. Convection superheaters are often of the horizontal type.

- **Integral**: Integral superheaters are a part of the boiler setting, and are also an integral part of the boiler or steam generator.

- **Separately Fired**: The separately fired superheater is located in a dedicated furnace, apart from the main steam generator and is independent of the steam generator operating conditions.

- **Platen**: Platen refers to how the tubes are arranged. A platen is an assembly of tubes set into a pattern of a gas-tight band, with inlet and outlet headers. They can be arranged horizontally or vertically with a spacing of 500-1000 mm between them. Figure 10 is a schematic of a platen tube arrangement. Platen tubes in a fabrication shop are shown in Figure 11.

Figure 10	Platen Tube Arrangement

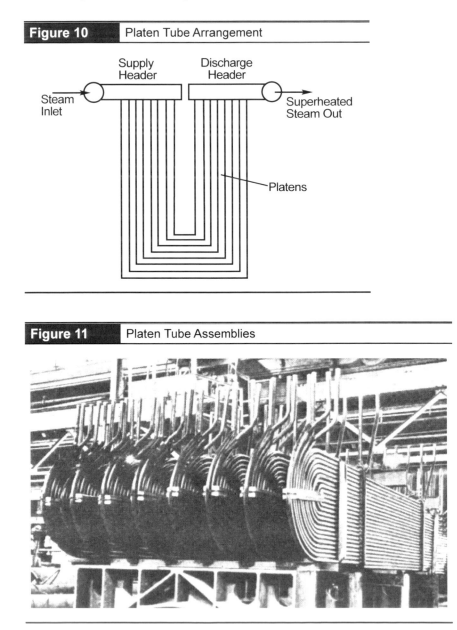

Figure 11	Platen Tube Assemblies

- **Convection Superheater**: If the superheater is shielded from the radiant heat of the furnace and is located within the path of the hot gases from the furnace, it is classed as a 'convection superheater'. The heat from the furnace is received by convection. Convection superheaters may be of horizontal or pendant design, and may be classified as either integral or separately fired.

The convection superheater has a rising steam temperature characteristic, which means that the superheated steam temperature will rise as the firing rate or boiler output increases. At low loads the steam temperature will be lower and at high loads the steam temperature will be higher. The reason is that at high loads, although there is an increase in steam flow through the superheater, there is also an increase in the mass of combustion gases flowing past the tubes, plus combustion gas temperature may increase due to the higher firing rate.

With this arrangement, if the steam temperature must be constant at all loads, some means of controlling the temperature may be required.

The steam generator shown in Figure 12 has a convection superheater only. The superheater is suspended (pendant type) in the gas path from inlet and outlet headers.

Figure 12	Steam Generator with Convection Superheater

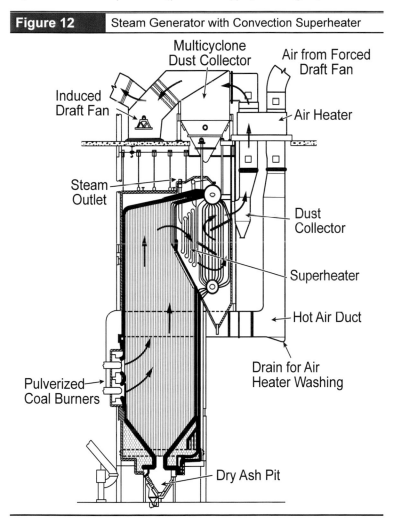

- **Radiant Superheater**: If the superheater is directly exposed to radiant heat from the furnace it is classed as a radiant superheater. The radiant superheater has a falling steam temperature characteristic, which means that the superheated steam temperature will be higher at low loads and will drop as the load increases. This is because the furnace temperature does not increase as rapidly as the steam flow does when the load increases.

- **Combination Superheater**: A combination superheater is one tube bank, with a radiant section, exposed to the radiant heat of the furnace, plus a convection section, away from the furnace, but in the combustion gas path. Combination superheaters are located at the top area of the furnace, and are situated partly in the flue gas duct between the conductive and radiant heating surfaces. The combination superheater combines the characteristics of the convection superheater and the radiant superheater. This results in a fairly steady steam temperature (see Fig. 13) at all loads.

Some steam generators have a radiant superheater in series with a convection superheater. This produces the same flat characteristic curve as a combination superheater. Figure 14 shows this superheater arrangement. The saturated steam from the drum goes first to the inlet header of a convection superheater, where the tubes are suspended directly in the path of the combustion gases. Leaving the convection section, the steam goes to the inlet header of a radiant superheater, the tubes of which are suspended in the furnace proper. Both of these superheaters are called pendant superheaters, since the tubes are suspended vertically.

Figure 13	Superheater Characteristic Curves

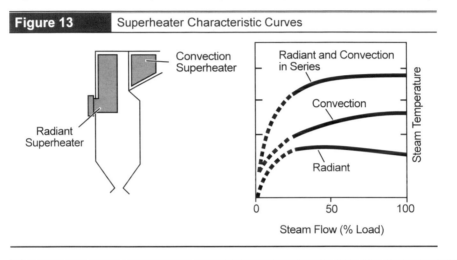

Figure 14	Superheaters in Series

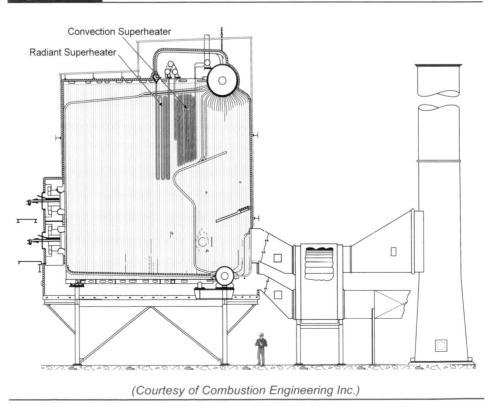

(Courtesy of Combustion Engineering Inc.)

Explain the purpose and design of a separately-fired superheater.

SEPARATELY-FIRED SUPERHEATERS

While the integral superheater is contained within the boiler setting and is an integral part of the boiler or steam generator, the separately fired superheater is located in a separate furnace away from the main steam generator. It is independent of the steam generator operating conditions.

Figure 15 illustrates a separately-fired superheater, contained within its own furnace and with its own burner for steam temperature control.

Figure 15	Schematic of Separately-Fired Superheater

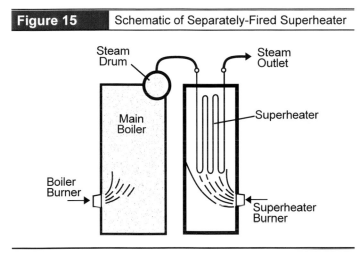

The disadvantages of the separately-fired arrangement is the higher first cost, lower operating efficiency, and requirement for more space. However, its advantage is that it provides a wider range of temperature control than the integral type. The design is limited to special industrial processes where carefully controlled and very high steam temperatures are required.

Figure 16 shows a twin furnace arrangement. The superheater is separately fired. By varying the firing rate of the individual furnaces, the temperature of the steam may be controlled independently from the saturated steam generated.

Figure 16	Twin Furnace Separately-Fired Superheater

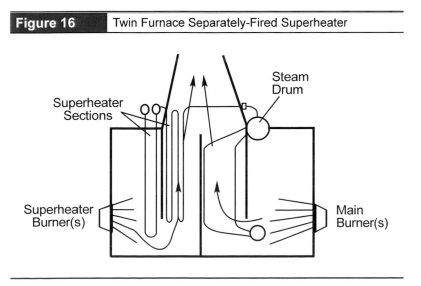

OBJECTIVE 5

Explain the purpose and describe the locations of reheaters. Explain the position and flow through reheaters in relation to superheaters.

REHEATERS

A reheater is similar in construction to a superheater. It is constructed of alloy steel tubing and the ends of the reheat tubes are connected to inlet and outlet headers by means of welded attachments.

The reheater receives steam, which has already expanded through part of a steam turbine and has dropped in pressure and in temperature. In the reheater, the steam temperature is increased to about the same temperature as was initially provided by the superheater. The reheated steam is then returned to the turbine for further expansion through the remaining turbine stages.

Figure 17 is an illustration of a steam generator with a superheater and a reheater. The steam path is shown, from the superheater to the turbine, back to the reheater, then back again to the turbine.

Figure 17	Superheat and Reheat Flows

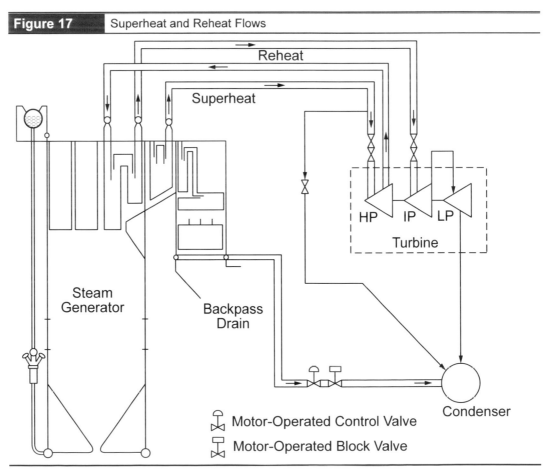

The reasons for reheating the steam to near original superheat temperature are:

- To prevent excessive condensation of the steam in the low pressure stages of the turbine
- To increase the cycle efficiency to some extent by increasing the proportion of available energy per kilogram of steam.

Reheaters are located in the furnace in areas of relatively high gas temperatures. As shown in Figure 17, they are often located between the radiant superheater and the convection superheater. They receive radiant heat and convection heat. Therefore, their outlet temperature profile is similar to that of a combination superheater, which is fairly steady, regardless of steam load.

The steam flow through the reheater changes as the turbine steam flow changes and as the superheated steam flow changes. Reheater temperature is controlled in the same way as superheater temperature.

Also, blowing soot from the wall tubes will decrease the reheat temperature, since the wall tubes will now remove more heat. Blowing soot from the reheater sections will increase the reheat temperature.

OBJECTIVE 6

Describe designs and locations of integral and separate economizers.

THE ECONOMIZER

An economizer absorbs heat from the flue gases after they have passed through the furnace, superheater, and reheat sections.

An economizer is a forced-flow, once through, convection heat transfer component to which feedwater is supplied at a pressure above that in the steam-generating section and at a rate corresponding to the steam output of the unit. The economizer is, in effect, a feedwater heater, receiving water from the boiler feed pump and delivering the water at a higher temperature to the steam generator or boiler.

Economizers are used, rather than additional steam-generating surface, to recover more flue gas heat, since the feedwater and, consequently, the economizer heat transfer surface, is at a lower temperature than the flue gases. Therefore, the economizer can further reduce the flue gas temperature and recover additional heat, which is ultimately returned to the boiler.

Integral Economizers

The integral economizer, as its name implies, forms an integral part of the boiler. It consists of vertical banks of carbon steel tubes, which run either between the boiler steam drum and an economizer water drum or between two economizer water drums. These tubes are usually located in the last combustion gas pass of the boiler, as shown in Figure 18.

Figure 19 shows some integral economizer arrangements.

In Figure 19(a), the economizer has two drums. Feedwater enters one side of the top, divided drum and flows downward, through one half of the economizer tubes, to the bottom drum. It then rises up the other half of the tubes, returning to the top drum again, and then to the boiler steam drum.

Figure 19(b) shows an economizer that has only one drum. The feedwater enters the lower drum and flows upward through the tube bank, making one pass, and then is discharged directly to the boiler drum.

Figure 19(c) shows another two-drum, integral economizer arrangement with a divided top drum. The feedwater flow is similar to that in Figure 19(a). However, crossflow baffles have been employed in this design to increase the number of times the flue gases pass over the economizer tubes.

Figure 18	Boiler with Integral Economizer

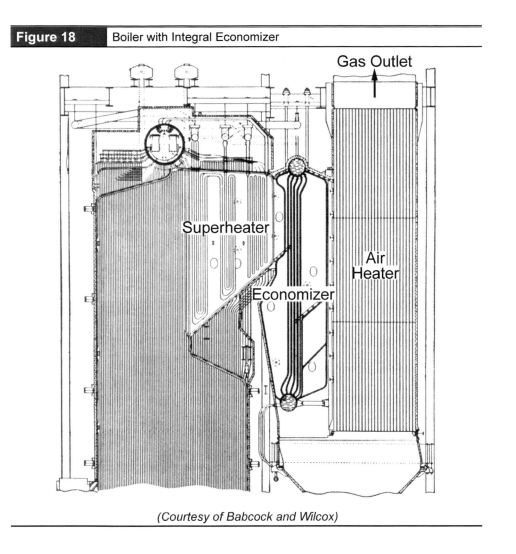

(Courtesy of Babcock and Wilcox)

Figure 19	Integral Economizer Arrangements

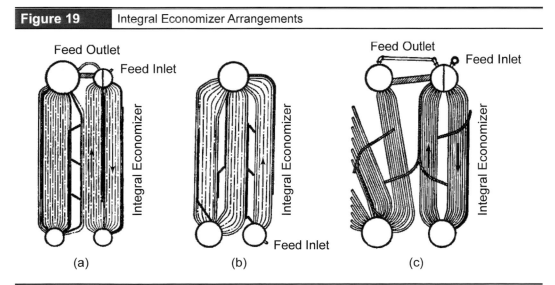

Separate Economizer

The separate economizer, which is the more common type, features rows of horizontal tubes, located outside the furnace proper. There are headers, but no drums, at the inlet and outlet of the economizer. Figure 20 shows a very early design (circa 1925) high pressure, coal fired boiler with a separate economizer. Figure 21 shows a separate economizer in a modern steam generating unit. In both designs, the combustion flue gases are directed over the outside surface of the economizer tubes.

Figure 20	Early (1925) Boiler with Separate Economizer

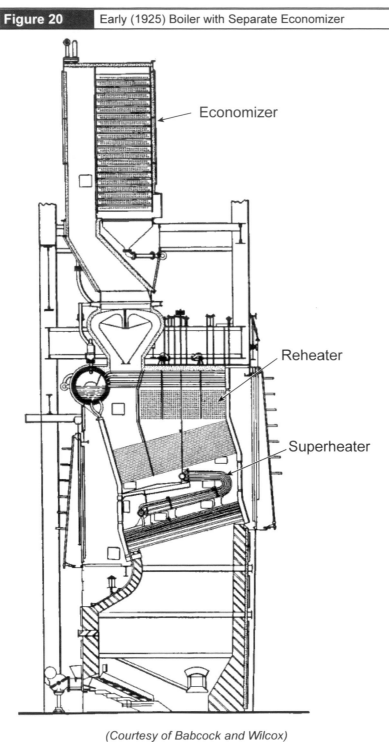

(Courtesy of Babcock and Wilcox)

Figure 21   Steam Generating Unit with Separate Economizer

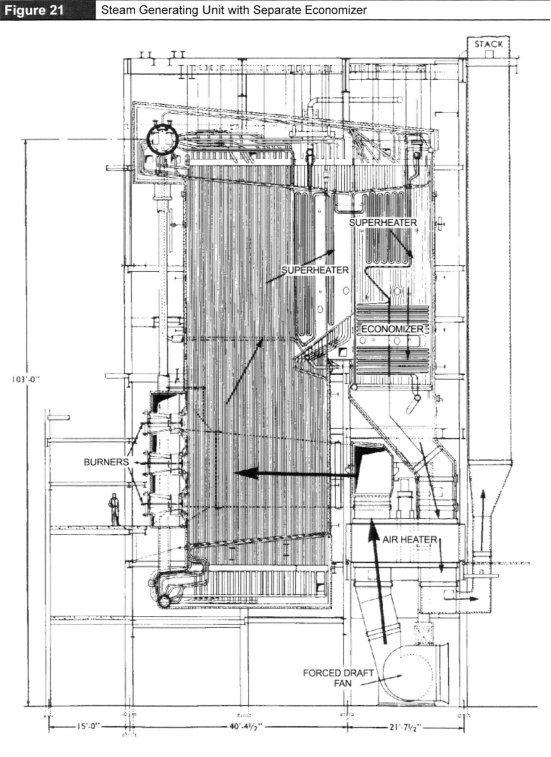

(Courtesy of Babcock and Wilcox)

The economizers in Figures 22 and 23 are of the bare tube design. They do not have extended surfaces, such as fins. The design in Figure 22 has an inlet header. It discharges directly to the boiler drum. The economizer shown in Figure 23 has continuous tubes looped between inlet and outlet headers.

Figure 22	Return Bend Loop Tube Economizer

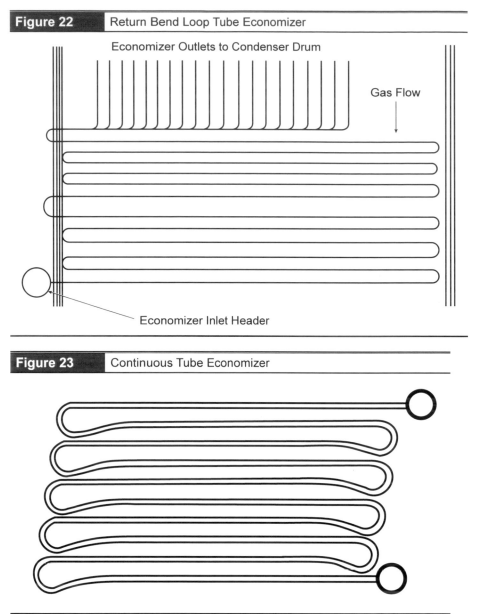

Figure 23	Continuous Tube Economizer

Figure 24 shows three-dimensional, cutaway view of complete, continuous tube economizer.

Figure 25 shows the location of a finned-tube economizer in a large watertube boiler. Fins attached to each tube provide extra surface area, thereby increasing the effective heating surface of the tube. This allows the overall size of an economizer to be decreased while maintaining the required heat transfer surface.

Figure 24   Continuous Tube Economizer

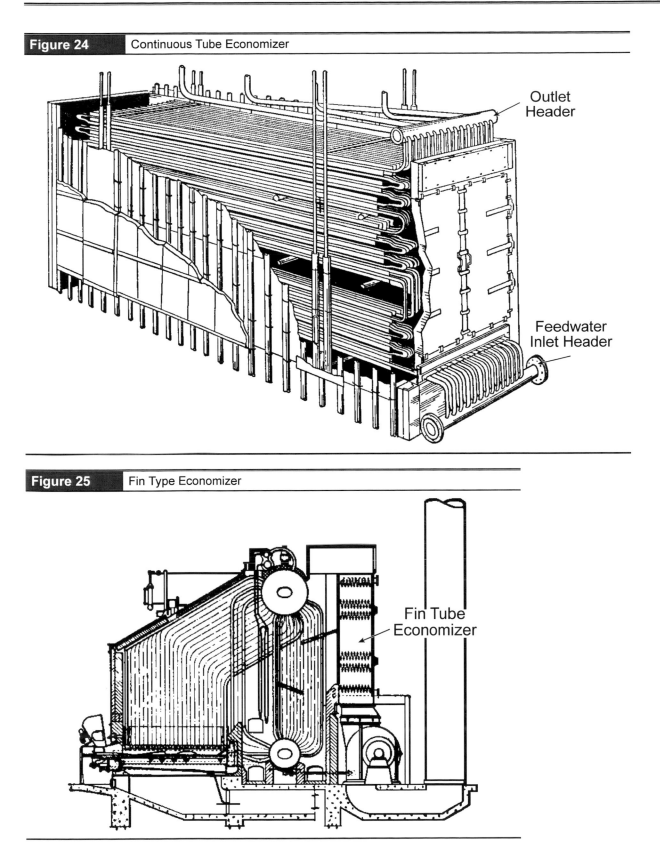

Outlet
Header

Feedwater
Inlet Header

Figure 25   Fin Type Economizer

Fin Tube
Economizer

Figure 26 shows the tube bundle arrangement of a utility boiler economizer. It is also a continuous coil design, but because of the large size, it is built in two sections. The feedwater enters through a single inlet header at the bottom and flows upwards through two sets of tubes, leaving through two outlet headers (see "intermediate headers" in the figure).

Figure 26 | Utility Boiler Economizer

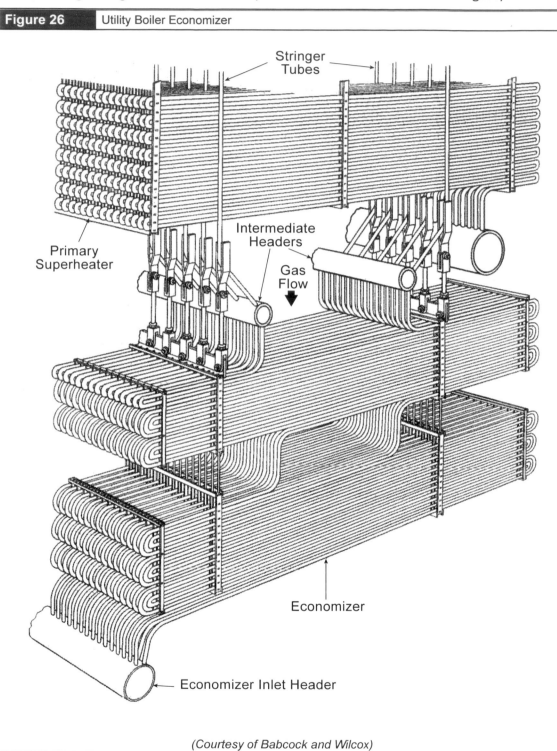

(Courtesy of Babcock and Wilcox)

OBJECTIVE 7

Describe the designs, operation, and location of plate, tubular, and rotary regenerative air heaters.

AIR HEATERS

An air heater, often called an air preheater, is usually the final stage of heat recovery from the boiler. It consists of heat exchange surfaces located in the path of the flue gases, usually between the economizer and the stack. The flue gases heat the combustion air on its way to the burners, thereby improving combustion efficiency and overall boiler efficiency. Air heaters are classed according to their operating principles into two types, recuperative and regenerative.

1. Recuperative Air Heaters
In the recuperative design, heat is transferred directly from the heating medium on one side of the heating surface to the air on the other side of the heating surface. There are two designs, one with plates and the other with tubes.

Plate Air Heater
A plate air heater is composed of welded envelopes complete with air inlet and outlet, airside spacers, and gas side spacers. The air passes through the envelopes, which are stacked side by side in the casing. Gas passages are formed by the spaces between the adjacent envelopes. The flue gas and the air pass through alternate passages in opposite directions and the heat from the flue gas transfers through the plate metal to the air. There are several design variations available to fit various duct configurations and the size of air heater depends upon the area of heat transfer surface required.

Figure 27 shows the general construction of one plate air heater. In this design, flue gases flow downward in a single pass. Air from the forced draft fan enters the bottom half of the air heater, at right angles to the gas flow, makes two passes and exits from the top half of the heater.

Figure 27	Plate Air Heater

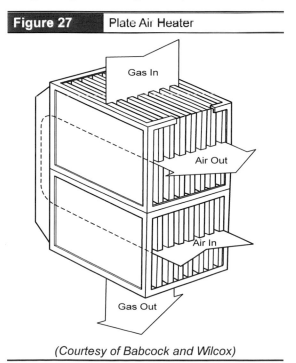

(Courtesy of Babcock and Wilcox)

Tubular Air Heaters

The tubular air heater is a recuperative air heater constructed of long, straight steel or cast iron tubes, which may be arranged either horizontally or vertically within the heater casing.

The vertical tube design is shown in Figure 28. Directed by baffles, the combustion air passes four times over the outside surfaces of the tubes, while the flue gas passes through the inside of the tubes. A by-pass damper is used to control the final outlet air temperature.

Figure 28	Tubular Air Heater

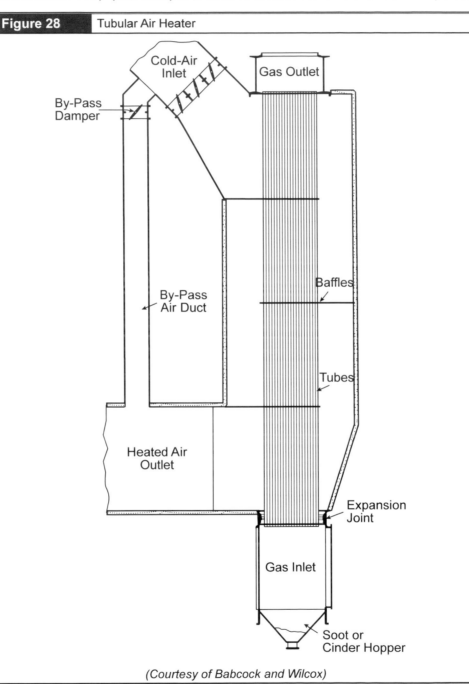

(Courtesy of Babcock and Wilcox)

Figure 29 illustrates several designs of tubular air heaters having various arrangements of gas and airflows. Notice that in the horizontal tube design (see bottom center figure) the combustion air passes through the tubes while the flue gas passes over the outside of the tubes. This is typical for horizontal tubes.

Figure 29 | Tubular Air Heater Arrangements

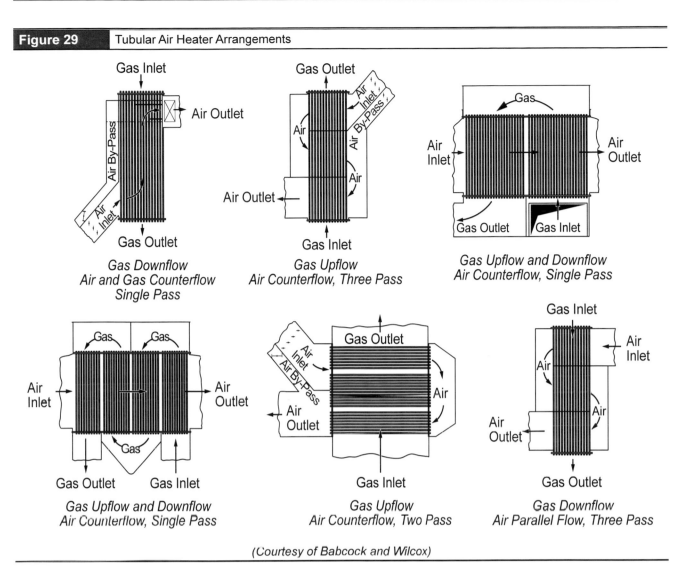

Gas Downflow
Air and Gas Counterflow
Single Pass

Gas Upflow
Air Counterflow, Three Pass

Gas Upflow and Downflow
Air Counterflow, Single Pass

Gas Upflow and Downflow
Air Counterflow, Single Pass

Gas Upflow
Air Counterflow, Two Pass

Gas Downflow
Air Parallel Flow, Three Pass

(Courtesy of Babcock and Wilcox)

Figure 30 shows a steam generator with a vertical tubular air heater. This air heater has a two-pass arrangement for the flue gases. The flue gases leave the economizer section, pass downward through one set of air heater tubes and then reverse and pass upward through another set of tubes. The combustion air travels horizontally across the surface of the tubes before being directed by ductwork to the boiler windbox and burners.

Air Heater Corrosion

Boiler fuels usually contain some amount of sulphur. The sulphur in the fuel is first oxidized to sulphur dioxide and then partially oxidized to sulphur trioxide. Sulphur dioxide in the presence of water vapor forms sulphurous acid and sulphur trioxide in the presence of water vapor produces sulphuric acid. Both of these acids will attack and corrode steel.

If allowed, this type of corrosion will occur at the cold end of the air heater, which is the gas outlet - air inlet end in a counter flow unit. To eliminate or reduce this corrosion, the temperature of the gas leaving the air heater must be kept above the dew point to prevent moisture from condensing on the air heater surfaces. Two methods to accomplish this are steam coils on the air side or by-passing some of the inlet air so the flue gas doesn't cool as much (see Fig. 29, bottom center figure).

Figure 30 Steam Generator with Tubular Air Heater

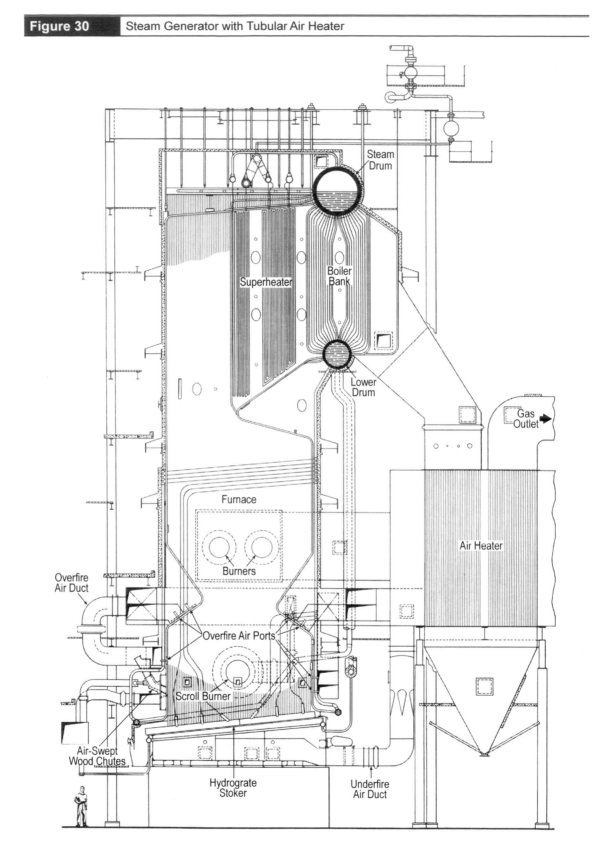

Steam
Drum

Boiler
Bank

Superheater

Lower
Drum

Gas
Outlet

Air Heater

Furnace

Burners

Overfire
Air Duct

Overfire Air Ports

Scroll Burner

Air-Swept
Wood Chutes

Hydrograte
Stoker

Underfire
Air Duct

(Courtesy of Babcock and Wilcox)

2. Regenerative Air Heaters

A regenerative air heater depends upon transfer of heat from the gas stream to a metal, or other solid surface, and then transfer of heat from this same surface to the combustion air.

In the rotary regenerative air heater, shown in Figure 31, the heat-transfer surfaces are moved alternately through the gas and air streams thus undergoing repetitive heating and cooling cycles (hence "regenerative"). Heat is transferred to or from the thermal storage elements. These are baskets containing sheets or plates of corrugated metal, which form the heat transfer medium.

Figure 31	Rotary Regenerative Air Heater

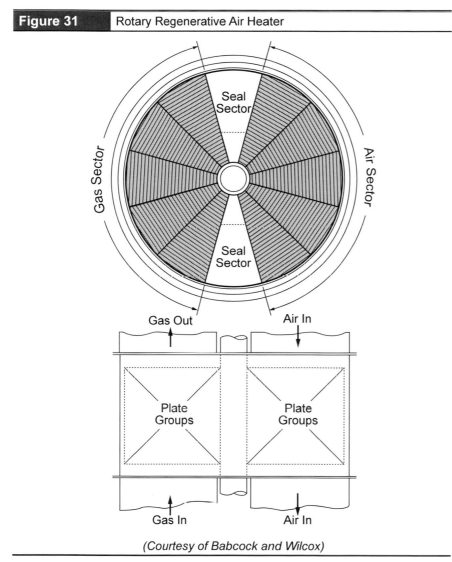

(Courtesy of Babcock and Wilcox)

Figure 32 shows a three dimensional view of the flows through the heater. The rotor revolves slowly (2 or 3 r/min.), exposing the corrugated metal plates alternately to the hot gases and the cold air streams. A central seal prevents the crossover leakage of air and flue gases within the heater.

The rotary regenerative air heater may be oriented in either vertical or horizontal position. The heater in Figure 32 has vertical orientation, while the heater in Figure 33 is horizontal.

Figure 34 shows a steam generator with the air heater arranged in a horizontal position, so that the flow of gas and air are in a vertical direction.

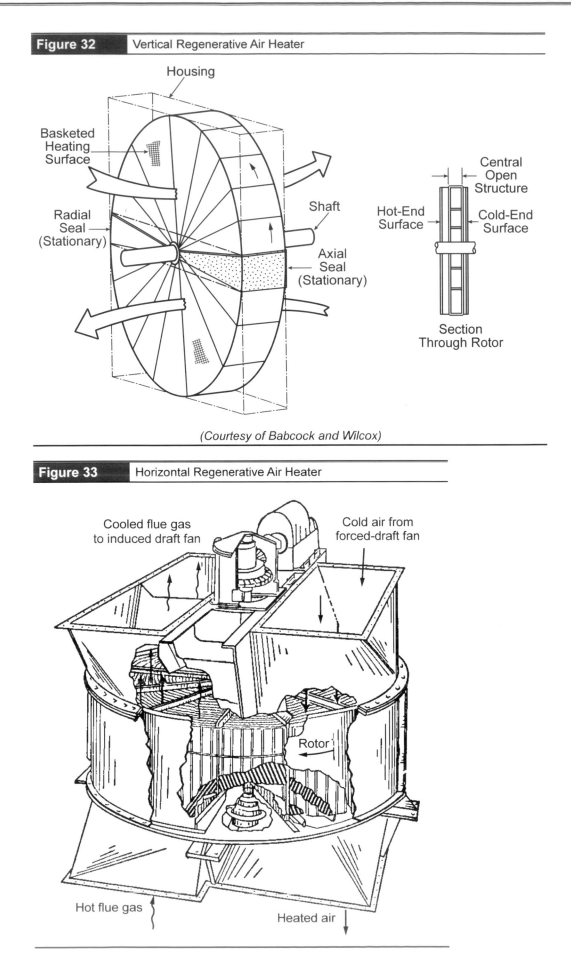

Figure 32   Vertical Regenerative Air Heater

Housing

Basketed Heating Surface

Radial Seal (Stationary)

Shaft

Axial Seal (Stationary)

Central Open Structure

Hot-End Surface

Cold-End Surface

Section Through Rotor

(Courtesy of Babcock and Wilcox)

Figure 33   Horizontal Regenerative Air Heater

Cooled flue gas to induced draft fan

Cold air from forced-draft fan

Rotor

Hot flue gas

Heated air

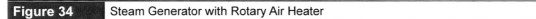

Figure 34 | Steam Generator with Rotary Air Heater

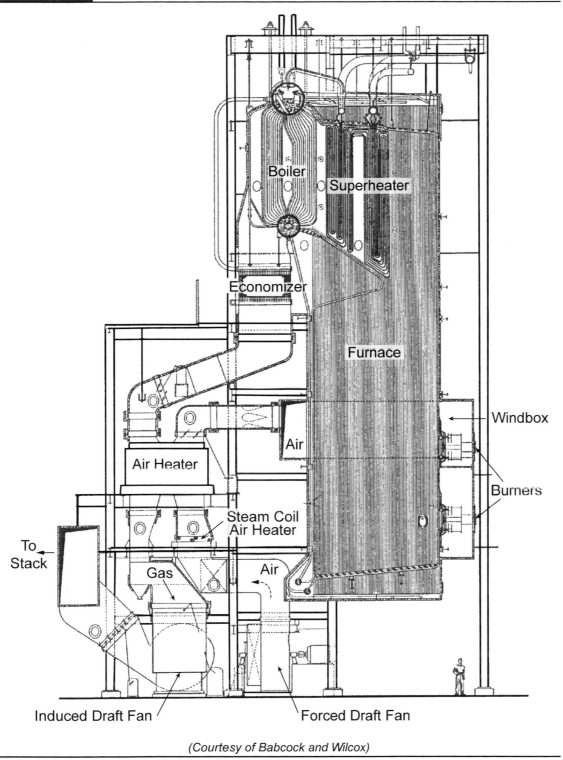

(Courtesy of Babcock and Wilcox)

OBJECTIVE 8

Explain operating care and considerations that must be given to the various heat transfer sections of the boiler.

CARE OF HEAT TRANSFER SECTIONS

The condition of heat transfer sections of a boiler must be monitored regularly. Any change in operating conditions must be documented and watched closely. The following is an overview of steam generator heat transfer sections and the main operating conditions to monitor.

Furnace Walls

Furnace wall tubes must be monitored for signs of external deposits. These may appear as glowing spots on the tubes, indicating a slag buildup, which can be removed by sootblowers. If a sootblower is not adjacent to the buildup, a change of firing pattern may work. Hot spots on tubes not caused by slag are a more serious problem. They indicate poor heat transfer through the tube walls. This may be due to deposits or lack of circulation on the waterside of the tube. Hot spots on tubes should be closely monitored and reported. Internal cleaning may be required to prevent tube ruptures.

Wet tubes on startup of the boiler are a normal occurrence, caused by condensation on the tube walls. As the boiler temperature increases, condensation will disappear. Tube leaks that develop will increase in size quickly. Due to the high pressures involved, water cuts the metal as it escapes. Report suspected leaks immediately as the unit may have to be taken out of service for repair.

Superheater Tubes

Superheater tube materials are generally hotter than wall tubes, since they are cooled by steam flow, not water flow. The condition of the tubes should be monitored for slag buildup, hot spots and sagging tube bundles. Slag deposits can be controlled by blowing soot or by changing firing patterns. Hot spots are serious and indicate tube overheating. The temperature of the tube may be taken using handheld pyrometers. Sagging tubes are a condition that develops over a long period of time, but should be measured on a regular basis.

The steam temperature out of the superheater sections should be monitored closely. Do not operate over the design outlet temperature of the superheater. This will reduce the life of the tube metal substantially. When starting a boiler, a steam flow is needed through the tubes for cooling. This is accomplished by venting through a superheater vent. The venting can be stopped after the boiler steam flow to the turbine or process is adequate for cooling.

If tubes develop leaks, they should be closely monitored. Leaks should be repaired as soon as possible.

Reheater Tubes

Reheater tubes are operated the same as superheater tubes. They are monitored for hot spots and for slag buildup. As the tubes also run very hot, tube sagging can occur over a long period of time. There is no steam flow through the reheater tubes before the steam turbine has a steam flow through it. Be careful not to increase boiler firing too rapidly and overheat the reheat tubes, during startup.

Economizer Tubes

Economizer tubes cannot be visually monitored, while the steam generator is on line. Pressure drops on the gas side can be monitored. Inlet and outlet boiler feed water temperatures can also be monitored. These delta P's and delta T's give an indication of gas side fouling and water side fouling respectively. Leaks can be detected by water in the flue gas or dripping out of the ducting.

When starting the boiler, it may be necessary to keep a flow of BFW through the economizer tubes to prevent overheating and fouling. If the boiler has an economizer recirculation line, it must be opened on startup and shutdown situations. Both internal and external surfaces of the economizer must be kept clean to provide desired efficiencies.

Air Preheaters

Air preheaters can be subject to fouling or corrosion. This is caused by condensation of vapours in the flue gases. The liquids formed are acidic and cause serious corrosion problems. The temperatures of the flue gas leaving the preheater must be kept above the dewpoint to avoid condensation. Some condensation is unavoidable during startups and shutdowns. Low ambient temperatures can also cause condensation. Steam coils on the airside or by-pass air mixing with the heated air at the preheater outlet are often used to keep the flue gases above the dew point.

Regenerative Air Heaters

As regenerative air preheaters have moving parts, there is some leakage between the inlet air and the flue gases. This leakage can be monitored by analyzing flue gas samples for oxygen content. It may also be evident by a loss of fan capacity.

The drive motors of air preheaters need to be monitored closely. If the preheater element stops, it causes a large upset in boiler operating conditions and the boiler may need to be cutback in load or shut down. Therefore, there are usually backup drives for the main drive. The backup drives need to be tested periodically to make sure they will function when required.

When the boiler is shut down, the air preheater should be inspected for signs of corrosion. Elements (sections of the air preheater) can be easily replaced in sections if required. The pressure drop through the airside and the gas side should be monitored. A rising pressure drop is a sign that fouling or corrosion may be occurring.

OBJECTIVE 9

Explain a typical water and gas temperature profile through a large steam generating unit.

WATER TEMPERATURE PROFILE

Figure 35 is included for interest, to show where the steam generator fits into a power plant cycle. The steam generator in this case is a pulverized, coal fired unit, which operates at 11.3 MPa, with a superheater outlet temperature of 538°C. The reheat temperature is also 538°C.

The steam generator water temperature profile is shown in more detail in Figure 36. Water is pumped to the economizer inlet at 254°C. Picking up heat from the flue gases downstream of the primary superheater, the water is heated to 280°C. The water from the economizer is piped to the steam drum. The temperature of the saturated steam and water mixture in the steam drum is 320°C.

The water temperature at the economizer exit is always below that of the steam drum to prevent steam production in the economizer. This results in lower water temperature in the boiler downcomers, which promotes and assists circulation.

The water and water/steam mixture in the steam generation tubes is at saturation temperature, in this case 320°C. The saturated steam going to the primary superheater is also 320°C. The temperature of the steam is raised in the superheater sections to 538°C. In this case the steam is heated in a convection superheater and then a radiant, secondary superheater.

The reheater increases the temperature of the steam from the H.P. turbine back up to 538°C. The steam from the reheater is then piped back to the intermediate pressure turbine. Here it expands through the I.P. turbine blades and the L.P. turbine blades before entering the surface condenser. The condensate from the surface condenser is pumped through a series of feedwater heaters before going back to the economizer and steam drum (Fig. 35).

GAS TEMPERATURE PROFILE

The gas temperatures through the coal fired steam generator are illustrated in Figure 36.

The F.D. fan takes ambient air at 28°C and delivers it to the air preheater where it is heated to 280°C. Some of the preheated air is then delivered through ducting to the burners. The remainder of the air goes to the coal pulverizers from which it will carry pulverized coal to the furnace.

The temperature of the furnace in a coal-fired boiler depends on the design of the furnace and upon the type and quality of the coal being fired. For this example we have used 1650°C in the furnace. The radiant superheater and reheater are exposed to radiant heat at the top of the furnace. The temperature of the flue gases downstream of the primary superheater is 1100°C. More heat is transferred in the reheater and the flue gas leaving the reheater is reduced to 843°C.

The flue gas then enters the economizer, where more heat is transferred to the incoming boiler feed water. The flue gas exits the economizer at 380°C. It then enters the air preheater, where it heats the incoming combustion air. The flue gas exits the air heater at 170°C, then passes through the electrostatic precipitators before going to the stack.

Figure 35 | Water and Steam Temperatures through a Power Plant Cycle

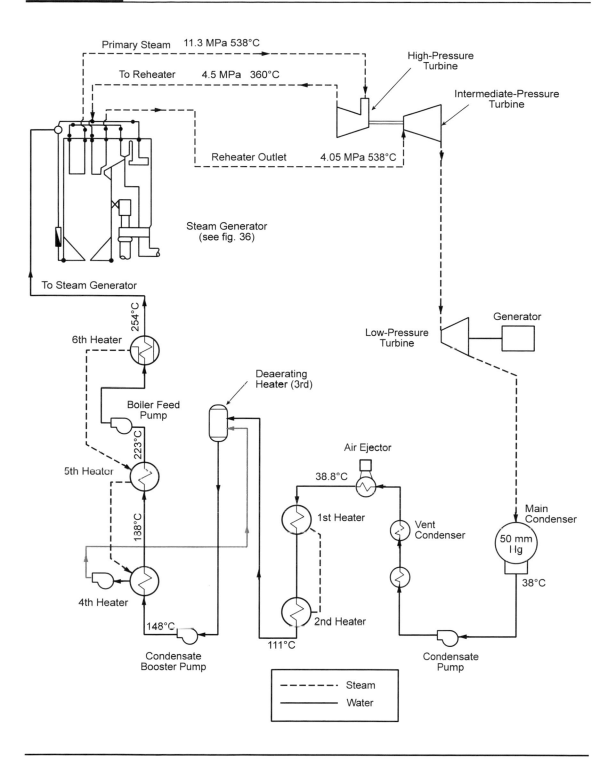

Figure 36   Gas Temperature Profile through a Steam Generator

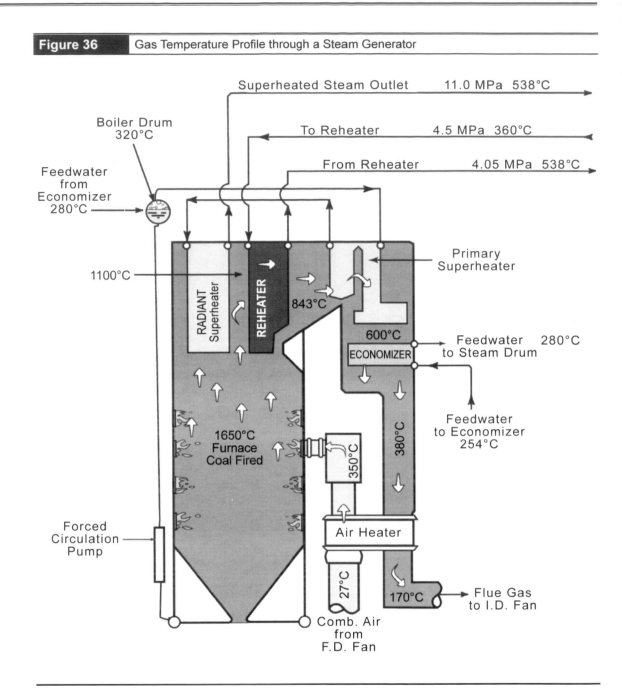

CHAPTER 4 - QUESTIONS

1. What materials are commonly used to construct furnace baffles?

2. Sketch and describe a membrane tube wall arrangement, showing tubes, fins, insulation and metal lagging.

3. State the advantages and disadvantages of separately fired superheaters

4. Using a simple sketch, describe the steam flow through a steam generator and turbine arrangement that incorporates a reheater.

5. Why are economizers used instead of additional steam generating tubes, when designing boilers? What is an integral economizer?

6. Explain the terms regenerative and recuperative as applied to air heaters.

7. Why is steam vented through the superheater vent when starting up a steam generator or boiler? When can the vent be closed?

8. What is the approximate temperature in the furnace of a coal fired steam generator? List the temperature drops of the flue gas as it passes through the various heat transfer surfaces of the steam generator.

ANSWERS: All answers are found within the content of the chapter.

High Pressure Boiler Fittings

LEARNING OUTCOME

When you complete this chapter you should be able to:

Describe the design and operation of common external and internal fittings attached to the pressure side of a high-pressure boiler.

LEARNING OBJECTIVES

Here is what you should be able to do when you complete each objective:

1. *Describe the design, installation, operation, and setting of a high-pressure pressure relief valve. Explain the Code requirements for size, capacity and locations of the pressure relief valves on a boiler.*

2. *Describe the code requirements for boiler pressure gauges, including attachment and locations.*

3. *Describe common designs, connections and components of high-pressure water columns and flat gauge glasses, including illumination and quick shut-off devices and bulls-eye glasses. Explain testing and maintenance of a high-pressure gauge glass.*

4. *Describe the float and probe designs for low-water fuel cutoffs and explain how these are tested.*

5. *Describe boiler steam outlet arrangements and fittings including gate, angle, and globe stop valves and globe, Y, angle, and spring-cushioned non-return valves.*

6. *Describe manual blowoff piping arrangements. Describe the design and operation of sliding disc, seatless sliding plunger, seat and disc, and combination valves. Explain manual blowoff procedures. Describe the requirements for a blowoff tank.*

7. *Explain the components of the steam drum internals of a watertube boiler. Describe the design and operation of various steam separation devices, including baffles, primary and secondary separators, and scrubbers.*

OBJECTIVE 1

Describe the design, installation, operation, and setting of a high-pressure pressure relief valve. Explain the Code requirements for size, capacity and locations of the pressure relief valves on a boiler.

DESIGN

NOTE: In the 2007 Edition of the ASME Code, Section I, the term "Pressure Relief Valve" replaced the previous terms safety valve, safety relief valve and relief valve. Therefore, most references in this Objective have also been changed to reflect the standardized ASME terminology.

Figure 1 shows the design of a high-pressure pressure relief valve.

The valve disc (D) is held firmly on its seat by the downward force of the heavy coil spring (J). The point (ie. set pressure) at which the valve will lift off its seat is adjusted by screwing the adjusting nut (L) up or down. This decreases or increases the compression of the spring (J) and, therefore the downward force on the valve disc. The adjusting nut (L) is prevented from turning after adjustment by the lock nut (N). When the valve has been set and the adjusting nut is locked, the cap (B) is reinstalled and the Boiler Inspector attaches his wire seal to the cap, preventing access to the adjusting nut (L).

This type of cast steel body valve is suitable for pressures up to 3450 kPa and temperatures up to 400°C.

Figure 1	HP Pressure Relief Valve Design

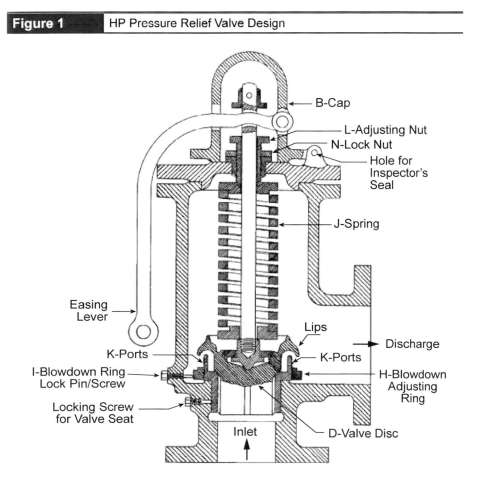

INSTALLATION

The following are paraphrased from ASME, Section I, PG-71.

A pressure relief valve must be connected to the boiler independent of any other connections and as close as possible to the boiler. It must be upright, with the spindle vertical. No valve of any type may be placed between the pressure relief valve and the boiler or on the discharge pipe from the pressure relief valve, if such a discharge pipe is used.

If there is a discharge pipe, its cross-sectional area shall not be less than the full area of the valve outlet and the pipe must be as short and straight as possible. A gravity drain of sufficient size must be provided in the discharge pipe of each pressure relief valve, where water or condensation might collect. Also, each valve must have an open gravity drain from the casing, below the level of the valve seat.

The discharge from a pressure relief valve shall be located or piped to be clear of platforms or running boards.

Figure 2 shows the discharge arrangement and dimensions for a typical pressure relief valve.

Here a riser pipe is supported independently of the valve to eliminate stresses on the valve. A combined elbow and drip pan is used in conjunction with the riser. Sufficient clearance is provided between the bottom of the riser and the drip pan to allow for expansion when heated to operating temperature. The drip pan and elbow both have open gravity drains to avoid liquid accumulation.

Figure 2	Typical Pressure Relief Valve Discharge Piping

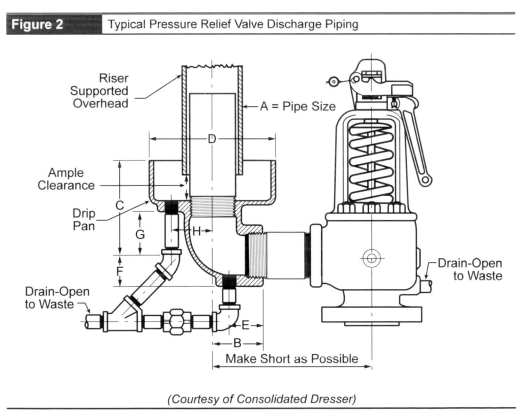

(Courtesy of Consolidated Dresser)

OPERATION

The disc of a pop-type pressure relief valve has a lip or skirt, as shown in Figure 3. This lip becomes exposed to steam pressure when the valve starts to open, thus increasing the effective area of the disc exposed to steam. The area below this lip is called the pop chamber.

As soon as the disc lifts slightly, the pressure of the steam acts on this increased area of the disc, resulting in a greater force being suddenly applied upwards against the spring. The sudden increase causes the valve to "pop" wide open and release steam to the discharge. Once open, the valve will remain open until the pressure drops below the popping pressure.

Figure 3	Pop-Type PRV Seat Arrangement

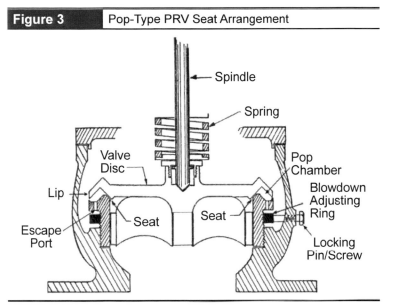

Figure 4 illustrates, perhaps more clearly, that as the valve begins to lift, steam rushes into the pop chamber, acts on an increased area as indicated by the shaded ring, causing the valve to "pop" to its full opening. The actual lifting force exerted on the disc by the boiler pressure depends on the area of the disc exposed to the pressure and on the freedom with which the steam can escape from under the lip.

Figure 4	Operation of a Pop-type Pressure Relief Valve

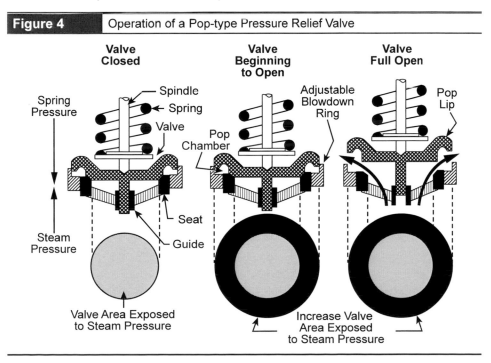

PRESSURE RELIEF VALVE BLOWDOWN

The difference between the pressure at which the pressure relief valve opens and the pressure at which it closes is called the **blowdown** of the valve. According to ASME Section I, PG-72.1, the pressure relief valve must be designed to operate with a minimum blowdown of 15 kPa or 2% of the set pressure, whichever is greater.

Referring back to Figure 3, the adjusting ring (commonly called the blowdown ring) may be screwed up or down to vary the amount of escape port opening.

- If the ring is screwed upward, toward the escape ports, the blowdown will be larger. This is because raising the ring decreases the opening of the escape ports, which causes less steam to escape and more steam to be directed against the valve lip. The resulting increase in lifting force on the disc causes the valve to stay open longer and to close at a lower steam pressure.

- Conversely, if the ring is screwed downwards, the blowdown will be less because the ring increases the opening of the escape ports, causing less steam to contact the lip and allowing the valve to close sooner.

Adjustment of the blowdown ring is done by removing the cap screw and inserting a screwdriver that will catch in notches on the outside of the adjusting ring. The screwdriver turns the adjusting ring in the desired direction. When the ring is in the desired position, it is locked in place by the lock screw.

To prevent unauthorized tampering with the blowdown setting, a cap screw is installed and held in place by a seal, which is installed by the Boiler Inspector.

PRESSURE RELIEF VALVE SIZING

The ASME Code Section I, Rules For Construction of Power Boilers, PG-67.1, states that each boiler shall have at least one pressure relief valve. Also, the boiler shall have two or more pressure relief valves if:

- The boiler has more than 47 m^2 of bare tube water-heating surface
- The boiler, if electric, has a power input of more than 1100 kW

PRESSURE RELIEF VALVE CAPACITY

ASME Section I, PG-67.2 says that "the capacity of the pressure relief valves for each boiler, shall be such that they will discharge all the steam that can be generated by the boiler without allowing the pressure to rise more than 6 percent above the highest pressure at which any valve is set, and in no case, more than 6 percent above the maximum allowable working pressure.

PG-67.3 states that "one or more pressure relief valves on the boiler proper shall be set at or below the maximum allowable working pressure (except as noted in PG-67.4). If additional valves are used, the highest pressure setting shall not exceed the maximum allowable working pressure by more than 3 percent."

Note: These are only two of many requirements found in PG-67.

With respect to superheater PRV's, PG-68.2 requires that every attached superheater shall have at least one pressure relief valve near the outlet. The superheater pressure relief valves may be included in the total relieving capacity for the boiler, but at least 75 percent of this relieving capacity shall be provided by the drum pressure relief valves.

OBJECTIVE 2

Describe the code requirements for boiler pressure gauges, including attachment and locations.

CODE REQUIREMENTS FOR PRESSURE GAUGES

The ASME Code, Section I, PG-60.6, gives the requirements for pressure gauges on a boiler. The code requires each boiler to have a pressure gauge attached to the steam space or to the water column or its steam connection. The gauges must be fitted with a shut off valve or cock. The connection to the gauge shall contain a siphon or other device to prevent steam from entering and damaging the gauge. Each boiler shall be provided with a connection of at least NPS 1/4 (6 mm) pipe size for the exclusive purpose of attaching a Boiler Inspector's test gauge to check the accuracy of the boiler gauge.

Figure 5 illustrates the arrangement for the gauge fittings.

The dial of the gauge will be graduated to approximately double, but in no case less than 1.5 times, the pressure at which the boiler safety valve is set.

In the case of a forced flow steam generator with no fixed steam or water line, pressure gauges shall be fitted in the following locations:

- At the boiler or superheater steam outlet, after the last section, which absorbs heat
- At the boiler or economizer feedwater inlet, upstream of any shut off valve used between any two sections, which absorb heat

In all cases, the material used for pressure gauges shall be suitable for the pressures, temperatures and fluids, encountered.

Figure 5	Gauge Fittings

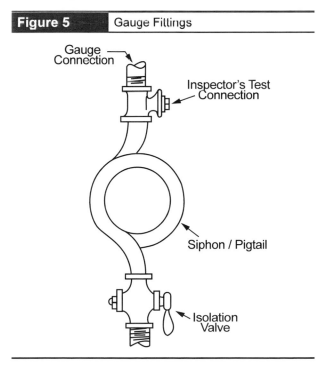

OBJECTIVE 3

Describe common designs, connections and components of high-pressure water columns and flat gauge glasses, including illumination and quick shut-off devices and bulls-eye glasses. Explain testing and maintenance of a high-pressure gauge glass.

WATER COLUMNS & GAUGE GLASSES

LOW WATER LEVEL IN A BOILER IS ONE OF THE TWO MAIN CAUSES OF BOILER ACCIDENTS!

(the other cause is improper furnace operation)

In order to visually determine the level of water in the boiler, at least one water gauge glass must be fitted to the boiler. The gauge glass, or glasses, may be fitted directly to the boiler shell or drum, but usually the gauge glass is attached to a water column (see Fig. 6 and, for more detail, Fig. 11)).

The use of a water column is preferred because the column acts as a reservoir and tends to stabilize and dampen water agitation, making the level easier to read. In addition, the column collects sediment that would otherwise deposit in the glass. The column on some boilers provides a place for the installation of high and low level alarms or for the installation of control components.

Figure 6	Water Column and Flat Gauge Glass

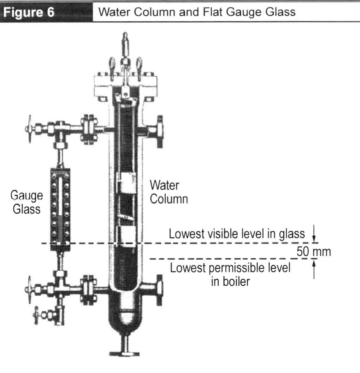

Gauge Glass

Water Column

Lowest visible level in glass

50 mm

Lowest permissible level in boiler

(Courtesy of Jerguson Gage and Valve Co.)

According to ASME, Section I, PG-60.1.1, boilers having a maximum allowable working pressure exceeding 400 psi (3 MPa) shall have two gauge glasses. Instead of one of the two required gauge glasses, two independent remote water level indicators may be provided.

Probably the most important requirement to consider from PG-60.1 is this:

"The lowest visible water level in a gauge glass shall be at least 2 in. (50 mm) above the lowest permissible water level, as determined by the boiler manufacturer." (see Fig. 6)

This requirement ensures that, as long as a water level is visible in the glass (and assuming the gauge glass is properly in service and properly maintained), the operator knows visually that the water level is not dangerously low.

FLAT GAUGE GLASS

For higher steam pressures, a flat glass type of gauge is used, consisting of thick, glass plates bolted within a forged, steel housing. The glass plates are lined with thin sheets of mica in order to protect the surface of the glass from the etching action of the steam and water. This type of gauge glass is shown attached to the water column in Figure 6 (also, see Figure 11 for more valve locations).

Figure 7 shows the constructional details of a flat glass gauge, in sectional view.

The steel body of the gauge is slotted in the centre to provide space for the water. This slot is covered on both sides by heavy flat glasses (B). Thin sheets of mica (C) protect the inner surfaces of the flat glasses. Gaskets (A) between the bolted covers and the outside surfaces of the glasses prevent straining of the glasses when the covers are tightened down.

| Figure 7 | Flat Glass Gauge Details |

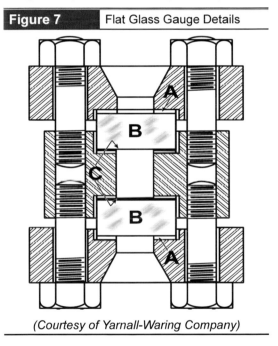

(Courtesy of Yarnall-Waring Company)

BULLS EYE GAUGE GLASS

The bulls eye gauge glass assembly is a high-pressure design suitable for pressures up to 20.7 MPa. This design uses individual port assemblies rather than using single pieces of flat glass for the back and the front of the gauge. Each port assembly consists of a flat glass, washers, gaskets, cover and screws. Figure 8 illustrates the port arrangement.

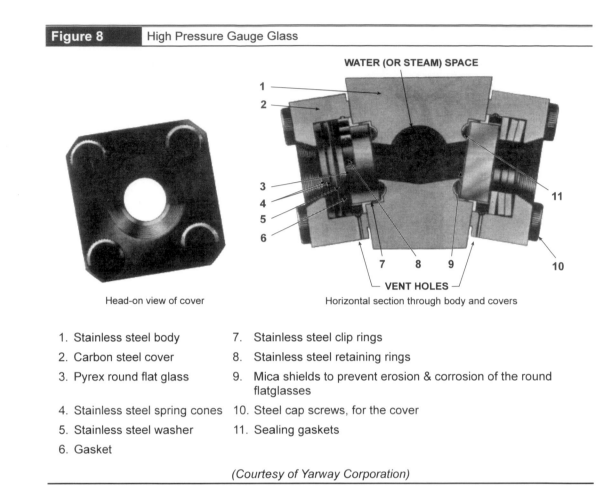

Head-on view of cover

Horizontal section through body and covers

1. Stainless steel body
2. Carbon steel cover
3. Pyrex round flat glass
4. Stainless steel spring cones
5. Stainless steel washer
6. Gasket
7. Stainless steel clip rings
8. Stainless steel retaining rings
9. Mica shields to prevent erosion & corrosion of the round flatglasses
10. Steel cap screws, for the cover
11. Sealing gaskets

(Courtesy of Yarway Corporation)

Bicolour Gauge Glass

A bicolour gauge glass is usually employed to give better visibility of the water level. The arrangement of this type is sketched in Figure 9. The light from the lamp shines through a vertical screen consisting of two strips of clear coloured glass, one green and one red. The gauge glass is so placed in relation to the glass strips that the green light will not pass through the gauge unless it is refracted by water, in the gauge. Similarly, the red light can only pass through that part of the gauge, which does not contain water.

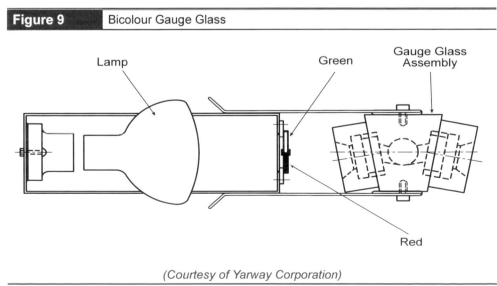

(Courtesy of Yarway Corporation)

Figure 10 illustrates one type of bi-colour, multi-port, bulls eye gauge glass, using the point-level method of indication. Instead of a water column, this gauge is attached to a circulating tie bar that has top and bottom connector blocks with gauge valves, plus a bottom connection for a drain line. The gauge glass consists of a number of sealed circular glasses or double bulls eye assemblies with spotlights connected at the back. The steam space is indicated in red while the water space is green.

Figure 10	Bulls Eye Gauge Glass

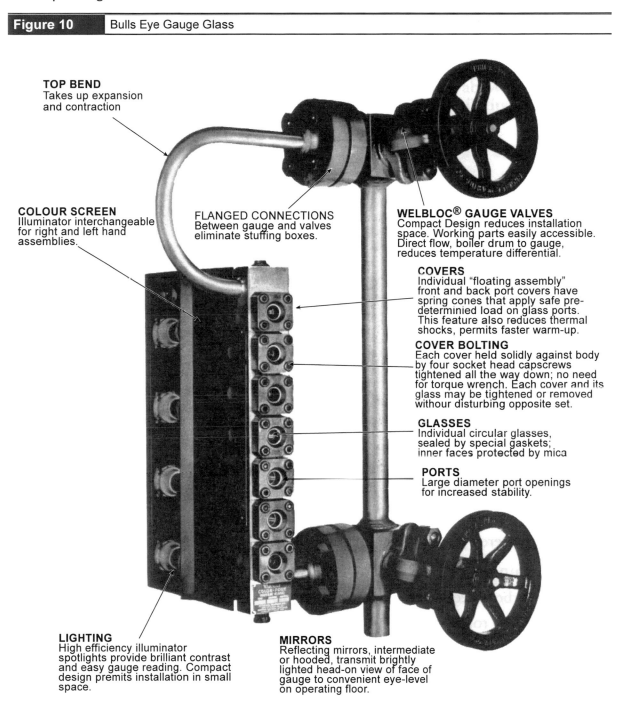

TOP BEND
Takes up expansion and contraction

COLOUR SCREEN
Illuminator interchangeable for right and left hand assemblies.

FLANGED CONNECTIONS
Between gauge and valves eliminate stuffing boxes.

WELBLOC® GAUGE VALVES
Compact Design reduces installation space. Working parts easily accessible. Direct flow, boiler drum to gauge, reduces temperature differential.

COVERS
Individual "floating assembly" front and back port covers have spring cones that apply safe pre-determinied load on glass ports. This feature also reduces thermal shocks, permits faster warm-up.

COVER BOLTING
Each cover held solidly against body by four socket head capscrews tightened all the way down; no need for torque wrench. Each cover and its glass may be tightened or removed withour disturbing opposite set.

GLASSES
Individual circular glasses, sealed by special gaskets; inner faces protected by mica

PORTS
Large diameter port openings for increased stability.

LIGHTING
High efficiency illuminator spotlights provide brilliant contrast and easy gauge reading. Compact design premits installation in small space.

MIRRORS
Reflecting mirrors, intermediate or hooded, transmit brightly lighted head-on view of face of gauge to convenient eye-level on operating floor.

(Courtesy of Yarnall-Waring Company)

Illumination

The gauge glass assemblies, shown in Figures 9 and 10, have built-in illumination. The lighting must be sufficient to shine through the filter glass assemblies and the gauge glass bulls eyes. The lighting assembly is fastened to the gauge glass. The light is shielded so it projects only through the gauge glass.

Flat glass sight glasses also have lighting assemblies attached to them. The light may be mounted in front of the glass to aid in viewing. If the flat sight glass is a see through design with two glasses, the light may also be mounted to shine from behind the glass.

QUICK SHUT-OFF DEVICES

Gauge glasses often have quick shut-off devices. Since the viewing area is made of glass, cracks are possible, resulting in steam leaks in the glass area. It becomes necessary to isolate the gauge glass, but from a safe distance.

Often chain valve arrangements are used to close the gauge glass block valves. In the assembly shown in Figure 11, the chains would be attached to the 'gauge glass steam valve' and the 'gauge glass water valve' and would be linked together to open or close both at the same time. The chains would be long enough and hang down far enough that they could be operated from the deck below.

The chain-operated valves can also be used when putting a gauge glass into service. This allows the operator to stand a safe distance away as hot steam warms up the glass. Only after the glass is fully warmed and no leaks are visible, should the operator go near the glass.

TESTING WATER COLUMN & GAUGE GLASS

Figure 11 is a diagram of a water column and gauge glass used for high-pressure service. The connections to the column from the boiler, plus the gauge glass connections to the column, must be proven free of any obstructions, using the following method:

1. Close the gauge glass top steam valve and the gauge glass bottom water valve in order to isolate the gauge glass before checking the column connections.

2. Close the column bottom water valve, then open the column drain valve. This permits steam to blow through the steam connection and the column, proving them free of obstruction. Close the column drain valve.

3. Close the column top steam valve. Open the column bottom water valve, then the column drain valve. Water flows through the water connection proving that this passage is clear.

4. Close the column drain valve and open the column top steam valve. This places the column back in operation.

5. Open the gauge glass top steam valve, then the gauge glass drain valve. This permits steam to blow through the top gauge connection, proving it is free of obstruction. Close the gauge drain valve.

6. Close the gauge glass steam valve. Open the gauge water valve, then the gauge drain valve. Water flow from the drain, proving that the lower connection is clear.

7. Close the drain valve on the gauge glass and open its steam valve to put the gauge glass back in operation.

Figure 11	Water Column and Flat Gauge Glass

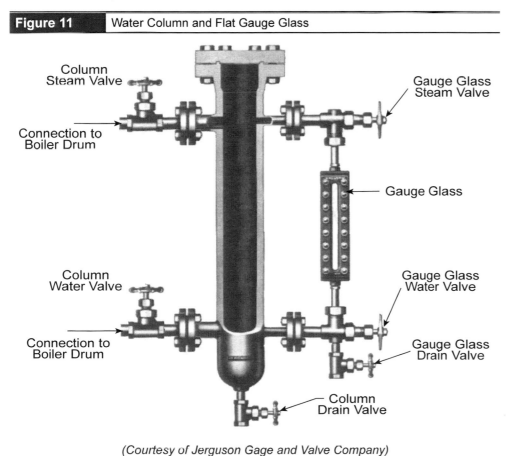

(Courtesy of Jerguson Gage and Valve Company)

GAUGE GLASS MAINTENANCE

At higher temperatures, gauge glasses are susceptible to corrosion, caused by alkalinity and silica in the water. Alkalinity causes thinning of the glass above the water line and its effect increases drastically as the pH of the water rises. Condensate, formed due to cooling of steam in the gauge glass, dissolves some of the silica in the glass and weakens it. This may result in eventual failure of the glass. Misalignment of fittings also causes gauge glasses to fail, due to mechanical stresses.

The following procedure is recommended when changing the glass in a flat gauge glass.

1. Close the steam and water valves on the gauge glass. Open the gauge glass drain.

2. Remove the bolted covers, glass, gaskets, and the mica. At this time, the threads on the studs should be coated with graphite and the nuts run down to clean the threads.

3. Remove any remaining gasket material, being careful not to create low spots on the surfaces of the joints. Scraping the gasket off the metal surfaces may form burrs.

4. Clean both ends of the gauge so gasket material will not plug the valves on the gauge.

5. Polish the gauge surfaces perfectly smooth. Check the surfaces to be sure that they are perfectly level with no high or low spots. This includes the surfaces of the gauge body and the bolted covers.

6. Apply molybdenum disulphide on the contact surfaces of the new glass. This permits the glass to slip into place easily. Never reuse old gauge glasses. Be sure that the glass is suitable for high temperature service.

7. Install a new gasket, new mica, and new glass on one side and install the cover. Replace the nuts on the cover.

8. Tighten the nuts on the cover evenly. It is best to start at the centre of the glass and tighten evenly on both sides of the glass.

9. Repeat steps 6, 7 and 8 on the other side of the glass.

10. If the boiler is in service, allow the new glass to warm up gradually by conduction of heat. Never open the gauge valves until the new glass is heated up.

11. With the drain valve still open, crack open the steam valve and permit steam to slowly blow through to heat the glass further.

12. When the glass is at operating temperature, close the drain valve and crack open the water valve to allow water into the glass.

13. If everything appears normal, and a water level is visible in the glass, open the steam and water valves fully. On high-pressure boilers, many gauge glass failures occur because the new glass was not heated gradually.

OBJECTIVE 4

Describe the float and probe designs for low-water fuel cutoffs and explain how these are tested.

LOW-WATER FUEL CUTOFFS

Normally, the water that covers the heating surfaces of a boiler keeps the metal at a safe operating temperature. However, if the water level becomes excessively low, heating surfaces may be exposed to hot gases with no water to provide cooling. The metal temperature may increase until the metal weakens and is unable to withstand the internal pressure. This may cause the metal to rupture, releasing pressurized steam and hot water from the boiler.

A low-water fuel cutoff device protects a boiler by shutting off the fuel supply to the burners if the water level drops to a predetermined low-low level.

CSA B51, clause 6.3.2.1 states:

- "Steam boilers not continuously attended by a certified operator, shall be equipped with at least two low-water fuel cut-off devices, each of which shall be independent of the other or others. These devices shall be installed so that they cannot be rendered inoperative. The installation shall be such that the devices can be tested under operational conditions. Note: The term 'tested under operational conditions' refers to a procedure that involves closure of the fuel supply valve or, in the case of an electric boiler not of the probe type, an interruption of the energy source".

Float Type Low-Water Fuel Cutoff

Figure 12 shows a float arrangement that combines a feedwater pump control switch with a low-water fuel cutoff and alarm. In this design, one mercury bulb with a two-wire switch controls the feedwater pump circuit, while a second mercury bulb with a three wire switch acts as a low-water fuel cutoff and alarm. As the water level drops, the float will close the two-wire switch to start the feedwater pump when the water is still above the lowest permissible level.

If the feedwater pump fails to start, or another problem causes the drum level to continue dropping, even when the pump is running, the bulb with the three-wire switch activates a boiler shutdown. The electrical circuit to the solenoid valve in the fuel line opens to shut off the burner and activate an alarm when the water in the boiler reaches the lowest permissible level.

Figure 12	Float Type Low-Water Fuel Cutoff

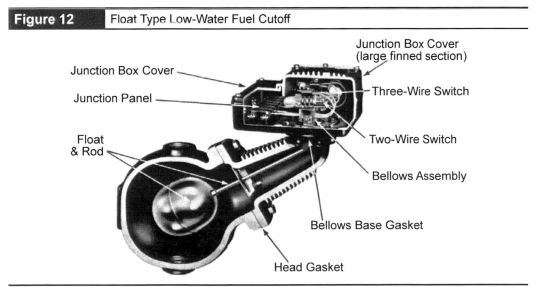

Probe Type Low-Water Fuel Cutoff

The probe design consists of electric probes (electrodes) immersed in the water. These probes may be mounted directly on the boiler shell, on the water column, or in a special probe housing. There are various probe arrangements. One common arrangement, shown in Figure 13, uses three probes, mounted in the water column.

Each probe has a specific purpose, with the shorter two acting to start and stop the feedwater pump and/or activate a feedwater valve. An alternate purpose of these two probes may be to activate high level (LSH) and low level (LSL) alarms. The longest of the three probes activates the low low level switch (LSLL), which de-energizes and closes the fuel shutoff valve.

Figure 13	Probe Type Low-Water Fuel Cutoff

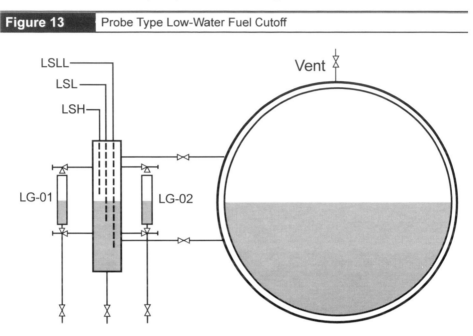

The probe design relies on the fact that water conducts electricity. When water covers a probe a circuit is completed through the water, between the probe and an electrical ground. If the water level falls below the probe, this electric circuit is broken.

TESTING LOW-WATER FUEL CUTOFFS

Regardless of their design, low-water fuel cutoffs must be inspected and tested on a regular basis. As specified in ASME, Section VII, they should also be thoroughly inspected and overhauled annually, to ensure good operating condition. Most jurisdictions have specific guidelines for the frequency of inspection and testing, guidelines which take precedence over ASME Section VII. Another important consideration is the boiler manufacturer's recommendations. Typical guidelines of the jurisdiction or the manufacturer may require the low water cutoff to be tested at least weekly or monthly.

To test the cutoff, first stop the water supply to the boiler. Then, with the burner in operation, drain water from the boiler. If the cut-off is working properly, the burner should shut down when the level is approximately 25 mm (1 in) above the bottom of the gauge glass.

To prevent sediment from collecting in the float chamber and impeding the action of the float, it is essential to routinely and thoroughly blow out the column and float chamber, using the drain valves. Before this procedure begins, the trip circuit must be by-passed to prevent unnecessary shutdown. This is done using a "defeat" switch or button, which is located nearby. This is NOT a latching button, but must be manually held in the 'defeat' position. This prevents the switch being inadvertently left in the 'defeat' position, which would leave the boiler unprotected.

OBJECTIVE 5

Describe boiler steam outlet arrangements and fittings including gate, angle, and globe stop valves and globe, Y, angle, and spring-cushioned non-return valves.

STOP VALVES

Every steam outlet, except safety valve, reheater, and superheater connections, is fitted with a stop valve, located as close as possible to the boiler. It is recommended that the stop valve be the outside-screw-and-yoke, rising spindle type. This allows easy indication, from a distance, whether the valve is closed or open. The advantage the threaded part of the spindle being outside the valve body (ie. outside screw design) is that it is not exposed to corrosion by the high temperature steam and water. Also, the valve may be easily lubricated.

Gate Stop Valve

The basic design of a gate type stop valve is shown in Figure 14. This stop valve features an outside screw and yoke with rising spindle. The handwheel is carried on the yoke and does not rise with the spindle. The locking lugs secure the bonnet to the valve body and are engaged by lowering the bonnet into the body and turning 45°. The bonnet is then seal welded to the body. The steel ring below the seal weld prevents stress at the bonnet joint due to welding.

Figure 14	Gate Type Outside-Screw-and-Yoke Stop Valve

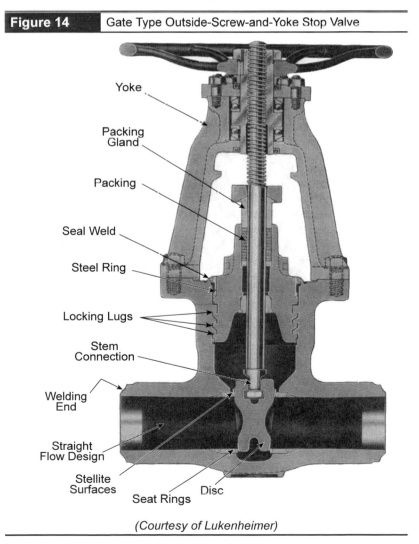

(Courtesy of Lukenheimer)

Angle Stop Valve

The angle type valve, shown in Figure 15, is another type of globe valve, which is also of the outside screw and yoke construction with rising stem. The steam flow is from the bottom and up past the disc, with a side outlet. This valve, often used in high-pressure applications, is a welded type. Note the drain valve for removal of condensate above the disc. The condensate is drained off before the main valve disc is opened. Thus, when the main disc is opened, no water is sent downstream to the steam header.

Figure 15	Angle Type Outside-Screw-and-Yoke Stop Valve

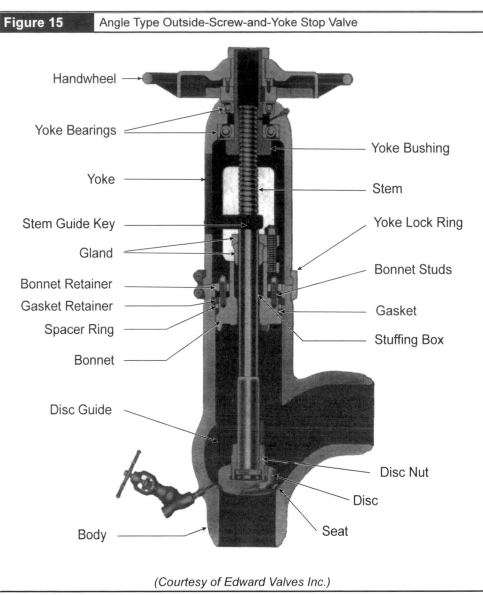

(Courtesy of Edward Valves Inc.)

Globe Stop Valve

Figure 16 shows the basic design of a globe type stop valve of the outside screw and yoke design, with a rising spindle. However, unlike the valves in Figures 14 and 15, the handwheel is attached to the spindle and rises with it. The valve disc fits into a replaceable seat. The steam flows up from the bottom, and passes between the valve disc and the seat. This design is excellent for throttling or for flow control applications.

Figure 16	Globe Type Outside-Screw-and-Yoke Stop Valve

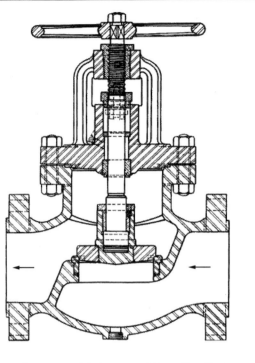

(Courtesy of Schutte and Koesting Co.)

NON-RETURN STOP VALVES

When two or more boilers are connected to a common main, it is recommended that each boiler be equipped with an approved, automatic stop-and-check valve, which shall be located closest to the boiler. This valve, also called the non-return valve (NRV), is in addition to the main boiler stop valve, which is located between the NRV and the main steam header. The space between the NRV and the boiler stop valve must be provided with an adequate drain valve.

The non-return valve is designed to prevent a back flow of steam from the header to the boiler if, for any reason, the boiler pressure drops below the header pressure. For example, if a boiler pressure part fails or ruptures, then the pressure in the damaged boiler drops below the steam header pressure. The non-return valve automatically closes and prevents steam from other boilers connected to the header flowing backwards into the damaged boiler.

The use of non-return valves makes it easier to bring a boiler on-line when it is supplying a common header with other boilers. The stem of the non-return valve can be put in the open position before the boiler is up to pressure. Steam from the other boilers, via the common header, does not enter the boiler because the valve disc is held closed by the higher header pressure. When the boiler steam drum pressure reaches the pressure in the main header, the NRV will automatically open and the boiler will "come on line", supplying steam into the header. Non-return valves allow the shutdown and startup of a boiler without the need to operate the manual stop valve.

Globe Non-Return Valve

The globe type non return valve, shown in Figure 17, features a rising stem with the handwheel carried on the yoke. When the handwheel is turned to raise the stem, the bottom of the stem withdraws from the disc piston and the valve is free to open when the pressure, at the inlet, is greater than that at the outlet. When the handwheel is turned to lower the stem, the stem will hold the disc piston tightly against the valve seat and the valve cannot open.

The equalizer connection, shown in Figure 17, connects the relatively high-pressure area over the disc piston to the high velocity, lower pressure area at the valve outlet. This allows the piston to be pushed up into the chamber, below the bonnet, when the valve opens. If the pressure at the outlet increases above that of the inlet, the equalizer connection will transmit this higher pressure to the area above the piston and the valve will close, thus preventing a reverse flow of steam.

Figure 17	Globe Non-Return Valve

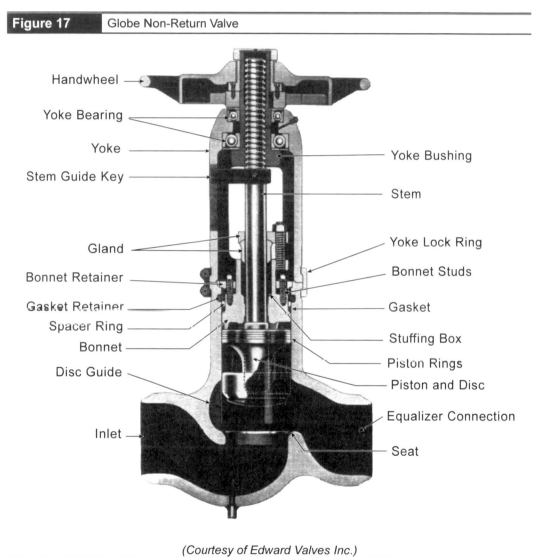

(Courtesy of Edward Valves Inc.)

Y-Type Non-Return Valve

Figure 18 shows a non-return valve with a Y-type body and weld connections. Like the valve in Fig. 17, this valve has an equalizing connection.

Figure 18	Y-Type Non-Return Valve

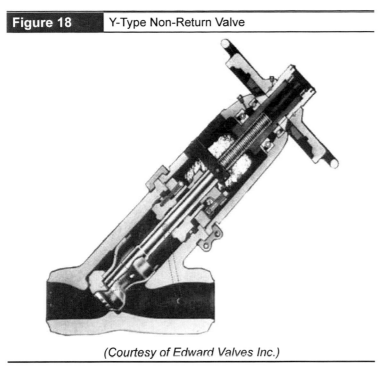

(Courtesy of Edward Valves Inc.)

Angle Non-Return Valve

Figure 19 shows an angle-type of non-return valve. The valve disc is attached to a piston, which works within a cylinder. When the valve spindle is backed off, as in Figure 19, the disc and piston are free to move. If the boiler pressure beneath the disc is greater than the header pressure at the valve outlet, the valve will open. If the header pressure exceeds boiler pressure then the disc will move to the closed position. The valve may be secured in the closed position by turning the spindle down against the disc. The piston serves to cushion the action of the valve when opening.

Figure 19	Angle-Type Non-Return Valve

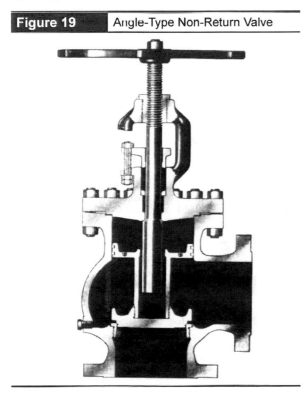

Spring Cushioned Non-Return Valve

In the spring cushioned non-return valve, shown in Figure 20, a spring is used, rather than a piston, to cushion the valve opening. Cushioning prevents the valve from chattering when the valve is opening and closing. It takes slightly more steam pressure to open a spring type non-return valve, since extra force is needed to overcome the spring tension.

Figure 20	Spring Cushioned Non-Return Valves

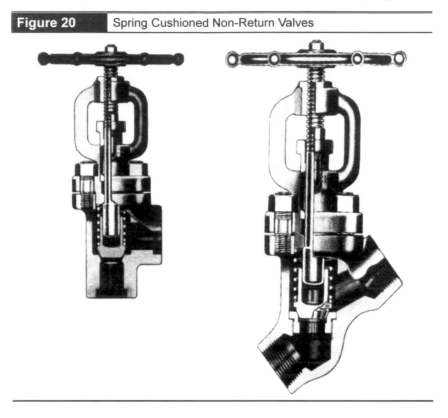

STEAM OUTLET ARRANGEMENTS

Figure 21 shows various arrangements of piping between boiler and steam header. Each arrangement features a non-return valve, always closest to the boiler, plus a stop valve at the header. Drains are provided in each case to drain the piping between the two valves.

If the boiler has a superheater, the non-return valve and block valve are located at the superheater outlet. There will be no valves between the boiler drum and the superheater inlet.

Figure 21	Non-Return and Header Valve Arrangements

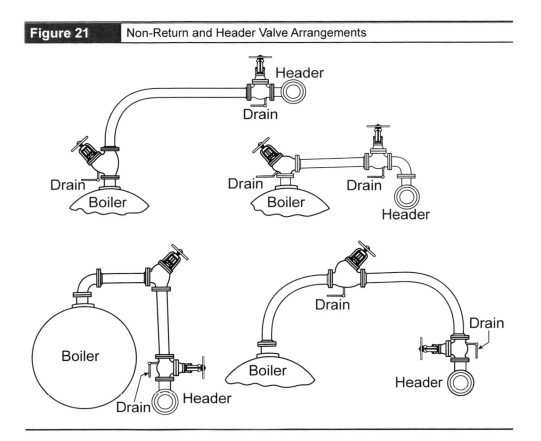

OBJECTIVE 6

Describe manual blowoff piping arrangements. Describe the design and operation of sliding disc, seatless plunger, angle and Y disc, and combination valves. Explain manual blowoff procedures. Describe the requirements for a blowoff tank.

BLOWOFF CONNECTIONS

The blowoff connection is made to the lowest point of the boiler in order to drain the boiler, blow mud and sediment out of the boiler, and lower the concentration of dissolved impurities in the boiler water. When the boiler is shut down for cleaning and inspection, the water may be drained out by opening the valves in the blowoff connection.

During the operation of the boiler, any sediment that has collected in the bottom of the boiler may be blown out. Dissolved solids also collect because as steam is produced from the boiler water, most of the dissolved impurities do not pass off with the steam, but remain in the boiler water. As a result, the water becomes highly concentrated with the dissolved impurities and may begin to foam and carry over. The concentration of dissolved impurities in the boiler water may be reduced by blowing out some of the heavily concentrated water through the blowoff connection. The boiler water is replaced with feedwater of relatively low concentration, or high purity.

The ASME Code, Section I, PG-59.3 gives the 'Requirements for Boiler Blowoffs'. Among other requirements it states that:

- "Except as permitted for miniature boilers... the minimum size of blowoff connections shall be NPS1 and the maximum size shall be NPS 2 1/2...". Also, PG-59.3.7 states that "A bottom blowoff pipe when exposed to direct furnace heat shall be protected by firebrick or other heat-resisting material...".

Figure 22 shows the blowoff line from the mud drum of a packaged watertube boiler.

| **Figure 22** | Packaged Boiler Blowoff Line |

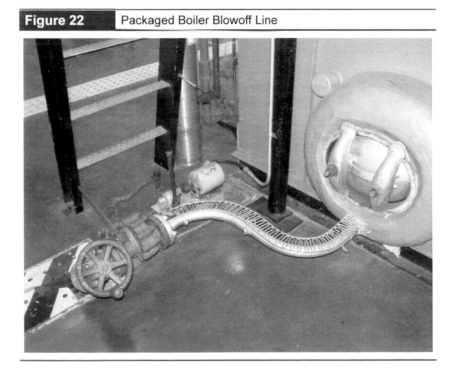

BLOWOFF VALVE ARRANGEMENTS

Every steam boiler with a working pressure exceeding 103 kPa shall be equipped with two approved blowoff valves, one of which must be a slow-opening type. A slow-opening valve is one requiring at least five 360° turns of the operating mechanism to change from full closed to full open.

Boilers are often equipped with one slow-opening valve and one quick-opening valve or they may be equipped with two slow-opening valves.

Figure 23 illustrates these two arrangements.

Figure 23	Blowoff Valve Arrangements

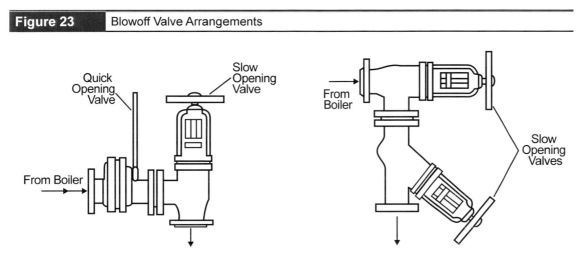

A quick-opening valve opens or closes by moving a lever through a small arc. If quick-opening valve and slow-opening valves are both used, the quick-opening valve must be located nearest the boiler. The quick-opening valve acts as a sealing, or guard valve, and the slow-opening valve as the blowing-off valve.

The fact that the blowing-off valve is slow-opening reduces the possibility of water hammer and associated damage to pipe and fittings. Blowoff flow changes slowly when the valve is adjusted.

The quick-opening valve should always be opened first, followed by the slow-opening valve. Then the slow-opening valve should be closed first, followed by the quick-opening valve. This sequence prevents high velocity erosion of the quick-opening valve, thus ensuring this valve always maintains a tight seal. The slow-opening valve will be subject to wear, since velocity will be high when the valve is partially open. However, this valve can be repaired or replaced without taking the boiler out of service, thanks to the quick-opening valve having positive shutoff.

This proper blowoff sequence for tandem valves is shown in Figure 24.

Figure 24 | Opening and Closing Sequences

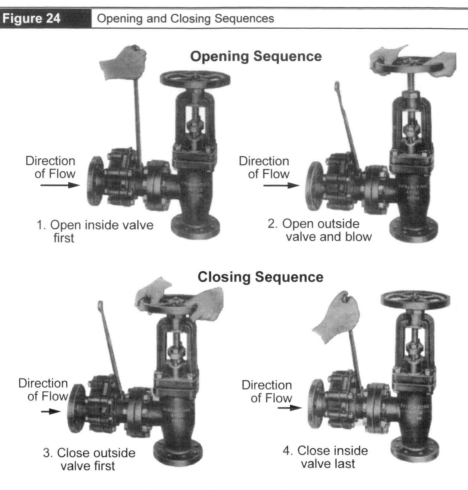

Opening Sequence

Direction of Flow →

1. Open inside valve first

Direction of Flow →

2. Open outside valve and blow

Closing Sequence

Direction of Flow →

3. Close outside valve first

Direction of Flow →

4. Close inside valve last

(Courtesy of Everlasting Valve Co.)

Figure 25 shows two slow-opening valves, arranged in tandem. The valve next to the boiler is an angle type and the other a straight through or Y-type. The blowoff sequence for the valves remains the same, with the valve nearest the boiler being opened first and closed last.

Figure 25 | Straightway and Angle Valves

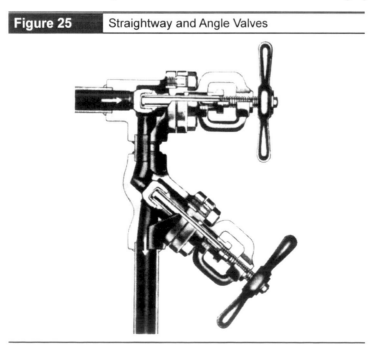

BLOWOFF VALVE TYPES

The most commonly used types of blowoff valves are:

- Sliding disc
- Seatless sliding plunger
- Seat and disc
- Combination

Sliding Disc

The general arrangement of a sliding disc is shown in Figure 26(a). The internal detail is shown in Figure 26(b). When the valve is in the closed position, the disc covers the opening. In the open position, the disc moves off to one side, opening a passage through the valve.

This valve is classed as a quick-opening and must always be used in conjunction with a slow-opening valve. It may, however, be converted to a slow-opening valve using a hand-wheel and gear arrangement, instead of the operating lever.

When used as a quick opening valve, moving the lever through a short angle, less than 90 degrees, operates the valve from full open to full closed.

Figure 26	(a) Quick-Opening Valve	(b) Sliding Disc and Seat

(Courtesy of Everlasting Valve Co.)

Seatless Sliding Plunger

The seatless, sliding plunger valve, illustrated in Figure 27, is a slow-opening, requiring at least five 360° turns of the hand wheel to move from full closed to full open.

When the handwheel is turned anti-clockwise, to open the valve, the non-rising stem rotates and raises the plunger so that the plunger ports coincide with the body inlet ports. The discharge then occurs downward, through the inside of the plunger and out through the bottom outlet.

When the handwheel is turned clockwise,to close the valve, the plunger lowers and closed off the inlet ports.

Figure 27	Seatless Blowoff Valve

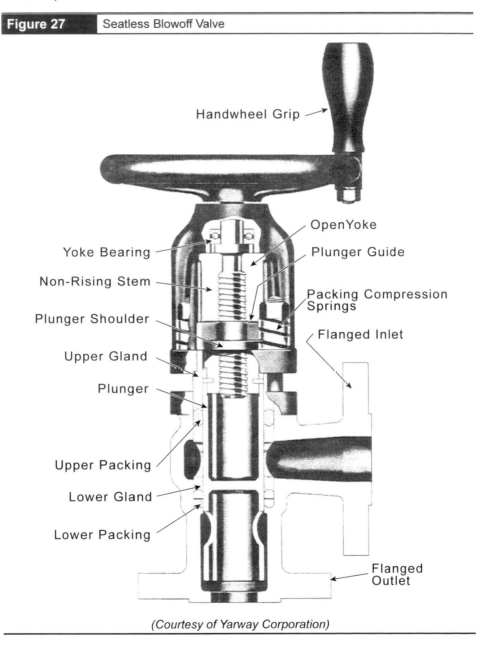

Handwheel Grip

OpenYoke

Yoke Bearing

Plunger Guide

Non-Rising Stem

Packing Compression Springs

Plunger Shoulder

Flanged Inlet

Upper Gland

Plunger

Upper Packing

Lower Gland

Lower Packing

Flanged Outlet

(Courtesy of Yarway Corporation)

Figure 28 shows the position of the plunger in open and closed positions.

Figure 28	Seatless Valve - Open and Closed

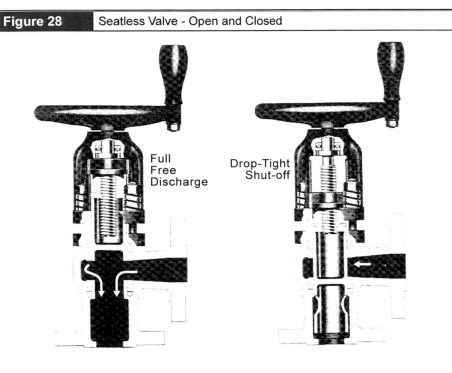

Full Free Discharge

Drop-Tight Shut-off

(Courtesy of Yarway Corporation)

Seat & Disc

The seat and disc valve is slow opening. It features a rotating, rising stem with an attached disc on the bottom. The disc is free to rotate and mates with the valve seat in the body. To minimize erosion, the surfaces of the disc and seat are made of very hard materials, such as stellite or monel. The seats are also threaded for easy replacement. These valves may be the angle type or "Y" type, as shown in Figure 29.

Figure 29	Seat and Disc Valves

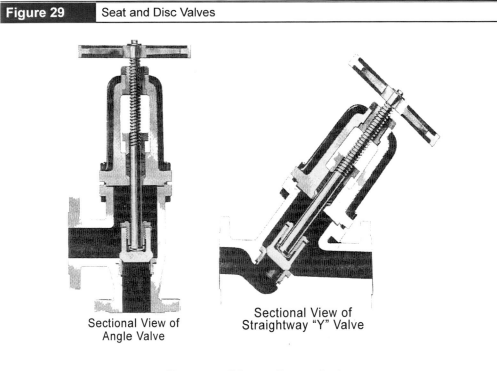

Sectional View of Angle Valve

Sectional View of Straightway "Y" Valve

(Courtesy of Yarway Corporation)

The valve shown in Figure 30 has an integral, welded-in stellite seat. Therefore, it is a hard-seat valve that resists erosion in water with high solids content.

Figure 30	Integral Seat Blow-off Valve

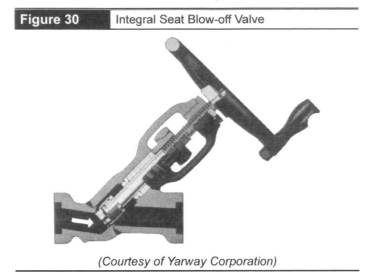

(Courtesy of Yarway Corporation)

Combination Valves

Two blowoff valves may be combined within the same valve body. This creates a very compact unit and eliminates bolted or welded connection between the two valves. A combination valve is shown in Figure 31. The inlet valve of this unit is the integral seat design, while the discharge valve is the seatless, sliding plunger design.

Figure 31	Combination Blowoff Valve

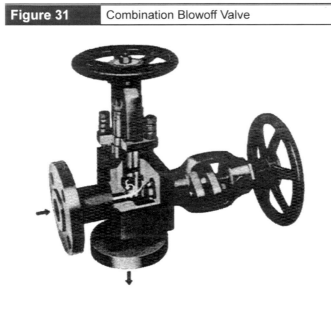

(Courtesy of Yarway Corporation)

MANUAL BLOWOFF PROCEDURES

To restate and reinforce what was stated earlier with regard to blowoff procedures, the ASME Code Section VII "Recommended Rules For The Care of Power Boilers", C2.427, recommends the following. These are direct quotes.

"If a quick opening valve and a slow opening valve are installed together on a boiler, then the quick opening valve would normally be opened first and closed last and blowing down is accomplished with the slow opening valve."

"In the case of a hard seat valve followed by a seatless valve, the hard seat valve should be opened last and closed first."

"In the case of two seatless valves where the plunger continues to move after port closure, the valve nearest the boiler should be opened last and closed first. If this is not done, the water trapped between the outer and inner valves would be placed under compression by the plunger travel after port closure."

"In any other combination of two identical valves, the sequence of operation should provide that the same valve is always opened last and closed first to save the other valve from throttling service and ensure tight closing of the combined system."

BLOWOFF VESSELS (TANKS)

CSA B51-09 governs the installation of blowoff vessels (tanks).

Section 6.5.1 states, "When the blowoff from a boiler having a working pressure exceeding 103 kPa (15 psi) is discharged into a sewer system, a registered blowoff vessel or other suitable registered device shall be placed between the boiler and sewer to reduce the temperature of the water entering the sewer system to 65°C (150°F) or lower"

Section 7.5 then specifies design requirements for blowoff vessels. A table (Table 2) is provided, which specifies the design pressure of a blowoff vessel in relation to the maximum pressure of the supplying boiler. Specifically, for a boiler presssure of 103 to 2060 kPa, the blowoff vessel must be designed for 30% of the maximum boiler pressure, but not less than 103 kPa, and for boiler pressures above 2060 kPa, the blowoff vessel must be designed for 690 kPa.

Another table (Table 3) specifies the minimum dimensions of blowoff vessels in relation to the steam evaporative capacity of the supplying boiler. For example, a boiler with steam capacity of 136 000 kg/h must have a blowoff vessel with a minimum diameter of 1220 mm and minimum volume of 2.27 cubic metres.

A typical blowoff tank, with component sizes as specified in CSA B51, is shown in Figure 32.

| Figure 32 | Blowoff Vessel (Tank) |

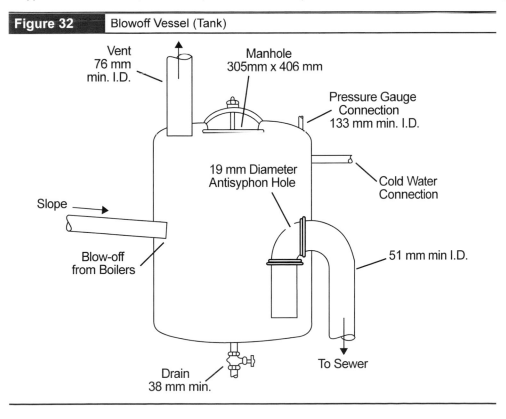

OBJECTIVE 7

Explain the components of the steam drum internals of a watertube boiler. Describe the design and operation of various steam separation devices, including baffles, primary and secondary separators, and scrubbers.

DRUM INTERNALS

Drum internals are fittings located within the boiler drum. They are divided into three classes, according to their purpose:

- First class: to remove moisture and impurities from the steam
- Second class: to distribute feedwater within the drum
- Third class: to provide continuous blowoff of concentrated boiler water

The term "drum internals" is taken to mean all the devices installed within the boiler steam drum, including the following:

- Steam separators
- Steam scrubbers
- Steam washers
- Chemical feed lines
- Internal feed pipe
- Continuous blowdown lines

STEAM SEPARATORS

The removal of impurities from the steam is extremely important. If the impurities are carried over with the steam, they form deposits in the superheater tubes and cause overheating of these tubes. If the steam is used to drive a turbine, deposits will form on the turbine blades and in the turbine control valves.

The impurities are in the form of solids, which are carried by the moisture in the steam. Therefore, removal of moisture will also remove the solid impurities. To remove the moisture from the steam before it leaves the drum, various types of separators are used.

Dry Pipe Separator

The dry pipe arrangement, shown in Figure 33, is a simple device for removing moisture from steam. The steam enters the pipe through holes in the top. It changes direction as it enters and exits the pipe, causing water droplets be thrown out and stay behind in the pipe. The water drains off through small holes at the bottom of the pipe.

Figure 33   Dry Pipe Separator (Side View)

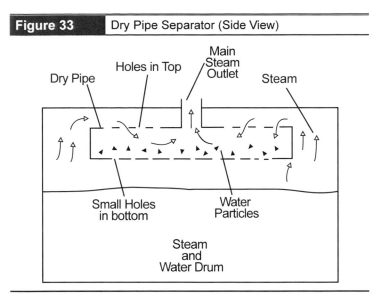

Cyclone Separators

Figure 34 shows a schematic arrangement of a cyclone steam separator with a small, corrugated scrubber fitted at the top. The steam-water mixture from the steam generating tubes (risers), initially enters the drum behind a baffle which direct it into the side of the cyclone separators. The cyclone action causes high centrifugal force, which throws the water to the sides of the cyclone. It drains down to the bottom and enters the water space of the drum. The steam leaves the top of the cyclone and passes through corrugated scrubber plates, which catch any further water droplets before the steam leaves the drum.

Figure 34   Cyclone Steam Separator

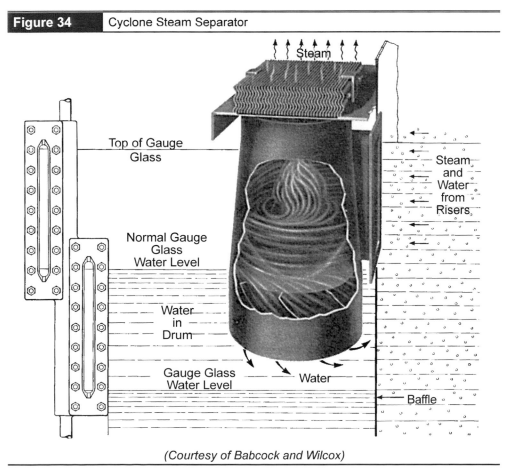

(Courtesy of Babcock and Wilcox)

STEAM SCRUBBERS

The steam drum, in Figure 35, illustrates the arrangement of the baffle plates, primary cyclone separators and secondary separator elements (scrubbers). The steam-water separation takes place in two stages. The primary separation removes nearly all the steam from the water so that very little steam can be recirculated back toward the downcomers.

The steam leaving the primary separators in high-pressure boilers still contains too much liquid (in the form of contained droplets) for satisfactory superheater and turbine performance. Therefore, the steam is passed through a secondary set of scrubber elements (usually closely spaced, corrugated parallel plates) for final removal of water droplets.

Figure 35	Cyclone Separators and Steam Scrubbers

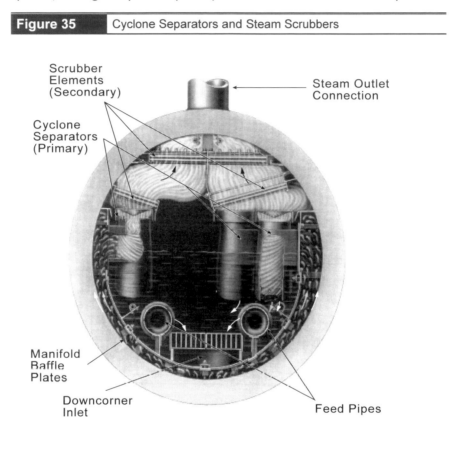

(Courtesy of Babcock and Wilcox)

Figure 36 is another internal view of a steam drum, which has a single row of cyclone separators. It has scrubbers at the cyclone outlets, plus the larger, corrugated scrubbers below the steam outlet.

The baffle that separates the riser tubes from the water circulating tubes (downcomers) and directs steam into the cyclones is also shown. Internal feed pipes are installed above this baffle to distribute feedwater along the length of the drum.

The amount of equipment inside these steam drums makes inspection of the steam drum somewhat difficult. Most of the baffle plates, cyclone separators, and scrubbers must be removed to gain access to the boiler drum surface or the tubes.

Figure 38 shows yet another separator and scrubber design. In this case the steam drum has horizontal, centrifugal separators. These are similar to the vertical units in action and, but the centrifugal components are mounted horizontally in the drum. Long separator drains extend down into the water. There is also a set of large secondary driers (or scrubbers), containing corrugated plates, for final removal of free moisture from the steam.

Note on Scrubber Corrugations:

Steam scrubbers (also called dryers), regardless of their mounting arrangement, consist of many thin metal plates, placed closely together. The steam passes between these plates and the free water attaches to the plates and runs downwards. To promote the contact of metal and water, the plates are corrugated, which causes the steam to change direction many times. A popular corrugation shape is the chevron, "V", shape and dryers with this design are commonly called CHEVRON DRYERS.

Figure 36	Cyclone Separators and Steam Scrubbers

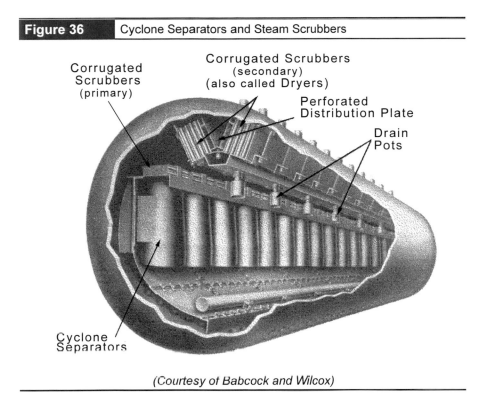

(Courtesy of Babcock and Wilcox)

STEAM WASHERS

Figure 37 is a another, cutaway diagram of a steam drum with a double row of cyclone separators. Two internal feedwater pipes are installed below the cyclones.

An additional feature is the steam washer. About 5% of the boiler's feedwater, instead of flowing to the internal feed pipes, is fed to the steam washer and sprayed into the steam that is flowing to the steam outlet. The purpose of this water spray is to absorb any gaseous impurities in the steam, such as gaseous silica, preventing it from leaving with the steam.

Figure 37	Steam Washer and Cyclone Separators

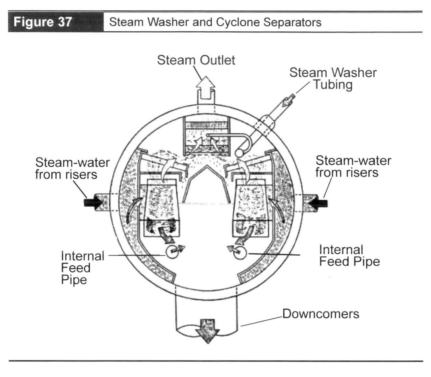

INTERNAL FEED PIPE

Figures 36, 37, and 38, in addition to illustrating the steam scrubbers and separators, also show the position of the internal feed pipe, or pipes. The internal feed pipe, through several holes drilled along its length, serves to distribute the incoming feedwater uniformly along the length of the drum. This uniform distribution avoids temperature shock to the drum and avoids turbulence. The location of the line is near the bottom of the water space, which is the "coldest" water area. Since the incoming water is relatively "cold", this location encourages the water to enter the downcomers, thereby enhancing the water/steam circulation pattern. Although not shown clearly, the baffle below the feed pipe also has holes drilled in it, which gives direct access to the downcomers. Other baffles separate the risers from the downcomers and prevent steam from directly contacting the incoming feed water.

CONTINUOUS BLOWDOWN LINE

Another important drum internal is the continuous blowdown line. Blowdown is the controlled removal of water from the boiler, for the purpose of controlling the concentration of dissolved solids. It continuously removes a controlled amount of concentrated water from the drum. The amount of blowdown is controlled by a special regulating valve with an indicator that shows the position (ie. the opening) of the valve.

Setting the continuous blowdown valve is done in conjunction with periodic testing of the boiler water dissolved solids. The continuous blow-down collecting pipe is located where the concentration of dissolved solids is greatest, which is several centimeters below the operating water level.

Figure 38 shows the relative position of the blowdown pipe.

Figure 38	Drum Internals

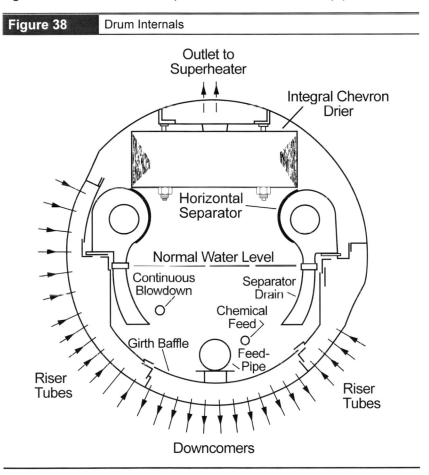

CHAPTER 5 - QUESTIONS

1. Describe the principle of operation of a high pressure relief valve and explain why the valve will shut at a lower pressure than that at which it opened.

2. a) Where is an inspector's gauge connected and what is its purpose?

   b) What is the purpose of the steam gauge siphon and why is it used?

3. a) Sketch a water column and gauge glass installation showing all necessary valves and fittings.

   b) Referring to this sketch explain how all the connections may be blown through to prove that they are clear.

4. a) Explain how a low water fuel cut-off protects a boiler from damage due to over-heating.

   b) Give three possible reasons for a low water fuel cut-off not operating properly and explain how to prevent these troubles from occurring.

   c) Describe the proper method of testing a low water fuel cut-off.

5. a) Describe the operation of an automatic stop-and-check valve.

   b) Under what conditions is this type of valve recommended on a boiler.

6. Describe an arrangement for the purification of steam, which uses two types of separating equipment within the steam drum.

7. A boiler has two manual blow-down valves, a quick opening and a slow opening. Using a simple sketch, describe the sequence of opening and closing the valves for blowing down the boiler.

8. Sketch a section of a steam drum showing all necessary internals. Indicate the position of the risers, downcomers and baffles.

ANSWERS: All answers are found within the content of the chapter.

Burner Designs & Supply Systems

Learning Outcome

When you complete this chapter you should be able to:

Describe the typical components of fuel supply systems and describe common burner/furnace designs for gas, oil, and coal-fired boilers.

Learning Objectives

Here is what you should be able to do when you complete each objective:

1. Describe a complete fuel gas supply system from fuel gas header to burner and explain the function of each component, including control and shut-off valves, auto-vents, and instruments. State the typical operating pressures.

2. Describe the design and operation of spud and ring burners, and explain high-efficiency, low NO_x designs.

3. Describe a complete fuel oil supply system from storage tanks to burners and explain the function of each system component.

4. Describe the design and operation of air, steam, and mechanical atomizing burners.

5. Describe a coal supply system from stockpiles to burners for a typical pulverized coal furnace.

6. Describe the design and operation of a pulverized coal burner and explain turbulent vertical, tangential, and cyclone furnaces.

7. Describe the design and operation of ball, impact, ball-race, and bowl mill pulverizers.

8. Describe the designs and operation of underfeed, overfeed, and crossfeed stokers for furnaces burning solid fuels.

OBJECTIVE 1

Describe a complete fuel gas supply system from fuel gas header to burner and explain the function of each component, including control and shut-off valves, auto-vents, and instruments. State the typical operating pressures.

BURNER GAS SUPPLY SYSTEM

Gas piping to boilers depends a lot on the size and design of the boiler. There are several possible arrangements, each with minimum requirements specified in ASME CSD1 code and CSA B149 Gas Code.

The typical components of a gas supply system to a multi-burner steam generator are illustrated in Figure 1.

Figure 1	Typical Gas Piping to Multi-burner Boiler

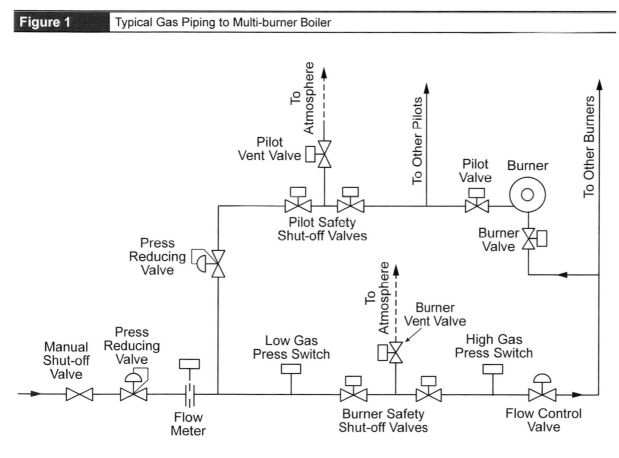

The gas enters through a manual isolation valve at plant pressure and is reduced to about 280 kPa in a pressure reducing valve or pressure control valve. A flow meter then measures the total gas flow to the boiler. The burner gas flows through a pair of safety shut-off valves (SSV's), which have an automatic vent valve between them, commonly termed a "double-block-and-bleed" arrangement. If abnormal conditions occur, such as low gas pressure or loss of combustion air supply, the SSV's will close and the vent will open, depressuring between the SSV's.

Downstream of the burner SSV's is a flow control valve, which modulates the gas flow to the burners to satisfy boiler steam load or the pressure of the main steam header. The gas then goes to a common burner header from which each individual burner is supplied. At each burner is an automatic shut-off valve to isolate only that burner.

Gas to the pilots is suppled from upstream of the first burner SSV. During a boiler start-up, this location allows gas to the pilots before the main burner SSV's are reset. A pressure reducing valve reduces pilot pressure to about 20 kPa. The pilot gas then flows through a pilot double-block-and-bleed arrangement, with two pilot gas SSV's and a vent to atmosphere. A boiler shutdown will cause the pilot SSV's to close and the vent to open, thus eliminating gas supply to all pilots. Each burner has an automatic shut-off valve on the pilot gas supply. This valve will open and close as directed by the burner start-up or shutdown sequence.

High and low gas pressure switches are included as safety devices in the system. If either high or low gas pressure occurs outside the allowable limits, unstable combustion and/or flame conditions may occur, with the ultimate potential to cause a furnace explosion. The pressure switches are designed to close the shut-off valves and thus stop all gas flow if the pressure limits (high or low) are exceeded.

The opening of the main burner flow control valve affects pressure in the main burner header, depending on the boiler load. At full load (all burners operating) the main burner pressure is about 70 kPa, while at reduced load it may drop to about 7 kPa.

The actual controls furnished with a gas-fired burner system will vary, depending on insurance carrier requirements, the manufacturer's specifications, or code requirements for that model of boiler. For comparison to the large boiler in Figure 1, a typical gas train for a smaller, heating boiler is shown in Figure 2. Only one main gas valve is required since this is a low-pressure boiler.

Figure 2	Gas Supply Train

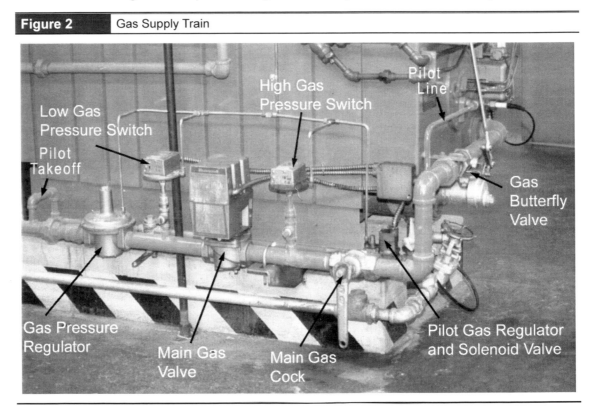

Figure 3 illustrates a gas supply train with an additional main gas valve. The main gas valves are operated by a motorized mechanism, rather than a diaphragm. There is also a gas line vent valve, which is solenoid operated and is normally closed when the gas valves are open. When the main gas valves are de-energized and go closed, the vent valve will automatically open to vent all gas pressure from between the two valves.

Figure 3   Gas Supply Train

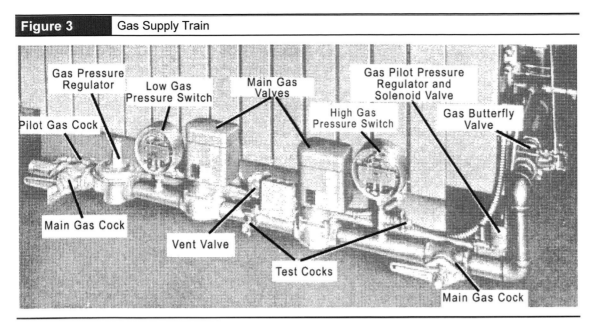

Safety devices and fittings, which are common to each of the gas supply trains illustrated, are as follows:

1. The **gas pilot pressure regulator** reduces the incoming header gas pressure. To ensure a satisfactory pilot flame, this regulator maintains a steady and constant pressure in the pilot gas line

2. The **main gas pressure regulator** controls the main gas pressure at a higher setting than the pilot regulator. This produces a steady flame and helps obtain the highest combustion efficiency.

3. A **low gas pressure cutoff switch** prevents the burner from operating when the gas pressure in the supply line drops below the pressure necessary to maintain a stable flame at the burner. Should the gas pressure drop below the switch setting, contacts will open to break a circuit, which causes the main gas valves to close. This switch is a normally open switch and usually has a manual reset.

4. The **high gas pressure switch** contacts are normally closed whenever the main gas line pressure is below a preset pressure. Should the pressure rise above this setting, the switch contacts will open, breaking a circuit causing the main gas valves to close. This safety device ensures stable combustion and correct air-fuel ratio during operation of the boiler. The switch is usually a manual reset type.

5. The **main gas valves** are ON/OFF, normally closed, single-seated gas valves. When the electric motors on the valves are energized, the valves are opened and fuel is provided to the burners. These valves operate automatically as directed by the boiler programming control.

6. The **gas butterfly valve**, under the control of the damper motor, regulates the rate of gas flow to the burner at all loads. The mechanical linkage for this valve can be seen in Figures 2 and 3, just above the butterfly valve. The linkage is connected to the same motor that opens and closes the air dampers, controlling the amount of combustion air to the boiler. Larger boilers will use air operated control valves to achieve this type of control.

OBJECTIVE 2

Describe the design and operation of spud and ring burners, and explain high-efficiency, low NOx designs.

GAS BURNER TYPES

Since natural gas is already in a gaseous state, there is no need for further atomization at the burner. However, the burner must be able to control the amount of air admitted to burn the gas and must be able to cause turbulent mixing of the gas and air. Most burners have the fuel entering the combustion air stream at (or close to) a right angle, which promotes good mixing. There are several different gas burner designs for steam generators; three common types are discussed briefly in this chapter.

Multi-Spud Burner

Figure 4 shows the multi-spud gas burner.

Figure 4	Multi-Spud Gas Burner

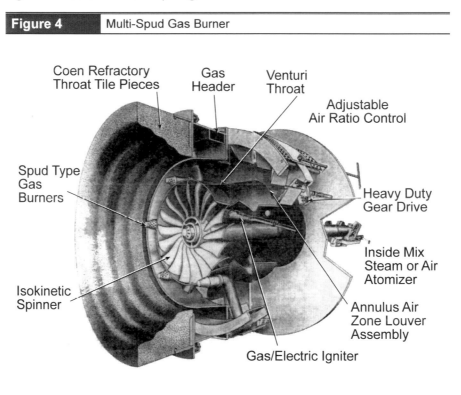

(*Courtesy of Coen Company, Inc.*)

In this burner, gas is supplied to a circular manifold, which has eight spuds (or jets) connected to it. The ends of these spuds are drilled with small holes, through which jets of gas issue. Combustion air from the windbox to the burner is controlled by register doors or louvres. Each spud has a shutoff valve so that it may be removed for cleaning, leaving the other spuds in operation. The burner may also have a centrally located oil gun for the burning of oil when desired.

Figure 5 gives another view of the multi-spud burner, showing the burner throat, the position of the spuds, and the impeller. The impeller, often called a swirl plate, ensures proper flame distribution around the burner throat.

Figure 5   End View of Spud Burner

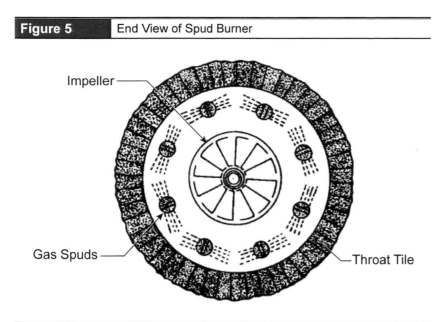

Figure 6 illustrates the airflow and flame pattern of a typical multi spud burner. This burner also has a recirculating flame pattern, which reduces the emissions of nitrogen oxides (NO_X).

Figure 6   Flows in Spud Type Burner Coen DAF Type

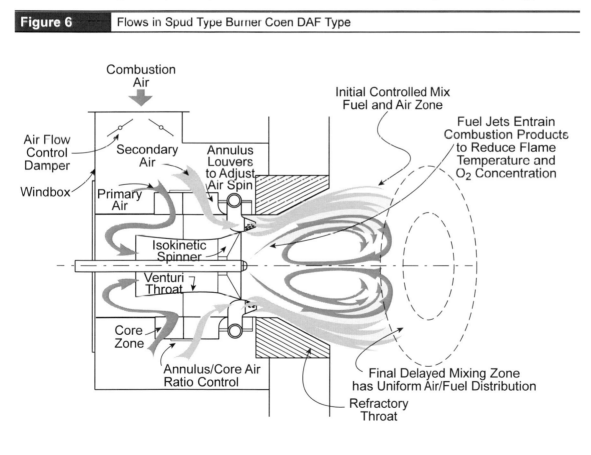

(Courtesy of Coen Company, Inc.)

Ring Type Burner

In this design, gas is supplied to a ring type manifold, which has numerous gas outlets drilled in it. Air is admitted through air register louvres and passes through the center of the ring. There it mixes with the gas issuing from holes in the ring manifold. This type may also have a centrally located oil burner. A ring type gas burner with removable oil gun is shown in Figure 7.

Figure 7   Ring Type Gas Burner

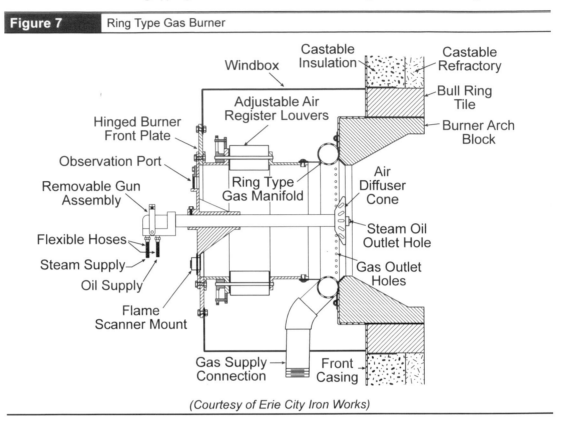

(Courtesy of Erie City Iron Works)

High Efficiency, Low NO$_X$ Burners

Nitrogen oxides (NO$_X$) are emissions that are formed during combustion, usually (but not always) due to high combustion temperatures. The NO$_X$ originates from three possible sources:

1. Thermal NO$_X$: The nitrogen and oxygen in the combustion air react at high temperatures to form NO$_X$. The thermal NO$_X$ reaction occurs rapidly above 1535°C. This is the greatest source of NO$_X$ and receives the greatest attention in its control.

2. Fuel NO$_X$: The nitrogen component of the fuel reacts with the oxygen in the combustion air to form NO$_X$. Since natural gas normally has a low nitrogen content, fuel NO$_X$ is not usually a concern.

3. Prompt NO$_X$: The nitrogen component of the combustion air reacts with hydrocarbon combustion products. This is a very minor source of NO$_X$ compared to total NO$_X$ production.

Pollution concerns and high fuel prices have made it necessary to make burners more efficient, using less oxygen and producing less NO$_X$. To use less oxygen, very thorough mixing of air and fuel is required. Burner manufacturers have different methods of achieving these results. Some burners use mixers or spin plates, separate air zones, or a system of feeding the air in stages.

To achieve lower thermal NO$_X$ the flame temperature must be kept as low as possible. This is achieved by using some form of flue gas recirculation. This involves mixing partly burned flue gas with the main flame, which results in a slower burning and cooler flame. Air staging is also used in which the combustion air is fed in several stages, separating the primary and secondary air to slow combustion. A third method is to adjust the fuel feed position, thus changing the flame pattern. Low NO$_X$ natural gas burners have a longer, more orange flame.

Example of a Low NO$_X$ Burner

Figure 8 shows an ASR (axial, staged, return flow) Burner, by Babcock Borsig Power, Inc., which feeds the combustion air in several stages. This separates the primary air and secondary air to slow combustion. This burner also recycles flue gas back to the burner outlet.

Figure 8	ASR Burner

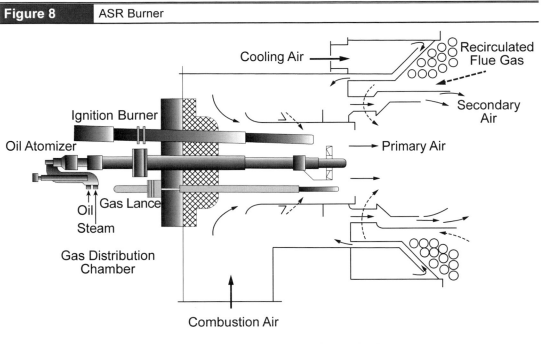

(Courtesy of Babcock Borsig Power, Inc.)

Referring back to Figure 6, The Coen Company's DAF (distributed air flow) burner uses an isokinetic spinner or swirl plate to generate a recirculation zone, which results in recirculation of combustion products into the flames, reducing the flame temperature. The result is a lower O$_2$ content of the flue gas and lower NO$_X$ emissions.

The chart in Figure 9 reveals the NO$_X$ reduction that is possible using Coen's DAF Technology. The graph compares NO$_X$ levels of different DAF burners, at different firing rates, to a standard gas burner on a package boiler. The standard burners run in the 100-200 ppm range, while the low NO$_X$ designs run in the 25-80 ppm range.

Figure 9	NO$_X$ Reduction Chart

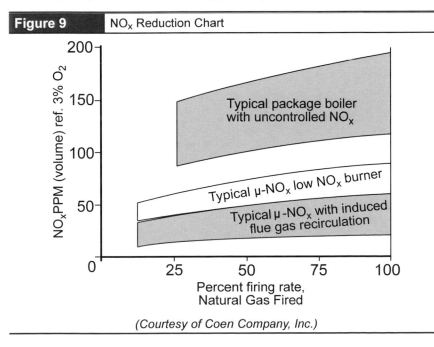

(Courtesy of Coen Company, Inc.)

OBJECTIVE 3

Describe a complete fuel oil supply system from storage tanks to burners and explain the function of each system component.

FUEL OIL HANDLING

The handling of heavy fuel oil involves storing, heating, pumping, and burning the oil. Handling of lighter oils involves the same operations with the exception of heating.

Storage Tanks

The storage capacity required at a particular plant primarily depends on the reliability and expedience of oil delivery from the supplier. If the plant is located in an urban, industrial area then storage capacity equal to one week's maximum consumption should be sufficient. However, if the plant is in a remote area it may be necessary to have storage capacity equal to three or more weeks' maximum consumption.

Storage tanks may be installed above or below ground. Above ground storage costs less and creates fewer pumping problems, plus all equipment is accessible for maintenance. However, this method requires greater space and an earth or concrete dyke around the storage tanks. This dyke must be sized to contain at least the total volume of oil stored, plus one third. Underground storage tanks, which may be steel or concrete, allow storage in confined areas, where ground space is limited, and permit storage close to the boiler room.

Figure 10 shows an oil storage tank for heavy fuel oil, showing the necessary connections. Piping to or from the tank should not be galvanized, since sulphur in the oil will react with the galvanizing zinc, causing sludge.

- The fill line should extend lower into the tank than the suction line or it should be fitted with a loop seal trap at the bottom so that it cannot vent oil vapors when the oil level in the tank is low.

- The vent pipe should drain back into the tank and the lower end should not extend more than 25 mm below the uppermost part of the tank. It should be visible from the fill connection, and be weatherproof and clog proof. Vents in above ground tanks should be fitted with flame arresters.

- The scavenging line is used to scavenge an empty tank with air, usually as part of the pre-entry procedure before personnel enter the tank for maintenance. The sludge pump connection allows the removal of sludge and water from the tank and the steam smothering line is used to smoother a fire in the tank.

- The manhole is bolted, has a gasket, and should not be used for any connections or for any purpose except inspection, repair and cleaning of the tank.

- The return line should extend below the level of the suction inlet or it should be fitted with a loop seal trap at the bottom so that it cannot act as a vent when the oil level in the tank is low.

- The heating coil is attached to a removable cover to allow access for repair. Steam to the coil is regulated by a thermostatic control valve, which controls the temperature of the oil in the suction line. The condensate from this coil discharges through a trap to the sewer.

- There are two suction connections with the lower one normally in service. The upper suction line is only used if water collects in the tank up to the level of the lower suction or if the lower suction begins to draw sludge from the tank. The latter is more common in heavy oil systems and is indicated by pump filters/strainers becoming plugged.

Figure 10 | Oil Storage Tank

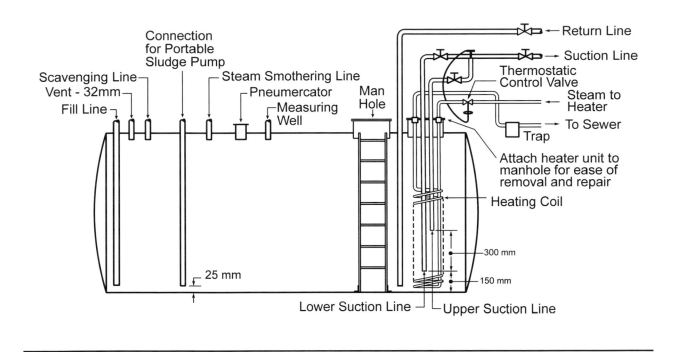

Oil Heating

Heavy fuel oil is heated in two stages. The first stage heats the oil to facilitate pumping and the second stage heats the oil to a temperature that will promote atomization in the burners. The oil temperature required for pumping is usually in the range of from 30°C to 55°C. Heating the oil for atomization requires an oil temperature of 70°C and 100°C, depending on the grade of oil and the burner design.

To heat the oil for pumping, a suction heater is located inside the storage tank. This usually consists of a pipe coil through which steam or hot water is passed. If steam is used it should not be above 170 kPa since higher pressures will result in high pipe surface temperatures, which tend to overheat and carbonize the slowly circulating oil. The use of electric heaters installed directly in the tank is not generally approved.

Condensate from the heating coil should be piped to waste to prevent the possibility of oil entering the boiler feed water system in the event of a leak in the heater coils. A closed system of circulating hot water may also be used in the suction heater, in which case steam coils or electricity are used to heat the hot water. This prevents both overheating of the oil and contamination of the steam.

Typical Oil Handling System

Refer to Figure 11.

The overall oil handling system includes the storage tank, the piping to and from the burners, and the necessary related equipment, such as heaters, pumps, strainers, plus control and measuring devices.

- The suction line has duplex strainers installed before each pump, to ensure clean oil to the pumps. The duplex feature allows one filter basket to be cleaned or changed while the other remains in service.

- This system has two gear type oil pumps, one driven by a steam turbine and one by an electric motor. The steam driven pump is normally in service, with the motor driven pump on standby. The pumps are positive displacement, requiring a pressure relief valve on the discharge. Two pumps are installed to avoid shutdown if repairs are necessary to one pump.

- The pump pressure required for mechanical atomization will depend upon the sprayer plate used in the oil burner nozzle and upon the quantity of oil needed for the boiler load. Typical pressures range from 345 to 1725 kPa. Steam atomizing burners use a lower oil pressure, ranging from 15 to 860 kPa.

- Downstream of the pumps are heaters and more duplex strainers. The oil at this point is at operating pressure and has been filtered twice.

- The oil preheater in the supply line to the burners raises the temperature of the oil for atomization and a thermostatic (automatic) control valve controls the steam supply. If oil temperature gets too high, a thermal overload valve will close and a portion of the oil will bypass the preheater and return directly to the tank.

- From the heaters, the oil flows to the burners. Flow control valves maintain the required operating flow to the burner headers. Individual burners are adjusted to maintain their desired flows. At low flow rates, the constant flow control valves will open and maintain a steady flow in the system by recycling oil back to the tank. Similarly, oil will be bypassed to the tank if the pressure in the supply line becomes excessive.

- The fill and return lines have a U bend on the bottom to prevent agitation of the sludge or water that has settled to the bottom.

Figure 11   Oil Handling System

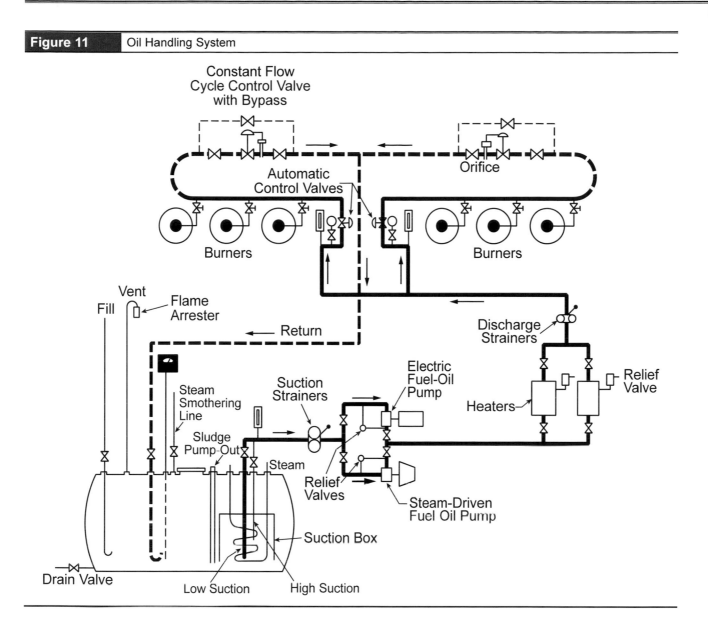

OBJECTIVE 4

Describe the design and operation of air, steam and mechanical atomizing burners.

OIL BURNER TYPES

The principal functions of an oil burner are to change the liquid oil into a fine mist, or vapour-like state, and to thoroughly mix this atomized oil with air so that combustion can take place quickly and efficiently.

Mechanical Atomizing Burners

Figure 12 shows a mechanical atomizing burner.

This design uses the fact that when oil is forced under pressure through a small orifice into an area of lower pressure it tends to break into a spray of fine droplets.

Figure 12	Mechanical Atomizing Burner

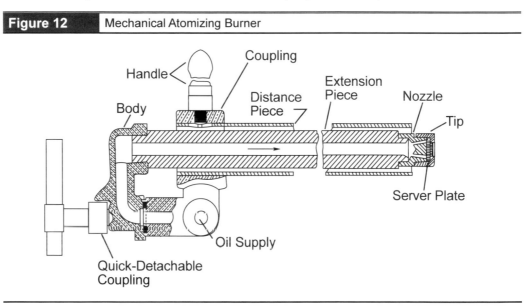

Referring to Figure 12, the oil is delivered to the burner nozzle under high pressure. Inside the nozzle, the oil passes through narrow tangent to a swirl chamber and the slots cause the oil to revolve rapidly in the swirl chamber. The oil is then forced through the nozzle orifice and leaves as a cone-shaped spray of fine droplets.

This design may be used for any grade of fuel oil, provided that, in the case of the heavier grades, the oil is preheated to the correct viscosity.

Figure 13 is a sketch of another mechanical atomizing burner, showing the nozzle parts disassembled.

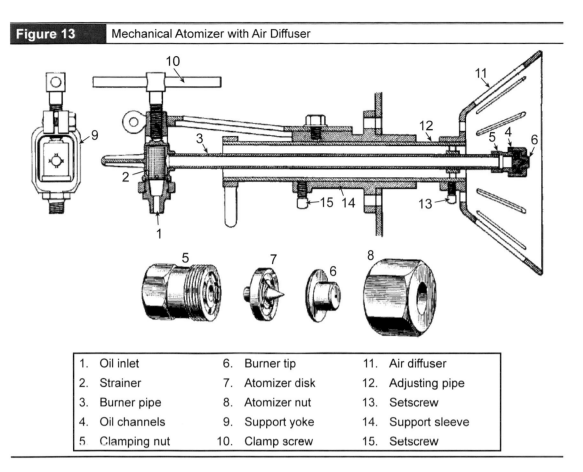

Figure 13 — Mechanical Atomizer with Air Diffuser

1. Oil inlet	6. Burner tip	11. Air diffuser
2. Strainer	7. Atomizer disk	12. Adjusting pipe
3. Burner pipe	8. Atomizer nut	13. Setscrew
4. Oil channels	9. Support yoke	14. Support sleeve
5. Clamping nut	10. Clamp screw	15. Setscrew

Steam or Air Atomizing Burners

Steam or air atomizer burners are widely used. They operate by producing a steam-fuel (or air-fuel) emulsion (mixture) that atomizes the oil through the rapid expansion of the steam when released into the furnaces.

The oil is pumped through an orifice and then blasted by a jet of high-pressure air or steam. Contact between the oil and the steam or air may occur inside or outside the burner tip, depending upon the design.

Figure 14 shows the internal mixing type, also called an emulsion atomizer. The oil and the steam are admitted to a mixing chamber and the mixture passes through the emulsion tube to the nozzle at the end where it emerges as an atomized spray into the furnace.

Figure 14 — Steam Atomizer Burner, Internal Mixing Type

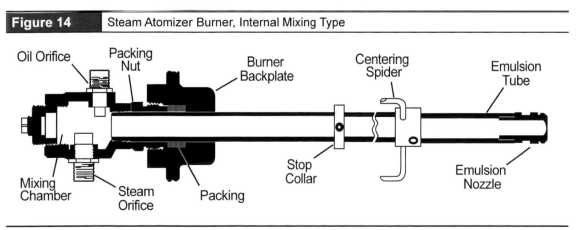

Figure 15 shows an external mixing burner. The oil is pumped under pressure to the central tube of the burner. Compressed air or steam is admitted to the annular space surrounding the central tube. The air or steam comes in contact with the oil at the burner tip, where atomization takes place.

Figure 15	Steam or Air Atomizing Burner, External Mixing

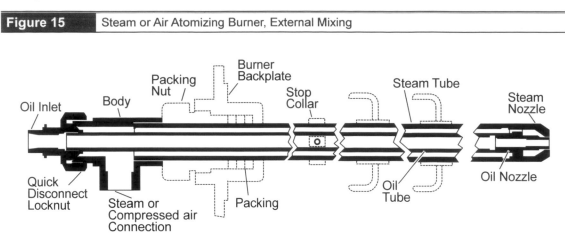

The external mixing burner is easier to clean and less likely to clog than the internal type. However, the internal type gives better flame control. Pressures required for atomization range from 140 to 550 kPa for the oil and from 690 to 1050 kPa for the steam or air.

The atomizing steam must be dry, since moisture causes pulsations, which can cause loss of ignition. The steam atomizer performs more efficiently over a wider load range than other types. It normally maintains efficient atomization down to 20 percent of rated capacity.

Compressed air may be substituted for steam during cold startups or during an emergency, when steam isn't available.

Figure 16 shows an alternate design of air atomizing burner, which is commonly used in packaged boilers. It is a low-pressure air-atomizing burner, using air at 7 to 14 kPa and oil at about 35 kPa.

Figure 16	Air Atomizing Oil Burner

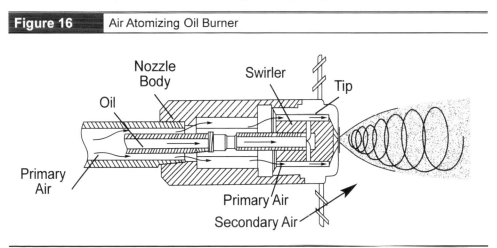

A small compressor, which is often belt driven from the forced draft fan motor, supplies atomizing, or primary air to atomize the light oil. The oil travels down a central tube while the primary air moves down the outer tube. The air blows the oil through an atomizer into a fine spray and swirls the oil mist into the furnace. The fuel enters the atomizing stream at or near right angles thus creating a shearing action on the fuel as it enters the atomizing stream.

Combustion air, also called the secondary air, is blown into the furnace by the forced draft fan. The combustion air swirls in the opposite direction to the oil mist, resulting in good, turbulent mixing, which creates good combustion.

Rotary Cup Oil Burner

Figure 17 shows a rotary cup burner.

Oil is delivered to a cup that is rotating at about 3500 r/min. Centrifugal force throws the oil from the lip of the cup in the form of a conical sheet of liquid, which quickly breaks into a spray. Primary air is supplied through an annular space around the cup.

Oil pressure in this case needs only to sufficient to deliver the oil to the burner, since atomization does not depend upon pressure. The burner in Figure 17 is designed for large, packaged boilers using No. 2 fuel oil.

Figure 17	Rotary Cup Atomizing Burner

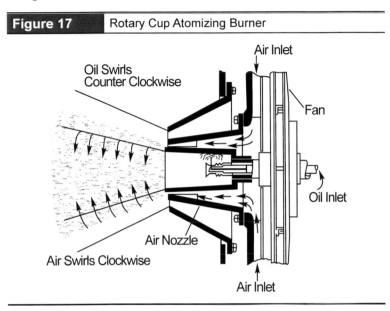

OBJECTIVE 5

Describe a coal supply system from stockpiles to burners for a typical pulverized coal furnace.

COAL HANDLING SYSTEMS

Coal handling is highly mechanized and even remotely controlled, in some cases. Together with the ash removal system, it accounts for a large part of the investment cost and is often the major maintenance item.

The purpose of the coal plant is to receive the incoming coal supply, place it on stock, and then transport it from stock to boilers when, and in the form, required. Coal delivery to the plant site may be required by water, rail or road, or the power plant may be located close to the coal supply.

Figure 18 illustrates a typical coal-handling layout.

In side view (a) the subsystems for unloading cars (the "track hopper") and the reclaim system at the bottom of the pile can be seen.

In side view (b), note the sequence of events.

- The coal is reclaimed and crushed to the proper size in the crusher house.
- The coal is then fed to the surge bin, where in-line magnets remove any metal. The surge bin also has load cells to track tonnage. Samplers are incorporated for quality checks.
- From the surge bin the coal is taken by conveyor belt to the in-plant silos, or coal-bunkers. The bunkers have load cells to monitor their levels.
- Each bunker has a coal feeder, which feeds to a pulverizer. The pulverized coal, now in the form of coal dust, is piped into the steam generator for combustion.

Plan view (c) is an overhead view of the coal handling operation. Note the flow of coal from the track hoppers to the storage pile, the reclaiming system, the crusher house, and the belt feeding system into the plant silos.

| Figure 18 | Views of Coal Handling Layout |

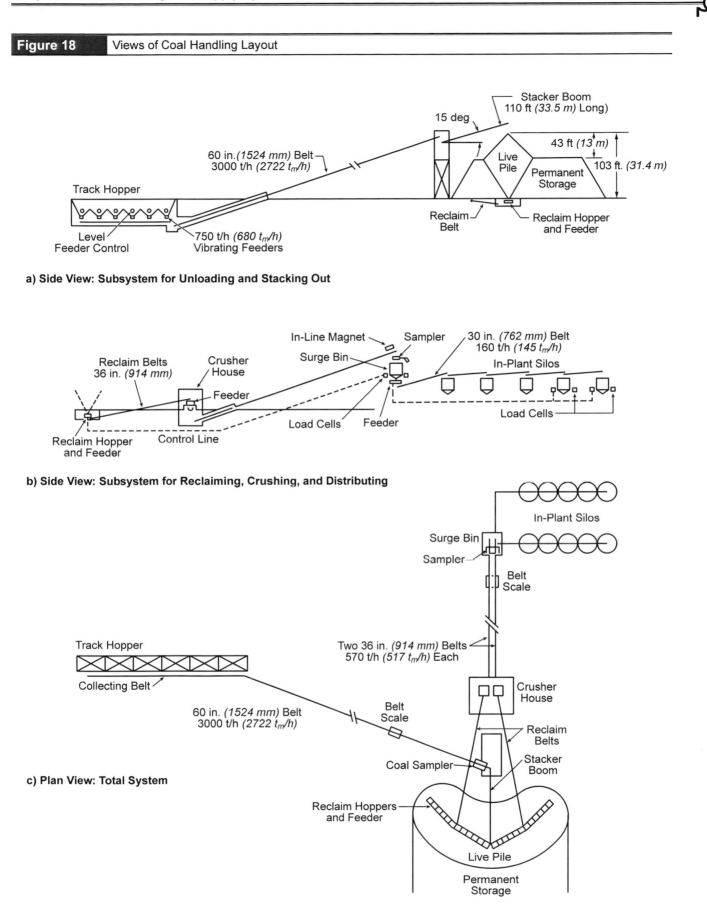

a) Side View: Subsystem for Unloading and Stacking Out

b) Side View: Subsystem for Reclaiming, Crushing, and Distributing

c) Plan View: Total System

(Courtesy of Babcock and Wilcox)

Figure 19 is a photograph of a coal pile, showing the crusher house and conveyor belts.

Figure 19	Coal Storage and Handling Area

(Courtesy of Babcock and Wilcox)

Figure 20 shows the layout (in plan view) of one power plant coal handling system, with the coal supply arriving by water or by rail. If the coal arrives by rail it is discharged by a rotary car dumper (or wagon tippler) as shown in Figure 21. The dumper incorporates a weigher.

Figure 20 Plan of Power Plant Coal Handling

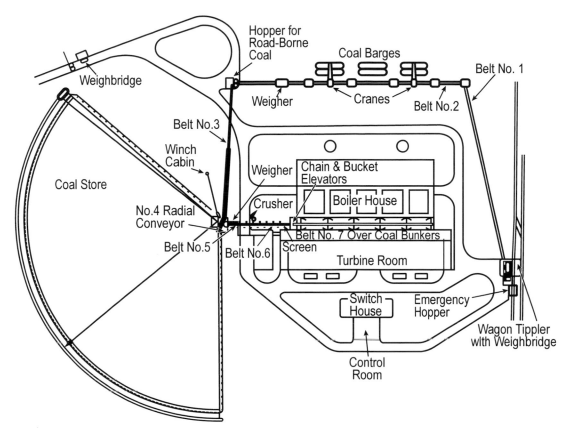

Figure 21 Rotary Car Dumper

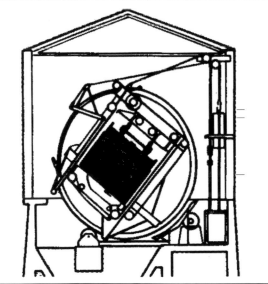

Coal that arrives by barge is unloaded by crane, using a clamshell bucket, as shown in Figure 22. It is discharged onto to a belt conveyor and weighed by a belt scale, Figures 23 and 24. The scale measures the speed of the belt plus the weight on a suspended section of the carrying run. Then, a integrator relates running weights to belt travel and calculates and records the tonnage of coal handled.

Coal can be fed onto a belt conveyor at any point and can be discharged wherever required, using a moveable tripper or over the head pulley, as seen in Figure 25.

Belt conveyors are the best method of handling the large quantities of coal required in a power plant. They can be sized to carry up to 1200 tonnes/h, moving at 4.25 m/s and with a maximum incline of about 18°, depending on the coal handled. Belts are made of a rubber and canvas composition, which has good tensile strength and is resistant to abrasion and corrosion.

| **Figure 22** | Coal Tower with Clamshell |

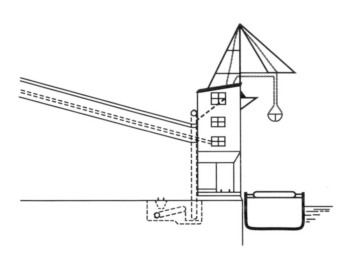

| **Figure 23** | Belt Scale |

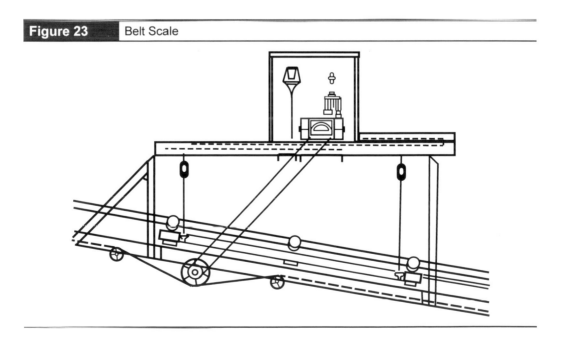

Figure 24   Belt Weighing Machine

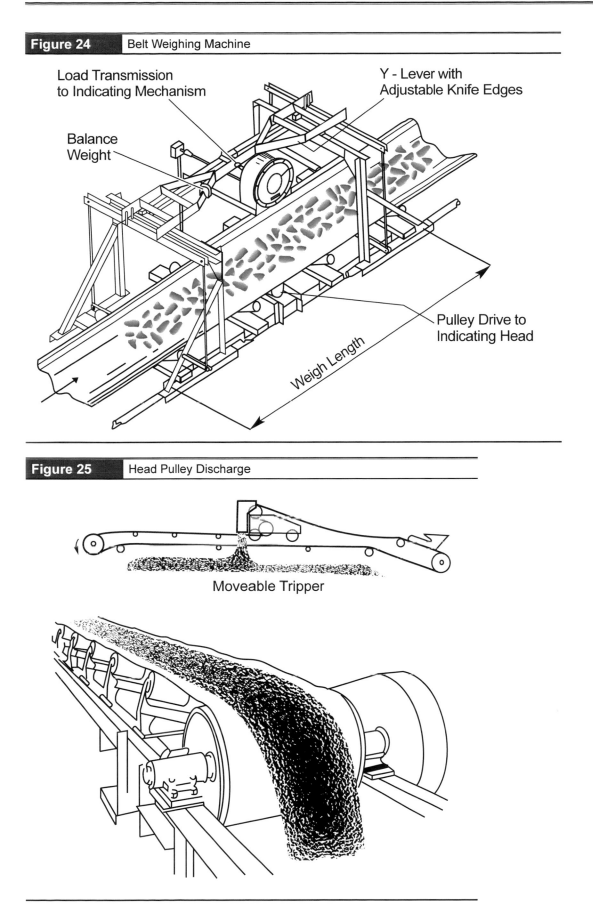

Load Transmission to Indicating Mechanism

Y - Lever with Adjustable Knife Edges

Balance Weight

Pulley Drive to Indicating Head

Weigh Length

Figure 25   Head Pulley Discharge

Moveable Tripper

When the incoming coal reaches the main supply conveyor it may be delivered directly to the boiler bunkers or sent to the stockpile for storage until needed. Normal practice is to first fill the bunkers and then send the remainder to the stockpile.

Magnetic separators are fitted to the belts that discharge into the bunkers. Their purpose is to extract any "tramp iron" that might be inadvertently mixed with the coal at the mine or during transport. These separators consist of electromagnets, which are suspended above the moving coal or fitted to the discharge pulley on the conveyor belt. The latter is shown in Figure 26. The magnetic material attracts to the pulley and then falls into a separate hopper. Screens are also fitted along the coal route to the bunkers to remove larger, non-magnetic objects, such as timber, stone, and even oversized coal. This prevents restrictions at the pulverizers.

Bunkers are usually sized to hold enough coal for about 12 hours of firing at full load. They must be designed to resist erosion and to ensure free flow of coal. Erosion is minimized by cladding the bunker walls with sheets of stainless steel or by covering the walls with a facing of concrete. Free flow of coal through the bunkers is achieved by keeping the coal as dry and clean as possible and by designing the bunker walls to reduce friction. If the coal is damp or friction is too high, the coal will stick, hang up, and produce "rat holes" or arches, as shown in Figure 27. Sticking coal can also be minimized by installing vibrators in the walls of the bunker.

Figure 26	Magnetic Pulley for Belt Conveyor

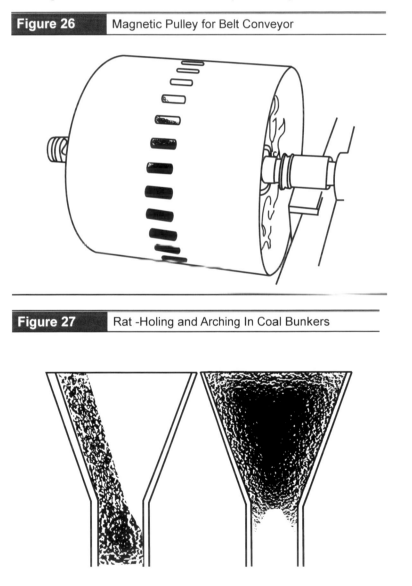

Figure 27	Rat-Holing and Arching In Coal Bunkers

Coal Storage (Stockpiling)

The coal stockpile must be large enough to provide reliable supply to the boilers during breaks in the delivery of new coal to the plant. These breaks may be frequent and of long duration for various reasons, including bad weather or transportation problems. It is usual to operate the coal handling plant only in daylight hours (except in emergencies) and to shut down at weekends.

Coal storage may be either **active storage**, from which firing equipment feeds directly, or **reserve storage**, which guards against delays in coal shipment, etc.

1. Active Storage

In active storage, the main requirement is easy access; the shape and depth of the stockpile is not important. In reserve storage, access is less important, but the stockpiling must be done very carefully to minimize spontaneous combustion and to reduce losses due to weathering.

Figure 28 shows one method of active coal storage, using a drag scraper. Several different drag scraper layouts are shown. A conveyor is used to add coal into the stock area and then the scraper bucket distributes the coal evenly. To transfer coal to the bunkers (called reclaiming), the scraper bucket is reversed and used to scrape the coal back into an underground receiving hopper.

Another method of active storage uses traveling conveyors or traveling bridges and cranes above the stock, which span the stock to deliver or reclaim the coal.

Figure 28	Drag Scraper Layouts

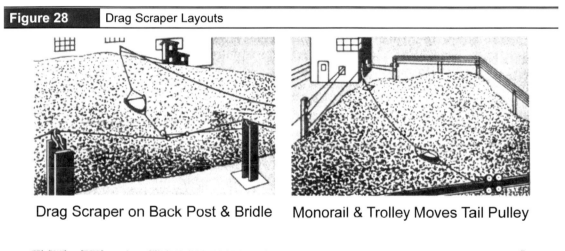

Drag Scraper on Back Post & Bridle   Monorail & Trolley Moves Tail Pulley

 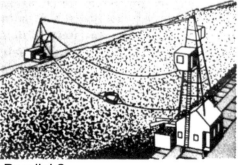

Radial Setup:
Back Post Moves on Track

Parallel 2 -
Tower Layout for Large Pile

Figure 29 shows an even more flexible stockpiling system using mobile equipment, such as bulldozers and scrapers. This method may be used for active storage, within limits, since it compacts the pile more, increasing the density of the coal. Coal stocks higher than 3 metres, regardless of purpose, require some compacting to exclude air.

Figure 29	Coal Handling with Mobile Equipment

Bulldozer mounted on a crawlerTractor

Scraper with Rubber-Tired Pime Mover

2. Reserve Storage

Reserve Storage requires extra consideration. The main aim when putting down a reserve stockpile is to minimize air and moisture within the pile. When coal is stockpiled for long periods, while exposed to atmospheric air, the coal will slowly oxidize and deteriorate. Oxidation causes combustible gases to release from the coal, reducing its heating value. An average loss in heating value is about 1% per year. There is also a danger of spontaneous combustion, since heat produced in the stockpile may result in temperatures that are high enough to cause the combustible gases to ignite.

Four substances in the coal seem to contribute most to the reactions involved in deterioration, heating, and spontaneous combustion. These are iron pyrites, water, oxygen and some hydrocarbons. The iron pyrites, water and oxygen combine to form iron sulphate and sulphuric acid, which, in turn, trigger carbon and hydrocarbon reactions with oxygen to produce methane gas.

Since it is impractical to only select coals that are low in iron pyrites, the solution to these problems is to use storage methods that will exclude (or minimize) oxygen and water. The best method is to pack the coal tightly and mix coal fines with the rough coal to fill all possible air spaces. Using heavy equipment to create the stockpile achieves the compacting and the fines

Figure 30 shows how coal piles should be layered and packed, compared to a loosely dumped pile.

Figure 30	Layering of Coal Piles

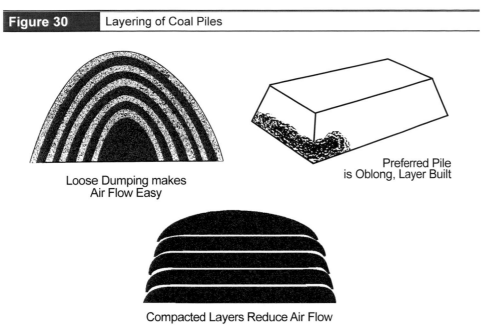

Loose Dumping makes
Air Flow Easy

Preferred Pile
is Oblong, Layer Built

Compacted Layers Reduce Air Flow

The temperature of a stockpile must be continuously monitored and recorded. Temperature probes or thermometers set in pipes are the usual method. If the temperature is 70°C or higher there is a threat of fire.

If temperature is high, but combustion has not yet occurred, preventative measures involve re-compacting the pile to seal off the air supply. If combustion occurs, CO_2 may be injected to extinguish the fire or the affected area of the pile may be dug out.

OBJECTIVE 6

Describe the design and operation of a pulverized coal burner and explain turbulent vertical, tangential, and cyclone furnaces.

PULVERIZED COAL BURNERS

After coal is pulverized (see Objective 7), the coal-air mixture passes through piping to the burners, located at the furnace. The air carrying the coal is known as primary air and ranges from 20% down to 10% of the total air requirements. Any excess air required for efficient combustion is included in the primary and/or secondary air. The other 80%-90%, called secondary air, combines with the primary air and coal at the burner. There are three general firing arrangements: horizontal firing, vertical firing, and tangential firing.

Horizontal Firing

Figure 31 shows a horizontal firing arrangement. The burner (or burners) is located in the front wall and flame travels horizontally across the furnace.

Figure 31	Horizontal Firing

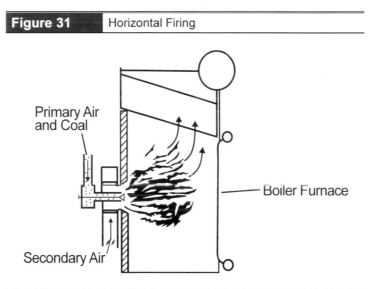

In other horizontal firing arrangements, the burners are located in the rear furnace wall or in both the front and rear walls.

Figure 32 shows one burner used for horizontal firing. It has a central coal nozzle with internal ribs, into which the mixture of coal and primary air (from coal pipe "2") enters. The spiral internal ribs provide uniform distribution and mixture at the burner outlet.

The secondary air is admitted to the burner housing surrounding the central nozzle through adjustable vanes (5). This provides turbulence and thorough mixing of the secondary air with the coal and air mixture at the nozzle outlet. Note that this particular burner also has provision to burn gas or oil, which may be necessary for startup.

| Figure 32 | Pulverized Coal Burner for Horizontal Firing |

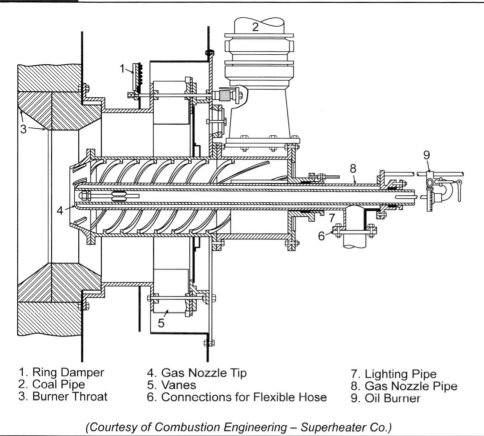

1. Ring Damper	4. Gas Nozzle Tip	7. Lighting Pipe
2. Coal Pipe	5. Vanes	8. Gas Nozzle Pipe
3. Burner Throat	6. Connections for Flexible Hose	9. Oil Burner

(Courtesy of Combustion Engineering – Superheater Co.)

Vertical Firing

Figure 33 shows a typical vertical firing arrangement. In this design, the burners are located in the furnace arch (at the top) and fire vertically downward. The flame then makes a U turn, upward, toward the furnace outlet. This pattern creates longer gas travel and greater residence time, promoting complete combustion.

| Figure 33 | Vertical Firing Arrangement |

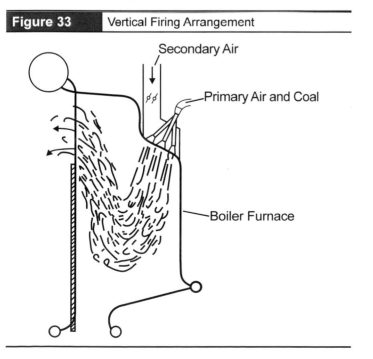

Secondary Air

Primary Air and Coal

Boiler Furnace

Vertical firing was developed for the slag-tap furnace (containing a molten pool of coal slag) to fire downward on the slag pool to keep it in a molten condition. However, this method is also successfully used in dry ash furnaces.

Figure 34 shows a multi-tip burner used in vertical firing. High velocity secondary air is mixed with the lower velocity primary air and coal to achieve good combustion.

Figure 34	Multi-tip Burner for Vertical Firing

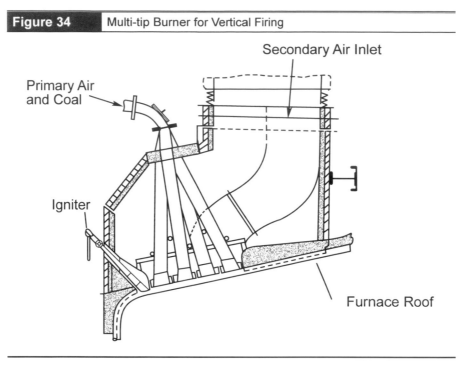

Tangential Firing

Figure 35 shows the tangential firing arrangement, which has burners in each corner of the furnace. The flames from the burners are directed tangentially, toward the center of the furnace. As the flames impinge upon each other, turbulence is produced and any unburned combustibles in the tail of one flame is caught up in the next flame. This promotes complete combustion of the coal. Figure 36 shows a single tangential burner, which has two coal nozzles plus provision for burning gas or oil.

Figure 35	Tangentially Fired Furnace

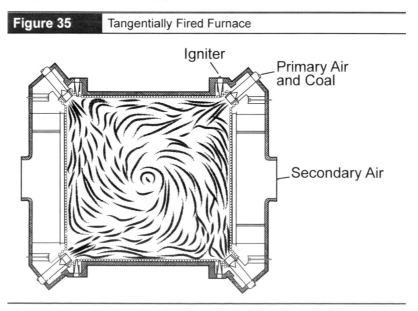

| Figure 36 | Tangential Burner |

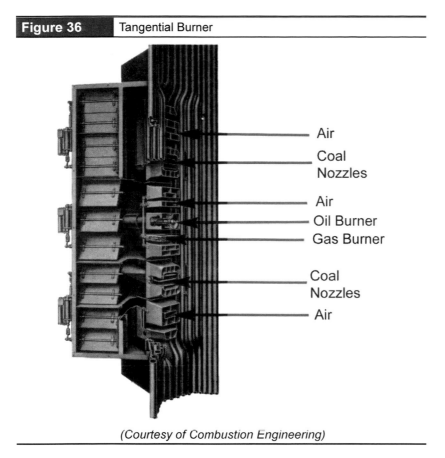

- Air
- Coal Nozzles
- Air
- Oil Burner
- Gas Burner
- Coal Nozzles
- Air

(Courtesy of Combustion Engineering)

Cyclone Furnaces

Figure 37 shows a cyclone furnace. This is a special furnace design that burns finely crushed coal (up 6 mm size), rather than pulverized coal. It consists of a water-cooled horizontal cylinder, which receives crushed coal and primary air. The primary air enters near the end of the cylinder in a tangential manner, which imparts a whirling (ie. cyclonic) motion to the coal.

Secondary air enters the barrel of the cylinder at high velocity (90 m/s) also in a tangential manner, thus increasing the cyclonic action of the coal. As the coal enters it is thrown against the cyclone walls by centrifugal force and is scrubbed by the secondary air. As the coal burns the ash melts into a slag, forming a layer on the walls of the cyclone. Excess molten slag drains from the cyclone into the main boiler furnace and flows into a slag tank.

An advantage of cyclone firing is that flyash emission is negligible, since the ash is retained and removed in molten state. Another advantage is the low power requirement for crushing, compared to the high power requirement for crushing and pulverizing.

Cyclone furnaces may be bin-fired or direct-fired. In the bin-fired system the coal is crushed to desired size and then stored in a bin before being fed to the cyclone. In the direct-fired system the coal is fed directly from the crusher to the cyclone.

| Figure 37 | Cyclone Furnace |

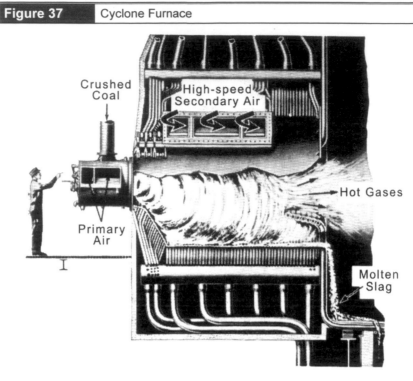

(Courtesy of Babcock and Wilcox)

Figure 38 shows more details of a cyclone furnace. Notice that the furnace is completely surrounded by water tubes.

| Figure 38 | Cyclone Furnace Details |

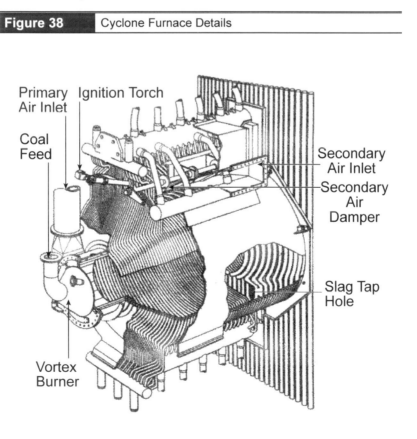

(Courtesy of Babcock and Wilcox)

Figure 39 illustrates three different arrangements of cyclones in relation to boiler furnaces.

Figure 39   Cyclone Furnace Types

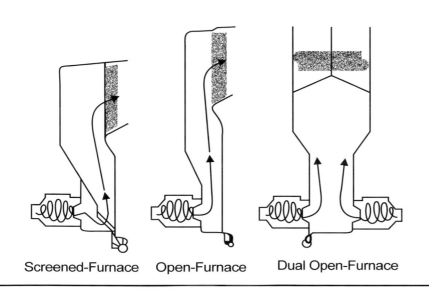

Screened-Furnace   Open-Furnace   Dual Open-Furnace

OBJECTIVE 7

Describe the design and operation of ball, impact, ball-race, and bowl mill pulverizers.

PULVERIZERS

A wide variety of devices have been designed to pulverize coals. Each design is particularly suitable for a type of coal and application. These pulverizers are commonly called mills, and the most common designs are described as follows.

Ball (or Tube) Mill

Figure 40 shows the principle of a ball mill, also known as a tube mill. The ball mill is a hollow, horizontal cylinder, which rotates on its axis at a speed of 18 to 35 r/min. The inside of the cylindrical shell has heavy cast liners. It is approximately half filled with forged steel or cast alloy balls, ranging in diameter from 25 to 51 mm.

Figure 40	Tube Mill

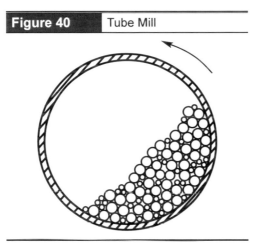

Coal is fed into the rotating cylinder where it intermingles with the balls. The continual cascading of the mixture causes pulverization, due to:

- Impact, as the balls fall on the large pieces of coal.
- Attrition, as coal particles slide over each other and the liners.
- Crushing, as balls roll over each other and over the liners with coal particles between them.

Referring to Figure 41.

Air flow constantly sweeps through the ball mill. Coal enters the air-swept mill through a feeder at the upper left, becomes pulverized, and is then carried out of the mill with the airflow, which is created by the exhauster at the upper right of the mill. The hot air not only carries the coal, but also dries it.

The pulverized coal from the mill passes through a classifier to regulate its size (ie. fineness). Oversized particles are returned to the grinding zone. This type of mill is particularly suitable for grinding anthracite and coke.

Figure 41 | Ball Mill

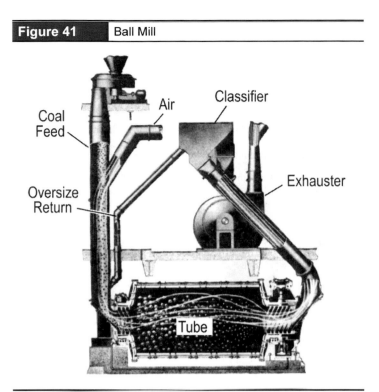

Impact Mill

Impact pulverizers (also known as "hammer mills") consist of a series of hinged or fixed hammers revolving at high speed (1200 to 1800 r/min) inside a chamber that is lined with wear-resistant, metal plates.

Figures 42 and Figure 43 show end and side views of a typical impact mill.

Raw coal is fed into the mill, where pulverizing results from the impact of the hammers on the coal and the attrition of the coal particles on each other and the mill surfaces. The pulverized coal is carried through the mill by a stream of hot air that is induced by an exhauster fan.

Figure 42 | C-E Raymond Impact Mill (end view)

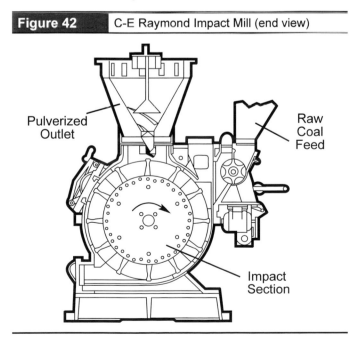

Figure 43   Impact Mill (side view)

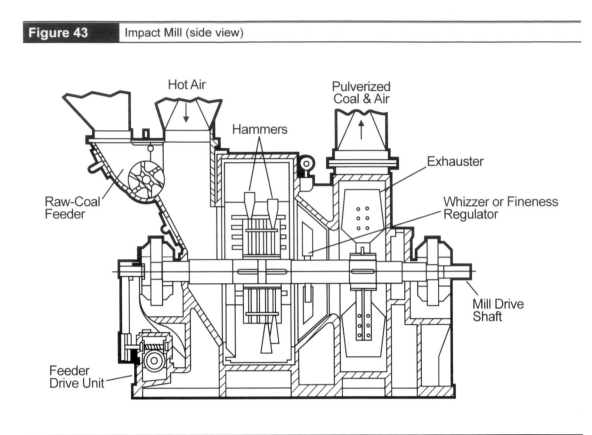

Ball Race Mill

Figure 44 shows a ball race pulverizer, which is a medium speed mill that uses crushing and attrition to reduce the size of the coal.

- The grinding action takes place between two grinding rings, called races, and a set of steel balls.
- The upper grinding ring is prevented from rotating and is pressed down upon the balls by a set of tension springs (see Fig. 45).
- The lower ring is rotated by gears, which are connected to the pulverizer driver.
- Coal is fed in from above the race and air enters from below.
- The air floats the pulverized coal up into the classifier and to the outlet.

These mills are suitable for all grades of coal.

Figure 44 | Ball Race Pulverizer

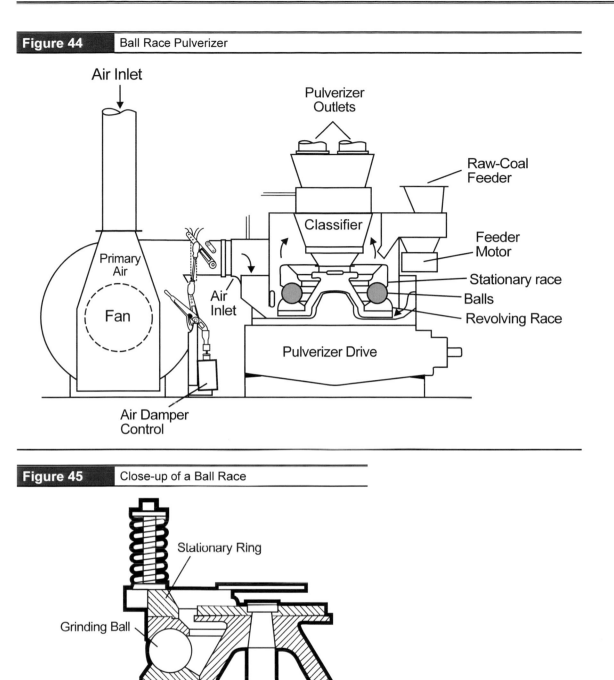

Figure 45 | Close-up of a Ball Race

Bowl Mill

The bowl mill pulverizer, shown in Figure 46, is a medium speed mill used for grinding all grades of bituminous coal. The rollers grind the coal between themselves and a slowly rotating horizontal table or "bowl". The coal is fed through a feed pipe to an inner cone, which then feeds the bowl. Air enters below the bowl and carries the pulverized coal upwards to the exhaust outlet.

Figure 46	Raymond Bowl Mill

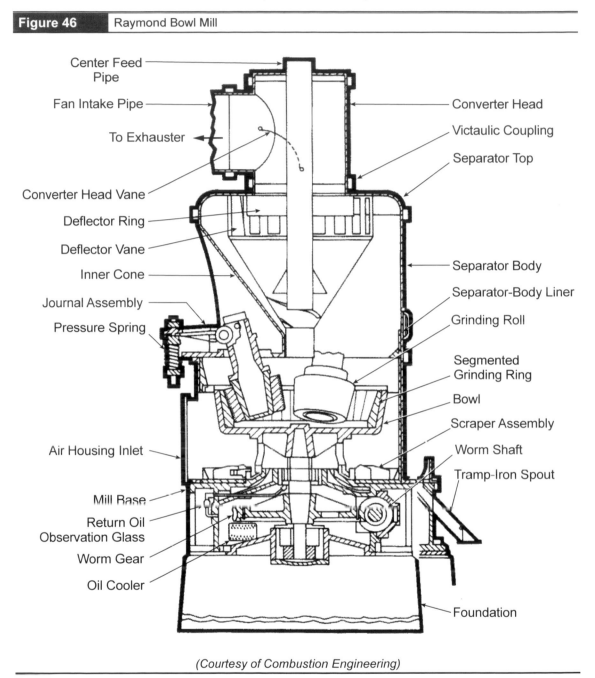

(Courtesy of Combustion Engineering)

OBJECTIVE 8

Describe the designs and operation of underfeed, overfeed, and crossfeed stokers for furnaces burning solid fuels.

UNDERFEED STOKER

Stokers are classified as overfeed, underfeed, or crossfeed, depending on whether the coal is fed into the furnace from above, below, or the side of the fuel bed.

The underfeed method is based on the upward flow of both fuel and air. Since fresh coal enters from beneath the burning fuel bed, the volatile matter, moisture, and air must pass through the active burning zone. This results in minimal soot and smoke.

Figure 47 shows a simple underfeed diagram.

Fresh (green) coal is fed upward between the two tuyeres (a tuyere is a nozzle or plate through which air is blown into a hearth). The ignition plane lies between the green coal and incandescent coke.

Figure 47	Underfeed Stoker

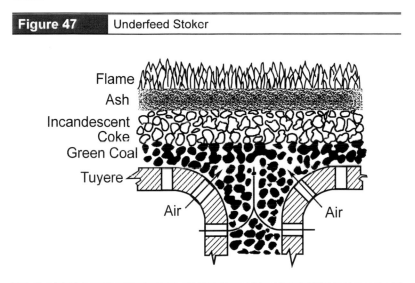

Underfeed stokers may be single retort or multiple retort type. In the single retort stoker, the coal is fed to the underside of the fuel bed by a ram or screw. The coal moves along a channel (called a "retort"), which extends into the furnace. As the ram fills the retort, the coal spills over on each side to feed the fuel bed.

Combustion air is supplied to a chamber on either side of the retort, below the grates, and passes through openings in the tuyeres on each side of the retort. During combustion the coal rises in the retort and is heated. The volatile compounds contained in the coal are distilled off, and burn as they pass through the incandescent portion of the fuel bed at the top. The carbon that remains ignites and burns on the side grates.

Multiple retort stokers have several retorts, which are inclined from the front of the furnace toward the rear of the furnace. Each retort is supplied with coal by a ram and the coal moves along the inclined retorts to the rear of the furnace where the ash is discharged.

Figures 48 and 49 illustrate the single retort underfeed stoker.

| Figure 48 | Single Retort Stoker - Side View |

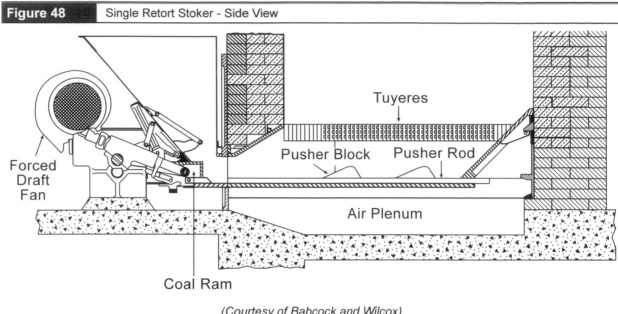

(Courtesy of Babcock and Wilcox)

| Figure 49 | Single Retort Stoker - End View |

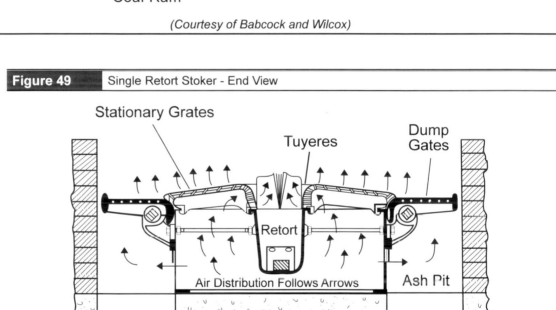

Figure 50 is a furnace view of a single retort, underfeed stoker, similar to that in Figure 49.

Figure 50	Underfeed Stoker

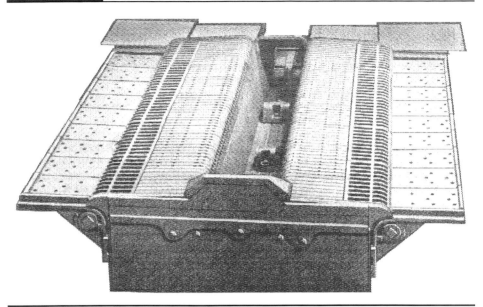

OVERFEED STOKER

An overfeed stoker, shown schematically in Figure 51, uses counter-current flow of coal and air, with coal flowing downward and air flowing upward. The coal bed receives fresh (green) coal on the top surface. The ignition plane lies between the green coal and the incandescent coke. The green coal is heated by the burning coal and by hot combustion gases rising from the grate. Anthracite and bituminous coals are suitable for this type of firing.

Figure 51	Overfeed Fuel-Bed

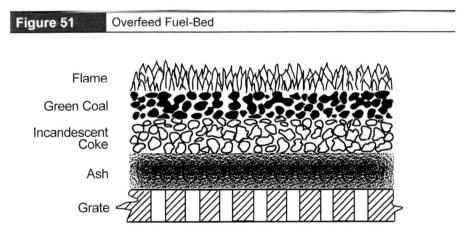

Spreader Stoker

The spreader stoker is the most versatile overfeed method. The coal is projected through the front wall of the furnace by a distributor, which may be a series of paddles attached to a rotating shaft below the hopper. Alternatively, jets of air or steam may propel the fuel into the furnace. Much of the coal is ignited in suspension, since most of the volatile matter is distilled off before the coal reaches the grates.

Uniform distribution of fuel occurs, due to the fact that the energy imparted to pieces of coal when struck by the distributor paddles, varies with the size of the pieces. Larger pieces fly to the back, while smaller pieces fall towards the front.

The grates may be the stationary, dumping, or continuous discharge (traveling) type. The continuous discharge spreader stoker has the advantage of higher burning rates than the dumping type, and eliminates periodic dumping of ash.

Figure 52 illustrates the spreader stoker distributor. The coal leaving the hopper is pushed by a reciprocating feed plate or pusher plate over the edge of a spill plate onto the revolving paddles of the rotor. The amount of coal entering the furnace is varied by changing the length of the feed plat stroke.

Altering the position of the spill plate or the speed of the rotor changes the distance the coal is thrown. Moving the spill plate back allows the coal to fall on the rotor blades sooner and the blades will throw the coal further into the furnace. Likewise, increasing the rotor speed will cause the coal to be struck with greater force by the blades and to travel further into the furnace.

Spreader stokers are characterized by rapid response to load changes and the ability to burn a wide variety of coals.

Figure 52	Spreader Stoker Feeder and Rotor

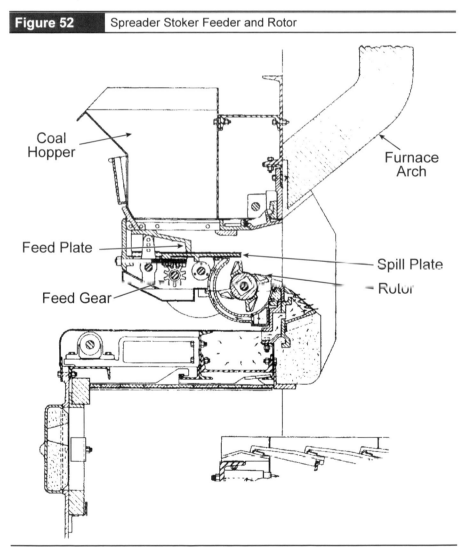

CROSSFEED STOKER

Figure 53 shows a crossfeed stoker, also called a traveling grate stoker. It consists of a moving grate, which extends into the furnace from the boiler front. Coal is fed by gravity from a hopper onto the front of the grate and burns as it is carried toward the rear of the furnace. By the time it reaches the end of the furnace the coal is completely burned.

Figure 53	Crossfeed or Traveling Grate-Stoker

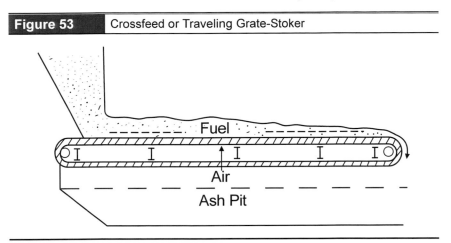

The ash drops from the end of the belt into an ash pit. The grate is driven by sprockets and moves slowly (approx. 5 mm/s). The depth of the coal bed on the grate is controlled by an adjustable gate, which varies the height of the opening from the hopper. Combustion air, supplied by a forced draft fan, passes up through openings in the grate. Often, overfire air is supplied above the grate to aid in burning the volatile compounds that are released from the fuel.

Figure 54 shows the crossfeed arrangement in more detail. The driving sprocket, driven by a constant speed motor (or a steam turbine in larger units), is located at the furnace front, with an idler sprocket at the rear. A large part of the combustion air is supplied at the side of the stoker and passes up through the grate. Dampers regulate the amount of air passing to different sections of the grate. The sections near the front, where the coal bed is thickest, require more air than the sections near the rear, where the fuel is almost completely burned. Overfire air jets supply additional air above the grate.

Figure 54	Crossfeed Stoker Arrangement

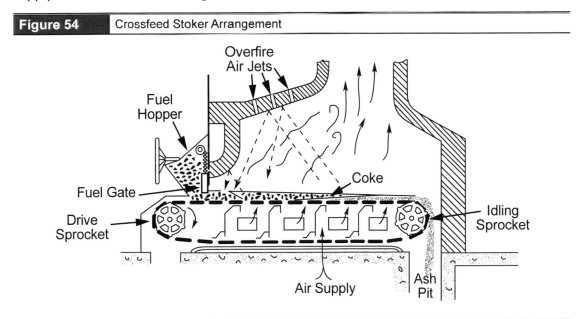

Figure 55 illustrates yet another traveling-grate stoker. It also shows a necessary part of a stoker-fired furnace, the furnace arch. This arch causes gases from the rear of the grate to mix with excess air from the front. The arch also maintains sufficient temperature to support combustion and radiates heat to the front of the coal bed to ignite entering coal and distill volatile matter off.

Figure 55	Traveling Grate or Crossfeed Stoker

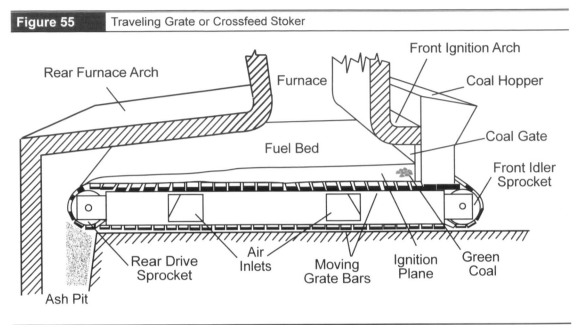

Types of Grates

The terms "chain grate" and "bar grate" refer to designs of the grate surface that carries the coal. The chain grate surface consists of a series of linked chains, similar to a bicycle chain, strung on rods. The grate is moved by sprockets and as the links travel over the sprockets they have a scissor-like action, which tends to loosen any ash clinkers that are adhering to the grate surface. Figure 56 shows a chain grate stoker.

Figure 56	Jet-Ignition Chain-Grate Stoker

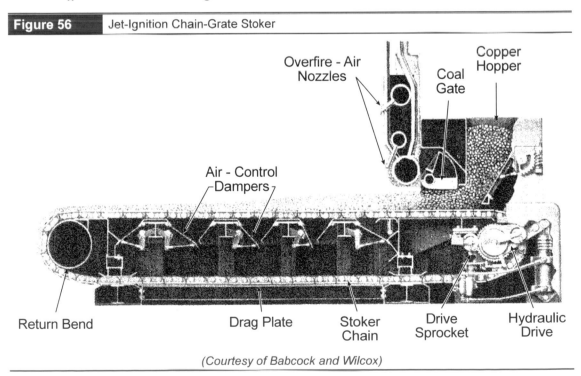

(Courtesy of Babcock and Wilcox)

Figure 57 shows a bar grate stoker in which rows of bars are carried by sprocket-driven chains.

Figure 57 Traveling Bar Grate

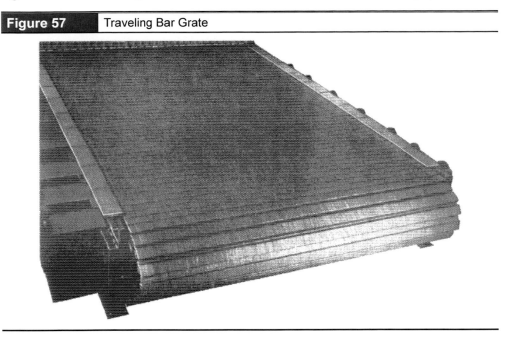

CHAPTER 6 - QUESTIONS

1. Make a simple sketch of a gas firing system. Briefly describe its operation.

2. How are nitrogen oxides (NO_x) formed in natural gas fired boilers? How do low NO_x burners reduce the amount of NO_x formed during combustion?

3. List the main components of a fuel oil supply system, from the storage tank to the burners. Briefly state the purpose of the components listed.

4. What are the three classifications of oil burners? Briefly describe how each type atomizes the oil for combustion.

5. Describe how coal is stockpiled at a plant site. Why is the method of layering the coal important?

6. Make a sketch of a tangentially fired furnace. Show the flame pattern in the furnace as well as the locations that primary and secondary air are introduced.

7. Briefly describe the method of grinding coal used in a bowl mill.

8. Sketch a cross-feed stoker and explain its operation.

ANSWERS: All answers are found within the content of the chapter.

Boiler Draft & Flue Gas Equipment

LEARNING OUTCOME

When you complete this chapter you should be able to:

Explain boiler draft systems and fans and describe the equipment used to remove ash from flue gas.

LEARNING OBJECTIVES

Here is what you should be able to do when you complete each objective:

1. Define and explain the applications and designs of natural, forced, induced and balanced draft.

2. Explain how draft is measured, monitored, and controlled in a large, balanced draft boiler. Explain the position of control dampers.

3. Describe typical draft fan designs, single and double inlet arrangements, and explain methods used to control fan output.

4. Explain the start-up and running checks that must be made on draft fans.

5. Describe typical windbox and air louver arrangements and distinguish between primary and secondary air.

6. Describe the design and operation of flue gas particulate clean-up equipment, including mechanical and electrostatic precipitators and baghouse filters.

7. Describe the design and operation of ash handling systems, including hydro and air systems, bottom ash systems, and scraper conveyor systems.

8. Describe the designs and operation of SO_2 recovery systems, including lime and wet gas scrubbing.

OBJECTIVE 1

Define and explain the applications and designs of natural, forced, induced and balanced draft.

DRAFT

Draft may be defined as the difference between atmospheric pressure and the static pressure of combustion gases in a furnace. Draft may be classified as either natural draft or mechanical.

Natural draft relies solely on the difference in pressure between the external atmosphere and the furnace to create air flow into the furnace. There is no assistance given by any mechanical device, such as a fan or blower.

Mechanical draft requires a fan to produce air flow into the furnace. There are three methods of creating mechanical draft. If the draft fan is located before the furnace and pushes the air into the furnace, it is called forced draft and the fan is called a forced draft (FD) fan. If the fan is at the outlet of the furnace and pulls the combustion gases out of the furnace and the combustion air into the furnace, it is called induced draft and the fan is called the induced draft (ID) fan. When both an FD fan and an ID fan are used at the same time it is called balanced draft.

Figure 1 illustrates the four draft arrangements.

Figure 1	Types of Draft

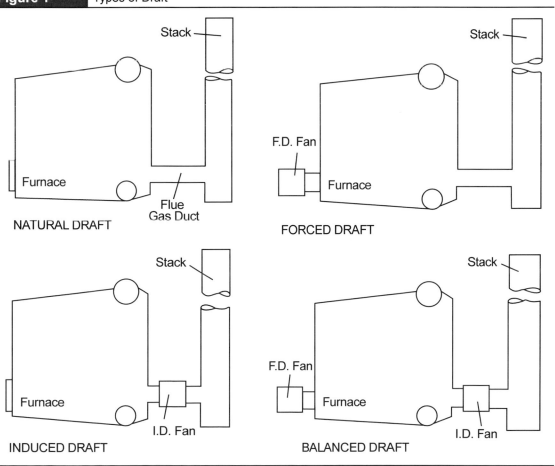

NATURAL DRAFT FORCED DRAFT INDUCED DRAFT BALANCED DRAFT

Natural Draft

Natural draft is created by the difference in pressure between the furnace inlet and the furnace outlet. Remember, fluids, including air, will only flow from a location of higher pressure to a location of lower pressure. Refer to Figure 2:

Imagine a column of atmospheric air at the inlet to the furnace and this column is the same height as the boiler chimney. The chimney, boiler and the outside air column form a large U tube. Due to the fire in the furnace, the combustion gases in the furnace and chimney are very hot, compared to the outside air. Therefore, the flue gases are less dense than the outside air. The column of outside air is cooler and more dense so there is greater pressure at its base than at the chimney base. This difference in pressure causes the "heavier" outside air to flow into the furnace and displace the "lighter" flue gases up through the chimney. This natural draft causes a continuous supply of combustion air to the furnace, without the aid of fans.

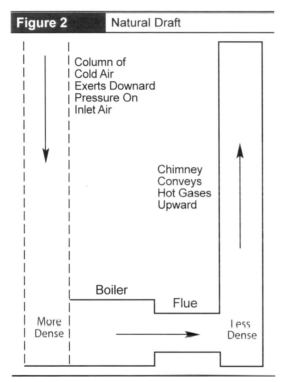

| Figure 2 | Natural Draft |

The amount of natural draft will depend upon:

- The temperature of the outside air; colder, denser air will increase the draft
- The temperature of the flue gases in the stack; hotter, less dense gases will increase the draft
- The stack height; the higher the stack is, the greater will be the draft.

The boiler operator has very little, if any, control over natural draft. The outside air temperature cannot be controlled. The height of the chimney is preset during design and is a fixed height. Therefore, only the gas temperature in the stack appears controllable. Unfortunately, increasing the firing of the furnace to achieve higher stack temperature is impractical, since it creates greater heat losses and, therefore, reduces efficiency.

The greatest difficulty with natural draft occurs during startup of a cold boiler. In this situation, there is no draft available, since the temperature in the chimney matches the outside temperature. The burner(s) must be started slowly and kept low until the chimney is warmed up sufficiently to produce adequate and sustained draft.

Stacks alone seldom provide sufficient draft to meet the requirements of larger boilers. For example, a 60 m stack provides a theoretical natural draft of 1 cm water gauge at the bottom of the stack. The resistance to air and gas flow in boilers with superheaters, economizers and air heaters, may require 50 cm water gauge, or more. These higher draft systems must use fans.

Forced Draft

Figure 3 shows a large steam generator with forced draft.

A **forced draft fan**, driven by a steam turbine or electric motor, takes suction from outside air, increases the pressure, and pushes (forces) the air into the furnace. This creates positive pressure (ie. higher than atmospheric), which forces the air and combustion gases toward the stack and out to atmosphere.

The furnace casing has slightly positive pressure, so it must be sealed to prevent outward leakage and must be strong enough to withstand the internal pressure.

Forced draft is easily controlled and eliminates problems associated with colder outside air, including during cold startup.

Figure 3	Forced Draft Boiler

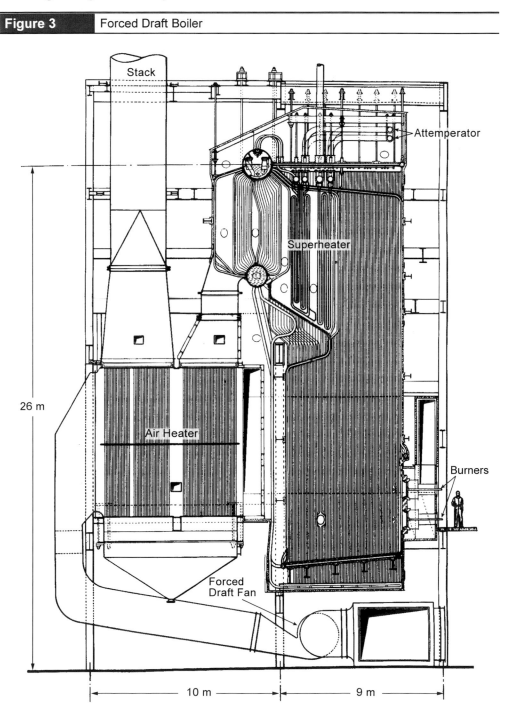

Induced Draft

In induced draft the fan is located in the flue gas path, between the boiler and the stack. The fan takes suction from the boiler, creating a slightly negative (less than atmospheric) pressure inside the casing. This negative pressure then allows atmospheric air to enter the furnace for combustion. The fan pulls the combustion gases out, increases the pressure, and forces them up the stack. The boiler casing must be sealed to prevent outside from air leaking into the boiler and must be made strong enough to withstand the external pressure of the atmosphere.

For the same required air flow, an induced draft fan must have a larger in capacity than a forced draft fan, for the following reasons:

- The I.D. fan must move a larger mass, since the flue gases contain the mass of fuel plus the mass of combustion air (eg. one kg of fuel, using 15 kg of air for complete combustion, produces 16 kg of flue gases)

- The I.D. fan must handle a larger volume of gases, since the temperature of the flue gas is higher than the air moved by an F.D. fan. The volume of each kilogram of gas increases as temperature increases.

- The I.D. fan must handle any air leakage into the boiler setting, which increases the total volume of gases.

Balanced Draft

An I.D. fan is not normally used alone to provide draft. Instead, a balanced draft system, using a combination of forced and induced draft, provides more efficient control, especially for larger boilers. The forced draft fan pushes combustion air into the furnace, while the induced draft fan draws out the combustion gases and forces them up the stack. The furnace pressure is maintained at or slightly below atmospheric pressure. Sealing and strength of the furnace are not as critical as in the purely forced or induced systems.

Figure 4 shows a steam generator with balanced draft.

| Figure 4 | Steam Generator with Balanced Draft |

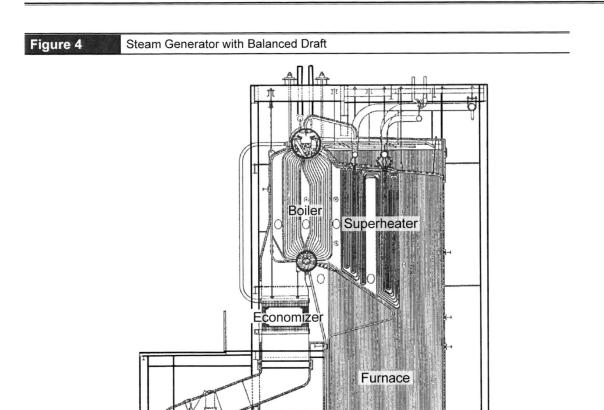

OBJECTIVE 2

Explain how draft is measured, monitored, and controlled in a large, balanced draft boiler. Explain the position of control dampers.

DRAFT MEASUREMENT

Remember, draft is the difference in pressure between the external atmosphere and the boiler internal. This pressure difference can be taken at various internal locations, so as to determine and monitor the availability of draft throughout the gas passes of the boiler.

Draft is measured by an instrument called a draft gauge and is recorded in "centimeters of water gauge" (cm wg). Ten cm wg is approximately equal to 1 kPa pressure.

Draft is usually monitored at the following locations in a boiler.

- Wind box
- Furnace
- Economizer inlet
- Air heater inlet
- Stack

Manometer

Draft measurement involves very small pressures for which a normal pressure gauge cannot be used. A simple draft measuring gauge consists of a glass U-tube, containing water, called a **manometer**.

Figure 5 shows a simple manometer, which is a U-tube with a measuring scale, graduated in mm and cm. The furnace pressure, connected to the left side of the manometer tube, is less than atmospheric. The higher, atmospheric pressure on the right side of the tube pushes downward, causing the level in the left side of the tube to rise. The difference between the two levels represents the draft. In this case, the difference is approximately 1.5 cm. Therefore, the draft is -1.5 cm wg (the minus sign indicates negative pressure in the furnace).

Figure 5	Manometer

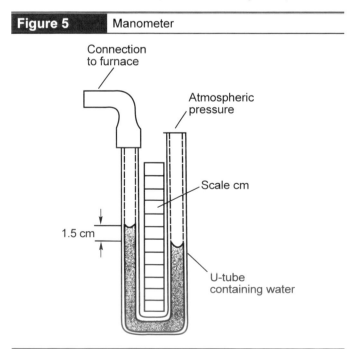

Diaphragm Draft Gauge

Figure 6 illustrates a more sophisticated draft gauge, which has superseded the U-tube. It is called a diaphragm draft gauge. A diaphragm is connected by a push rod, range spring, and linkage to a pointer. The top of the diaphragm is exposed to the atmosphere, while the bottom of the diaphragm is exposed to the pressure on the boiler side (at whichever location is being measured). Difference in pressure determines the position of the diaphragm and this, in turn, is transferred proportionately to the pointer. The pointer indicates the actual pressure difference (ie. the draft) on a scale, calibrated in cm of water.

Figure 6	Diaphragm Draft Gauge

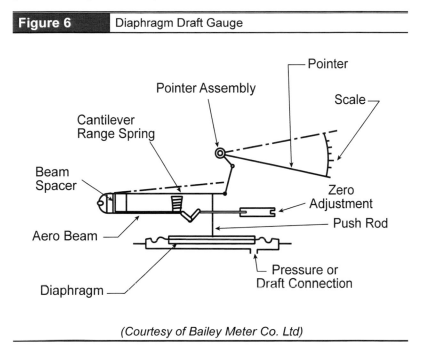

(Courtesy of Bailey Meter Co. Ltd)

Figure 7 shows one method of displaying the draft.

Three locations are shown: the windbox (which is between the FD fan and the furnace), the furnace itself, and the air heater (which is just before the stack or the ID fan inlet). Notice the different scales and the progressive reduction in draft from the windbox to the air heater.

Figure 7	Typical Draft Gauge Display

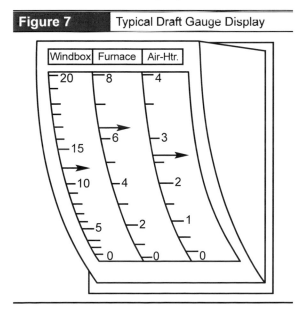

Control of Balanced Draft

Figure 8 shows the locations of the equipment used to control boiler draft.

- The FD fan controls the flow of combustion air to the boiler, using dampers at the fan inlet. A damper drive unit controls the damper position in response to a signal from the combustion controls. The sole purpose of these dampers is to ensure the correct amount of combustion air enters the furnace for the firing rate necessary to obtain the desired steam output.

- The combustion air passes through the air heater, where it is heated by exchange with the hot flue gases leaving from the boiler. In some cases, the exact volume of air entering the furnace is controlled by primary and secondary air louvres, located at the burners.

- The ID fan removes the hot flue gases from the boiler. Dampers at the inlet of the fan respond to a damper drive unit, which controls their position. Usually, the sole purpose of the ID fan dampers is to control the furnace pressure. If the pressure increases, the dampers will open more to take more flue gases from the boiler.

In fact, the above description is somewhat simplistic. Many control systems involve sophisticated interaction between the FD and ID damper controls, in order to maintain the required draft. Both sets of dampers may be adjusted to ensure either a slightly negative or slightly positive furnace pressure, regardless of the firing rate.

Figure 8	Balanced Draft Control Equipment

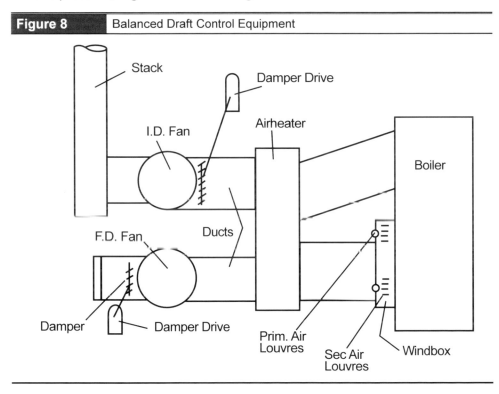

OBJECTIVE 3

Describe typical draft fan designs, single and double inlet arrangements, and explain methods used to control fan output.

7-11

DRAFT FANS

Most draft fans are centrifugal design. Blades mounted on an impeller, rotate within a spiral or volute housing. Air or flue gas enter the center of the impeller and are thrown out by the blades at high velocity. The fan supplies sufficient energy to the air or flue gas to initiate motion and overcome all friction. The blades do the actual work, while the housing collects and directs the air or flue gas to and from the impeller.

Figure 9 illustrates a centrifugal fan that is suitable for FD fan service. It has impeller blades that are curved backwards (ie. opposite to the direction of rotation) and a vane-controlled inlet.

Figure 9	Forced Draft Fan

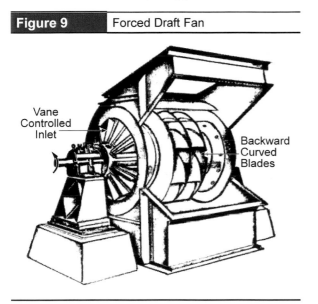

Figure 10 illustrates a centrifugal fan with radial tip blades and double inlet (ie. suction at both ends), suitable for service as an ID fan.

Figure 10	Induced Draft Fan

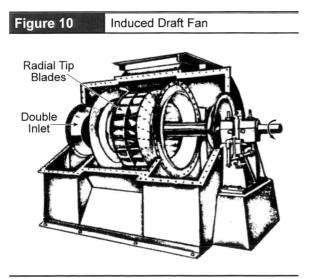

Fan Components

Figure 11 shows typical components of a large, centrifugal fan, using front and side views.

Figure 11	Centrifugal Fan Parts

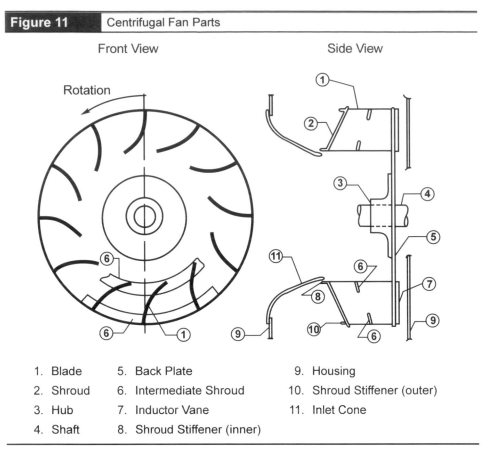

Front View   Side View

1. Blade	5. Back Plate	9. Housing	
2. Shroud	6. Intermediate Shroud	10. Shroud Stiffener (outer)	
3. Hub	7. Inductor Vane	11. Inlet Cone	
4. Shaft	8. Shroud Stiffener (inner)		

Blade Designs

The blades of FD and ID fans are classified into six basic types. They are defined by the shape of the blades and the direction in which they point in relation to the direction of rotation of the impeller.

Figure 12, in particular the cross-section on the right, illustrates the six designs. Note the direction of rotation is clockwise.

The **air foil** fan is primarily used for moving clean air or non corrosive gases. Although expensive, it is also the most efficient design and is often used as an F.D. fan. **Backward curved** or **backward inclined** blades are most common in high speed F.D. fans. ID fans normally use **straight radial**, **radial tip** or **forward curved** blades, which run at lower speeds and are better suited to move dust laden and hot flue gases.

Figure 12	Types of Fan Blades

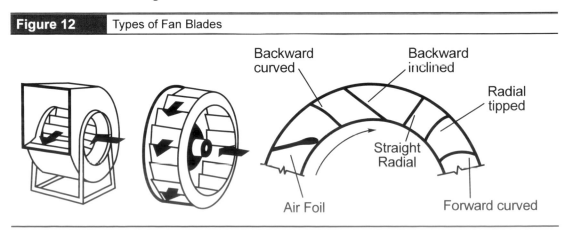

Fan Inlets (Single & Double)

The fan inlet may be single (entering at one side of the impeller only) or double (entering at both sides of the impeller), as shown in Figures 13 (a) and (b).

The single inlet fan creates a thrust load on the bearings, due to the pressure difference across the backplate. Inductor vanes are often installed on the backside of the backplate on a single inlet fan to help minimize thrust.

The double inlet balances the pressure across the impeller, creating a relatively thrust free operation.

Figure 13	Inlet Fans

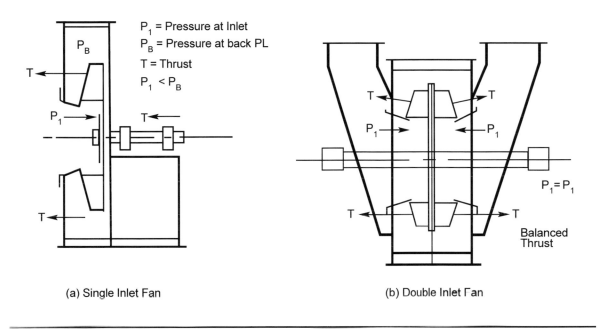

P_1 = Pressure at Inlet
P_B = Pressure at back PL
T = Thrust
$P_1 < P_B$

(a) Single Inlet Fan   (b) Double Inlet Fan

FAN OUTPUT CONTROL

The output (ie. flow) of a fan is controlled by one of the following methods:

- Inlet dampers or vanes
- Outlet dampers
- Variable fan speed

Inlet Damper or Vane Control

Figure 14 shows an ID fan with double inlet and a set of horizontal dampers (aka. louvres) at each inlet. These louvres are linked together and controlled simultaneously to ensure the same flow is available to both sides of the impeller. This design is ideal for handling both hot air and flue gases.

Figure 14	ID Fan

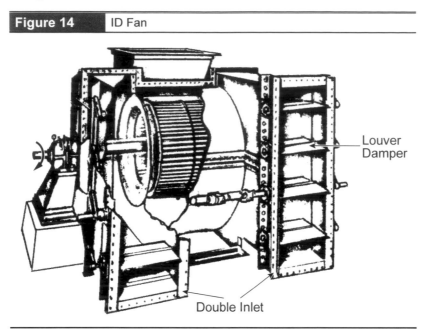

Louver Damper

Double Inlet

Refer back to Figure 9; it shows another design, using control vanes, which are mounted very close to the fan inlet. Each vane is triangular, but collectively they form a circular set of vanes that open and close at the inlet. One advantage of inlet vanes is that the air enters the fan with a spin in the direction of wheel rotation. This results in less power requirement, especially at low loads and, therefore, a more efficient operation at partial loads.

Outlet Damper Control

Outlet dampers throttle the air leaving the fan. The resistance produced by the damper causes the fan to operate at a higher discharge pressure. This requires more power at partial loads and results in a less efficient operation. Compared to inlet dampers, outlet dampers have lower initial cost and are simpler to operate, but require more power to the fan.

Variable Speed Control

Variable speed involves changing the speed of the fan to achieve the desired flow. Common methods include variable speed motors, magnetic couplings, fluid drive units and steam turbines. The latter is popular in power plants since it helps to achieve more efficient heat balance.

Variable speed control is the most efficient method of fan control in terms of power consumption, but usually has the highest initial cost. Variable speed is often used in combination with damper control.

OBJECTIVE 4

Explain the start-up and the running checks that must be made on draft fans.

FAN STARTUP

- Ensure all debris, tools, rags, etc., are removed from the immediate fan and driver area.
- Visually check the fan and driver; look for loose nuts, plates or bolts, disconnected rods, etc.
- Ensure the fan inlet screen is clean and clear of frost, rags or debris.
- Check the dampers and damper drive connections for tightness.
- Check the oil in the fan and driver bearings. If the level is low, fill it to the correct level with recommended oil. If the oil is dirty or polluted with water, change it to the fan manufacturer's recommended oil.
- Open cooling water to the water- cooled bearings.
- Generally look for any condition which might impair the proper operation of the unit.
- If the drive unit is a steam turbine or engine, open drains and slightly open the steam supply and exhaust valves to warm up the unit. Open the steam exhaust valve wide, after warm up.
- Start fan, listen for unusual noises, feel bearings and fan casing for excessive vibration, check bearing lubrication, check for fan leaks, especially around seals.

FAN RUNNING CHECKS

- Look for signs of oil, water, air or hot gas leakage
- Listen for unusual noises.
- Note unusual smells, such as those caused by hot bearings, leakage of gases, motor shorts, etc.
- Check bearing oil levels.
- Check all indicators for the fan and driver, such as bearing temperatures, fan suction and discharge pressures, manometers, air or gas flows, etc.
- Feel all bearings for normal temperature and vibration.
- Check rotation of bearing oil rings.
- Generally look for any unusual condition; a change normally indicates problems.

Check these items frequently during the first hour of operation, since most problems occur shortly after start up.

After the fan has been operating for some time, continue the running checks less frequently, but on a regular schedule.

START-UP OF BALANCED DRAFT FANS

Preamble

In modern generating stations, the boiler ID and FD fans are high capacity units, which are capable of developing very high or low pressures in the furnace enclosure. Many furnace are tall with large, flat waterwall surface areas that cannot be economically built to withstand the negative pressure that an ID fan can develop. If started incorrectly, an ID fan is easily capable of developing sufficient negative pressure to collapse the furnace.

Also, centrifugal fans perform work when they are moving air. If a fan is started in such a way that it is delivering air as it comes up to speed the driver of the fan will be required to develop increasing power as the fan moves progressively more air. On electric driven fans, this will cause abnormally high current draw, which may trip the electric motor on current overload and/or cause the rotor to overheat. Due to this, fans should always be started with their inlet/outlet dampers closed. This limits inrush current to the motor and prevents uncontrolled pressure excursions in the furnace.

Start-up Sequence

a) Check bearing oil, cooling water, etc.

b) Stroke fan dampers and check interlocks

c) START ID FAN as follows:

- Establish an air flow path through the boiler by opening burner air registers and FD fan dampers. This will reduce the furnace pressure drop (due to ID fan damper leakage) when the ID fan is started.
- Close ID Fan outlet dampers.
- Start ID fan drive and watch it come up to speed.
- Put the ID fan (furnace draft) control on "auto".

d) START FD FAN as follows:

- Close FD Fan outlet dampers.
- Start FD fan drive and watch fan come up to speed.
- Put FD fan control on "auto"

e) As the FD dampers open to purge the furnace, the ID dampers should follow to control the furnace draft

OBJECTIVE 5

Describe typical windbox and air louver arrangements and distinguish between primary and secondary air.

WINDBOX & AIR LOUVRES

The windbox is an extension of the main air ducts and serves as a distributing chamber for the air to the individual burners. It is a large chamber, located where the burners enter the boiler so that all burners receive their air from the windbox. Air pressures are stabilized in the windbox, allowing each burner to receive the same amount of air.

Each burner has a set of louvres, which allow air to pass from the windbox into the burner proper. These louvres are often called air registers. In some boilers, the air registers are manually adjusted and locked into place, with no need for further adjustment. In other cases, the air registers are automatically moved to the open or closed position by the boiler controls or by the individual burner logic. For example, in multiple burner boilers, it may be desirable to have the registers closed on all burners that are not in service.

PRIMARY & SECONDARY AIR

Primary air is air that mixes directly with the fuel in the first (ie. primary) stage of combustion. In gas or oil burners, the primary air is usually mixed with the fuel immediately upon leaving the fuel nozzle. If air atomization is used, some of the primary air mixes with the fuel before it leaves the nozzle. In pulverized coal burners, the primary air is mixed with the coal before it enters the burner. The air helps to carry the coal powder. Primary air for solid bed combustion is supplied from below the bed and flows up through the bed where it mixes with the fuel at the combustion zone.

Secondary air is air that is supplied to the burner downstream of the primary combustion zone. It helps to burn the volatile matter that is expelled from the fuel during primary combustion, thereby making the combustion process more complete and efficient. In gas, oil and pulverized coal burners, the secondary air enters the burner around the outside of the primary combustion nozzles and surrounds the main flame. In solid fuel furnaces, the secondary air is admitted above the fuel bed.

Figures 15 to 18 illustrate typical burner arrangements for gas, oil, pulverized coal, and solid fuel furnaces. Note the references and locations of primary and secondary air in each case.

Figure 15	Primary and Secondary Air to Burner

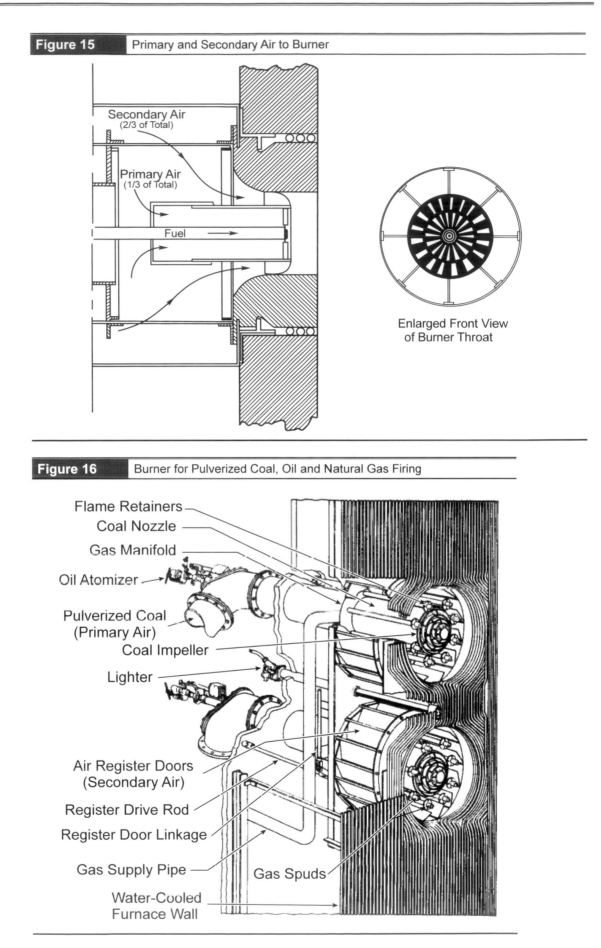

Figure 16	Burner for Pulverized Coal, Oil and Natural Gas Firing

Figure 17	Tangential Firing

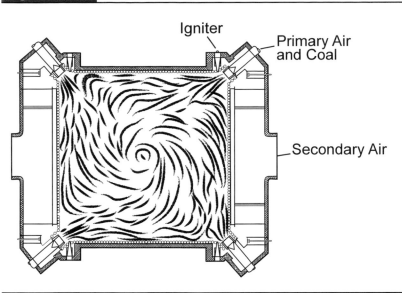

Figure 18	Solid Fuel Bed

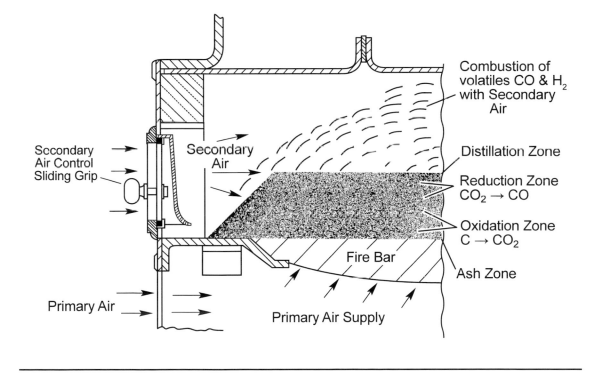

OBJECTIVE 6

Describe the design and operation of flue gas particulate clean-up equipment, including mechanical and electrostatic precipitators and baghouse filters.

SOLID POLLUTANTS IN FLUE GAS

Solid pollutants are particles that result from combustion and are released to atmosphere, or have the potential to be released to atmosphere. These pollutants, generally called ash, consist mainly of the non-combustible components of the fuel. Oil fired and gas fired boilers produce no ash. Boilers that burn coal and other solid fuels produce considerable amounts of ash.

With stoker firing, most of the ash can be removed from the furnace, quenched with water and sent to a suitable landfill for disposal. However, with pulverized coal firing, the high turbulence between the coal and the combustion air causes most of the ash to be carried out with the stack effluents.

Ash and soot cannot be prevented from entering the flue gas, since they are natural results of combustion. However, they can be prevented, by various methods, from entering the atmosphere. These methods involve precipitation and/or filtering of the particles.

Mechanical Precipitators

For our purposes, "precipitation of solids" may be defined as the removal of solids from a gas stream. Mechanical precipitation relies on the fact that when a moving particle changes velocity (whether in magnitude or direction) a force is created on that particle.

In mechanical precipitators, this principle is used to cause solid particles to separate from the flue gas stream. Figure 19 illustrates two methods of achieving this separation.

In **Figure 19(a)**, the particle-laden flue gas from the boiler enters the precipitator at the left, with a certain velocity, through a relatively narrow duct. It then enters the diverging section, "A", where the duct gets larger. This reduces the forward velocity of the gas. Due to their larger mass, the ash particles resist the change in velocity, and the force of their momentum pushes them toward the hopper.

At point "B", the velocity of the gas is lowest, plus the direction of flow turns upward. At this point, a downward force (gravity plus centrifugal force) is exerted on the dust particles, pushing them into the hopper. This is aided by the relatively slow velocity of the gas, which helps the particles to escape the flow. At point "C", the duct converges and the stream must now accelerate as it passes through a narrower space. As the velocity increases, the force will pull the particles backwards.

Figure 19(b) shows another variation in mechanical precipitator design. In this case, there is an enlargement of the duct in area "B", causing the gas flow to reduce. Also in area "B" are a series of baffles, which cause the flow to abruptly turn before continuing on to the outlet at "C". The sudden turn causes ash particles to hit the baffle surfaces and be deflected downwards into the hopper. This design has the advantage of saving space and neater, more streamlined ducting.

Figure 19 Particle Precipitators

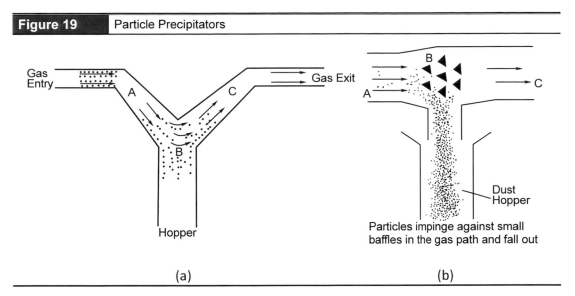

(a)   (b)

Cyclone Precipitator

Figure 20 shows a very effective method of ash removal, using a cyclone precipitator with water spray. In this design, the gas stream enters with high velocity from the narrow section, A, and into the larger section, B. The entry line is tangential to the shell, which causes the gas to have a swirling, cyclonic action.

Water is continuously sprayed from above, causing the ash particles to become heavier, mud-like masses. The centrifugal force of the cyclonic action pushes the particles to the walls, where they run down to the bottom and settle as sludge. The sludge can be removed as required.

A serious drawback in this design occurs when the flue gases contain sulphur dioxide (SO_2), from the combustion of sulphur. SO_2 in water forms weak sulphuric acid, which is very corrosive to iron-based metals. It is also a soil pollutant and an irritant to human skin. In order to use water spray, there must be a safe and acceptable method to dispose of the acidic water. The scrubbing water may be treated with lime or dolomite slurry. Both of these compounds exhibit an alkali chemical behavior (pH >7). The acidic (pH <7) scrubbing water is thus neutralized to about a pH of 7 and sulphur is retained in solid form in a non polluting waste compound.

Dry cyclones are used extensively, but their effectiveness is somewhat limited because the separating forces on the dry, lighter ash particles are much less.

Figure 20 Cyclone Precipitator

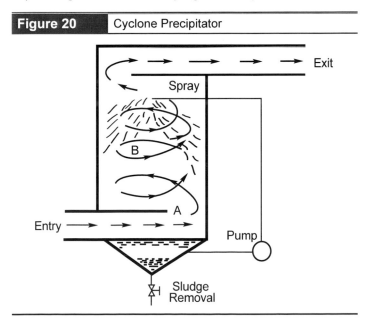

Electrostatic Precipitators

An entirely different principle of separation is used in the electrostatic precipitator. It relies on the principle of magnetic attraction of charged particles to oppositely charged surfaces.

Figure 21 shows a simplified electrostatic collector in an electrostatic precipitator.

- Ash laden flue gas from the boiler enters the precipitator, which contains a negatively charged discharging electrode.
- An external DC source supplies a high DC voltage to the electrode.
- The passing ash particles receive a negative electrical charge and become attracted to the positively charged collector wall (the collecting electrode).
- At the wall the particles collect into heavier particles, which then fall to the hopper below.

The closer the ash particles come to the charging electrode, the greater is the electrostatic effect. Therefore, for good precipitation of ash, the distance between the collector wall and the electrode must be kept to a minimum.

The accumulation of particles on the walls of the collector may become thick enough to fill the gap between the wall and the electrode. In this case the precipitator is "shorted" and the charging electrode begins conducting to the wall, thereby losing ability to charge incoming ash particles. This can cause the passages to become clogged. To prevent this, a "rapper" device, with small, hammer balls continuously raps the walls. This causes the compacted particles to fall into the hopper.

Figure 21	Electrostatic Collector

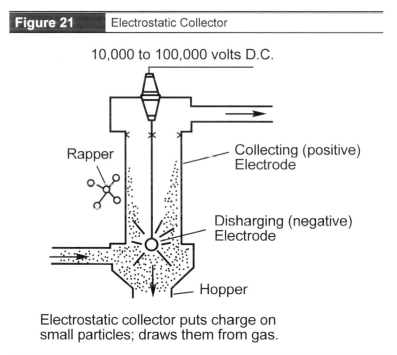

Electrostatic collector puts charge on small particles; draws them from gas.

Figure 22 shows a complete electrostatic precipitator.

Since the distance between the electrode and collecting surfaces must be small, several collecting surfaces must be used. Rows of flat, vertical collecting plates alternate with rows of high-voltage electrodes. The rappers in this design are more sophisticated mechanisms, with separate rappers for the collectors and the electrodes.

Figure 22	Electrostatic Precipitator

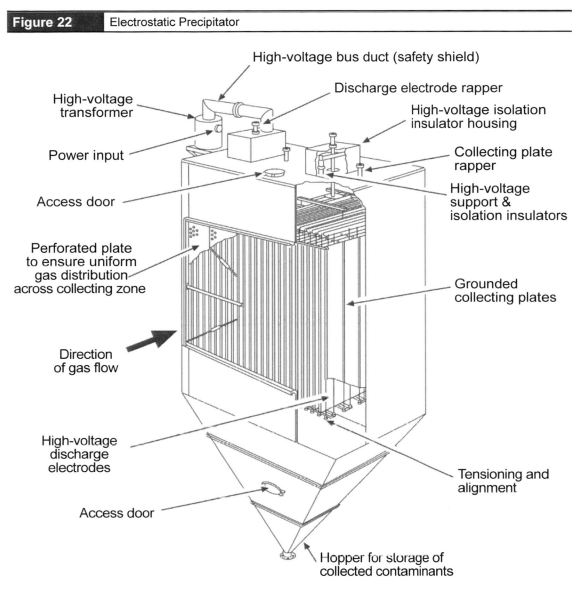

Since the distance between electrodes and collecting plates is very small, one or more cyclone precipitators usually precede the electrostatic unit to reduce the volume of ash particles. With efficiencies as high as 90%, electrostatic precipitators are usually used as final polishers of the flue gas. Efficiency will be adversely affected by:

- Higher than normal flue gas temperatures; charging ability of the ash particles is reduced as temperature increases.
- Idle or defective rappers, causing internal build up and shorting out of the electrodes

Bag House Filters

With certain coals, some flue gas particles cannot be easily charged. Therefore ash removal by electrostatic precipitators is ineffective. In this case, an alternative method is to pass the gas through fabric filters. A common arrangement is called a bag house, in which many filter bags are arranged in parallel rows. The fabric of the bags allows the flue gas molecules to pass through, but not the ash particles.

Figure 23 illustrates a bag house.

Due to its size, cost and installation, a fabric bag cannot be discarded when it gets clogged. A rapper system, similar to that of the electrostatic precipitator, shakes the compacted particles from the bags. Jets of air may be used instead of or in combination with the rappers.

Some fabrics, such as polyamide or acrylic fibers, may operate safely at 290°C and may accept gas up to 315°C for short periods.

Figure 23	Bag House Filters

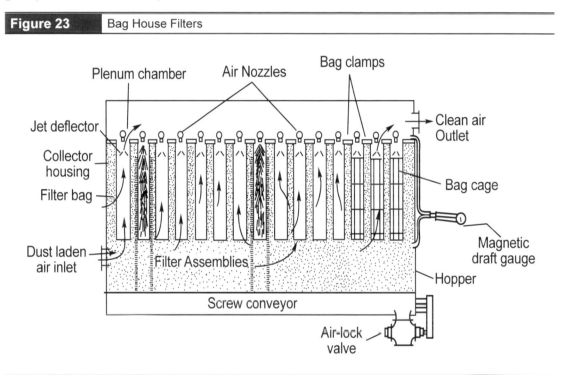

OBJECTIVE 7

Describe the design and operation of ash handling systems, including hydro and air systems, bottom ash systems, and scraper conveyor systems.

ASH HANDLING SYSTEMS

Ash handling systems receive the ash from the furnace bottom and from the precipitators and then dispose of it. The particular system used depends upon the method of firing and the size of the boilers. A plant with small, stoker-fired boilers may be arranged so that trucks can be driven into the basement and the ash dumped directly into them from the ash pit. Medium sized plants may use a pneumatic system that removes the ash from the pit and transports it to an outside storage bin, or silo. Trucks then remove it from the silo. Large, pulverized coal fired plants use more elaborate systems, which may be hydraulic, pneumatic or a combination of both.

Figure 24 shows a typical ash handling system for a large plant, using both hydraulic and pneumatic methods.

- Ash from the dry bottom furnace is quenched and collected in a water-filled ash hopper. Sticky slag that discharges from the furnace with the dry ash disintegrates when quenched with water.

- The ash is periodically removed from the hopper through a hydraulically-operated gate and forced, by a jet pump or hydraulic ejector, through a pipeline to a fill area.

- As the ash leaves the hopper, it passes through a clinker grinder, which reduces the size of large pieces, to permit passage through the pipeline.

- When the ash water mixture reaches the fill area, the water is drained off to a clarifying basin before entering any stream, river or lake.

- Flyash is collected from three locations, the economizer section, the dust collectors and the bottom of the stack. The flyash from the economizer is sent to intermediate storage bins by an air pressure system supplied by a blower.

- Flyash is removed from the intermediate bins, dust collectors and stack by a vacuum system. A mechanical blower or pump creates the vacuum.

- The vacuum pump pulls the air/ash mixture through a primary, mechanical separator and then a secondary, cyclone separator where the ash is removed.

- Before the air discharges to atmosphere, it passes through air washers to remove any remaining flyash.

- The fly ash is carried from the bottom of the primary and secondary separators by another blower-operated air pressure system, which carries it to storage silos. Trucks haul the flyash from the storage silos.

While Figure 24 shows a dry bottom furnace, a similar ash handling system could be used for a wet bottom, slag tap furnace. In this case, the molten slag drops into a water-filled hopper. The water is agitated by jets to aid in the disintegration of the slag, which also passes through a clinker grinder, before entering the ash-handling pipeline.

Figure 24 Ash Handling System

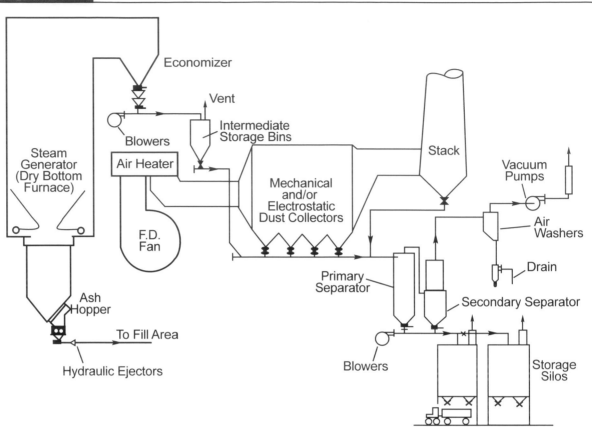

Types of Ash Handling Systems

There are three common main types of ash handling systems:

- Hydro, or water-powered system
- Pneumatic, or air-powered system
- Mechanical system

1. Hydro System

The hydro system uses jet pumps to move a mixture of water and ash through a closed pipeline to the disposal area.

Figure 25 is a schematic of a jet pump, used to handle abrasive solids. The pump is a simple device with no moving parts and three main components: body, nozzle and diffuser. High-pressure water enters the nozzle, where it mixes with ash from the hopper. Together they pass through the venturi diffuser, which increases the velocity and creates a low pressure area at the nozzle. Difference in pressure between the diffuser and the discharge causes movement (ie. pumping) of the mixture.

To minimize erosion, the jet pump is made of abrasion-resistant alloys. The piping, downstream of the jet is also designed for abrasion resistance, especially the elbows.

Figure 25	Jet Pump for Ash Removal

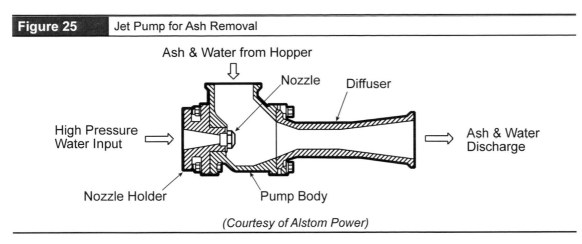

(Courtesy of Alstom Power)

2. Pneumatic System

A pneumatic system uses a stream of air or flue gas to move the ash. The air movement is created by upstream pressure or downstream vacuum.

Figure 26 shows a vacuum-to-pressure, dry, pneumatic, flyash system. A mechanical exhauster creates a vacuum on the upstream system, from the precipitators to the surge transfer tank and bag filters. A mechanical blower pressurizes part of the system, from the transfer tank to the flyash silo.

Figure 26	Pneumatic Flyash Removal System

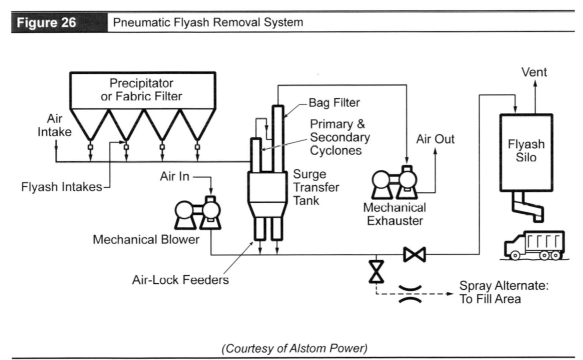

(Courtesy of Alstom Power)

3. Mechanical System

Mechanical ash removal involves the use of solids handling equipment, such as scraper conveyors, bucket elevators, and conveyor belts. Figure 27 shows the most common mechanical arrangement, which uses a submerged scraper conveyor. The scraper operates below the water level of the bottom ash pit. A steeply sloped belt conveyor is used to de-water the bottom ash mixture and transport it to the clinker grinder.

Figure 27 | Submerged Scraper Conveyor

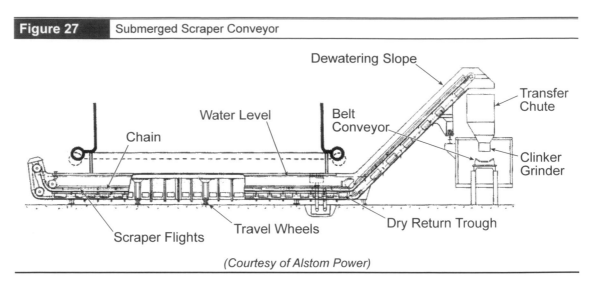

(Courtesy of Alstom Power)

Bottom Ash Hoppers

Bottom ash hoppers may be dry or wet. In the dry type the bottom ash pit is dry and lined with an insulating material. The ash is crushed and removed dry. Dry bottom hoppers are not normally used on boilers that produce more than 180 000 kg/h (180 tonnes/h) of steam. In a wet bottom system, the ash hopper is filled with water. The wet system has the following advantages:

- It cools the ash and helps to break it up into smaller pieces
- It keeps the slag submerged so that large masses do not fuse together
- The water helps in the removal of the ash

Figure 28 shows side views (internal and external) of intermittent-removal ash hoppers. Note the water level, clinker grinder, and jet pump. Jetting nozzles are also used to remove slag from the sides of the hopper. During normal operation, each hopper is usually drained only periodically (approximately every 8 hours).

Figure 28 | Wet Type Bottom Ash Hopper

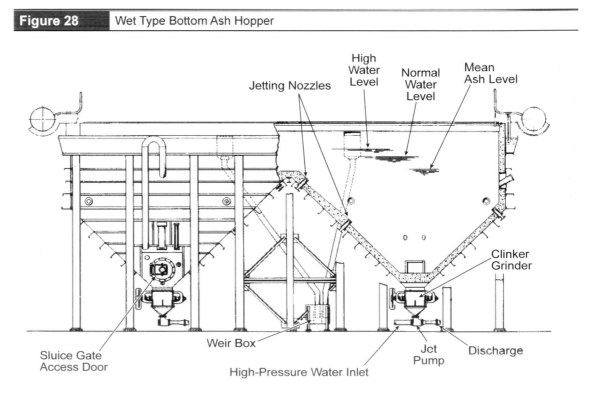

(Courtesy of Alstom Power)

OBJECTIVE 8

Describe the designs and operation of SO₂ recovery systems, including lime and wet gas scrubbing.

SULPHUR DIOXIDE RECOVERY SYSTEMS

Recovery systems for the removal of SO_2 from flue gas can be classified into two major types:

- Wet scrubbers
- Dry scrubbers

Wet Scrubbers

Figure 29 shows a flue gas wet scrubbing system, which operates as follows.

- A slurry of lime/limestone is pumped to the venturi scrubber. The boiler flue gas enters the scrubber and contacts the slurry, which absorbs sulphur dioxide, fly ash and lesser amounts of oxygen from the flue gas.
- The resulting solution of spent absorbent and gases then goes to the bottom of the spray tower.
- Upon entering the spray tower, the remainder of the flue gases separate from the absorbent. The boiler ID fan draws the flue gas up through the spray tower.
- Meanwhile, a solution of the absorbent slurry is pumped from the holding tank to the spray tower where it sprays into the rising flue gases, further absorbing any remaining traces of sulphur dioxide.
- Another water spray at the top of the spray tower cools the hot flue gases. The flue gases discharge to the stack and out to atmosphere.
- Spent absorbent drains from the spray tower to the scrubber effluent holding tank, where the dissolved sulphur compounds and fly ash precipitate out of solution.
- Fresh lime is added to the slurry to regenerate the spent absorbent. The slurry contains 5 to 15 percent suspended solids, consisting of fresh lime, absorption products and flyash.
- To regulate the accumulation of solids in the slurry, a bleed stream from the scrubber effluent holding tank is pumped to the solid/liquid separation section of the system, which includes the clarifier, process water tank, and vacuum filter. Here, solids are removed and disposed of, while the liquids are recycled back to the scrubber effluent holding tank.

Figure 30 shows the layout of a similar scrubbing system.

Again, flue gas is scrubbed in absorbers, which contain a series of sprays. The gas comes in contact with lime or limestone slurry, which absorbs about 90% of the SO_2. After passing through a mist eliminator at the top of the absorber, the flue gas goes to the stack. There are subsystems for slurry preparation, waste slurry dewatering, and solids disposal. Solid products are disposed of by mixing the de-watered sludge with flyash and sending to a landfill.

Figure 29 | Flue Gas SO₂ Scrubbing System

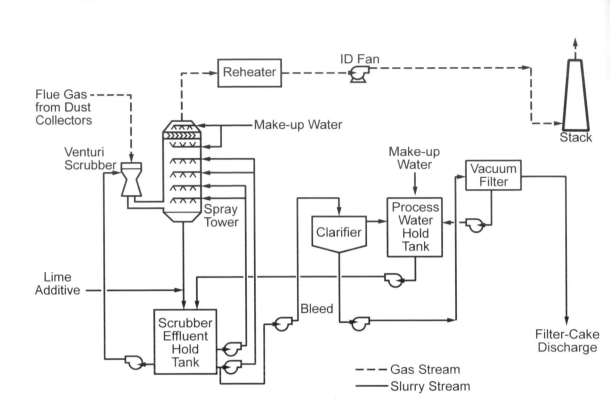

(Courtesy of Alstom Power)

Figure 30 | Power Plant Lime Scrubbers

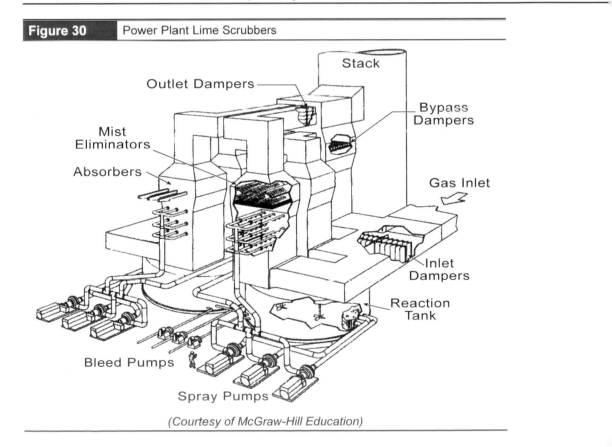

(Courtesy of McGraw-Hill Education)

Figure 31 shows another type of wet scrubber. It is a simple loop, absorber tray tower in which flue gas enters at the bottom and flows into the absorber tower quench section. A lime slurry is sprayed into the gas stream through nozzles. This is the initial stage of SO_2 absorption.

The flue gas then passes through a perforated tray where further SO_2 is removed due to the violent flow action. Any liquid droplets entrained in the upward flowing flue gas are removed by moisture separators before the clean flue gas passes out to the atmosphere. The sludge is disposed of from the bottom of the scrubber.

Figure 31	Wet Tray Tower Scrubber

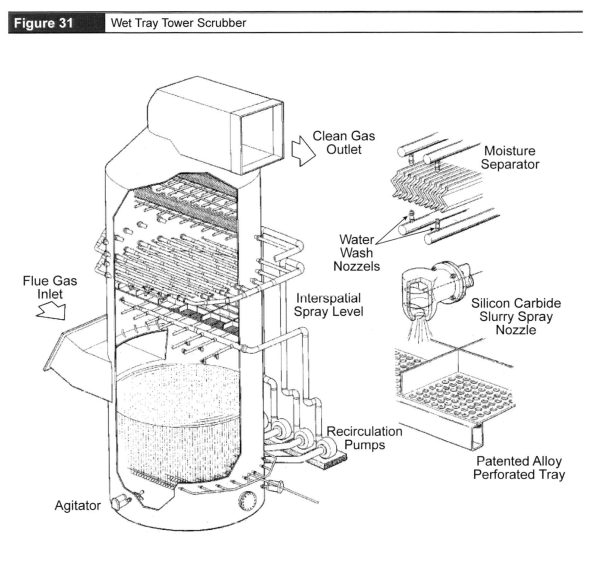

(Courtesy of Babcock and Wilcox)

Dry Scrubbers

Dry scrubbing is the main alternative to wet scrubbing for SO_2 removal. The advantages of dry scrubbing over wet scrubbing include:

- Simplicity of construction
- Waste products are dry
- Fewer operating components
- Less costly construction materials

In the dry scrubbing process, the hot flue gas is used to dry a finely atomized slurry of alkaline reactants. As the slurry dries, a majority of the SO_2 in the flue gas reacts with the reagent. The reacted material, now a dry powder, is removed along with the flyash in the precipitators or bag-house filters.

Figure 32 shows a utility boiler with dry scrubber and baghouse. Unlike a wet scrubber installation, the dry scrubber is located before the dust collector.

Figure 32	Utility Boiler with Dry Scrubber

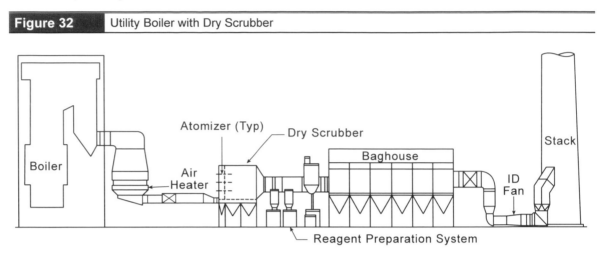

(Courtesy of Babcock and Wilcox)

Figure 33 shows the horizontal scrubber of Figure 12, with atomizing air nozzles. Flue gas leaves the air heater at a temperature of 121°C to 177°C and then passes through a finely atomized spray of alkaline slurry. The atomized droplets absorb SO_2 while the hot flue gases dry the slurry into a powder. The dried products are removed from the hopper at the bottom of the scrubber or continue to the precipitator for removal. This design is common with industrial or utility boilers.

Figure 33	Pneumatic Horizontal Nozzle Dry Scrubber System

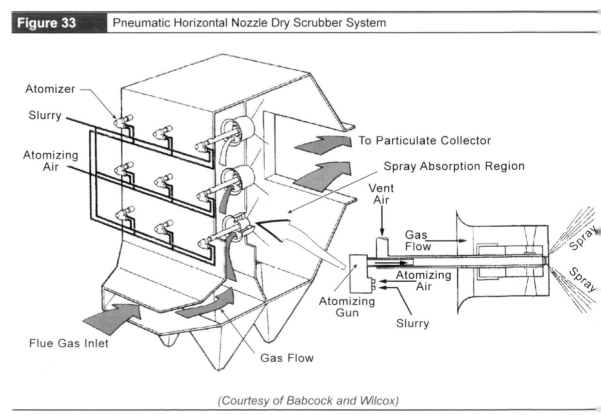

(Courtesy of Babcock and Wilcox)

Figure 34 shows a dry scrubber with vertical flow spray nozzles. Here the flue gas flows in at the top, where it is sprayed by nozzles that point downward.

Figure 34	Pneumatic Vertical Nozzle Dry Scrubber

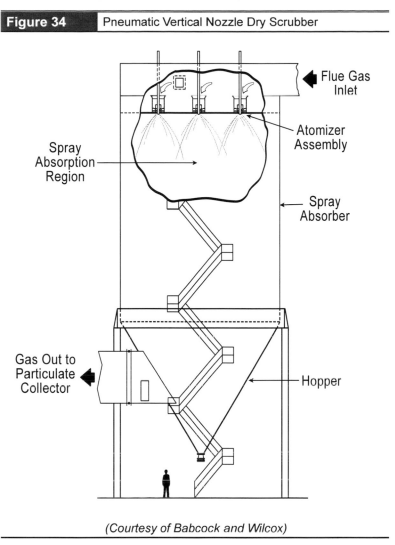

(Courtesy of Babcock and Wilcox)

Reagents

Lime is the most common absorbing reagent in dry scrubbers. Limestone is the preferred reagent with wet scrubbers. Lime is much more expensive than limestone. Therefore, the operating cost for a dry scrubber is higher than for a wet scrubber. The dry scrubbers are often used in smaller plants or where reagent cost is not the main factor, such as in plants using lower sulphur coals.

CHAPTER 7 - QUESTIONS

1. What factors affect the creation of natural draft in a boiler?

2. With the aid of a single line sketch, explain the following:
   a) How balanced draft is created and controlled in a boiler.
   b) What pressure is normally maintained in a boiler that operates under a balanced draft system?

3. List the advantages and/or disadvantages of the following types of fan output control:
   a) Inlet dampers or vanes
   b) Outlet damper
   c) Variable speed

4. Briefly discuss the difference between primary and secondary air louvers for a boiler.

5. List the steps that you feel should be followed in the starting of a draft fan.

6. With the aid of a simple sketch, explain the principal of operation of a cyclone precipitator.

7. What are the advantages of the wet type of bottom ash removal system?

8. With the aid of a simple sketch, explain the principal of operation of a lime wet scrubbing unit used for the removal of sulphur dioxide from flue gas.

9. List the advantages that dry scrubbers, used for sulphur dioxide removal, have over the wet type scrubbers.

ANSWERS: All answers are found within the content of the chapter.

CHAPTER 8

Boiler Control Systems

LEARNING OUTCOME

When you complete this chapter you should be able to:

Explain the components and operation of automatic control systems for boiler water level, combustion, steam temperature, and start-up.

LEARNING OBJECTIVES

Here is what you should be able to do when you complete each objective:

1. Describe on-off and single element control of boiler feedwater.

2. Explain swell and shrinkage in a boiler. Describe the components and operation of a two-element feedwater control system, explaining the interaction of the controllers.

3. Describe the components and operation of a three-element feedwater control system.

4. Describe the components and operation of a direct combustion control system.

5. Describe the components and operation of a 'steam flow – airflow' combustion control system.

6. Describe the components and operation of a 'fuel flow – airflow' combustion control system.

7. Describe the components and operation of an 'airflow – fuel flow' combustion control system.

8. Describe the components and operation of a multi-element combustion control system.

9. Describe steam temperature control methods and equipment, including attemperation (desuperheating), gas recirculation, gas bypass, and tilting burners.

10. Describe the automatic, programmed start-up sequence for a gas-fired boiler.

OBJECTIVE 1

Describe on-off and single element control of boiler feedwater.

ON-OFF BOILER FEEDWATER CONTROL

In on-off feedwater control, water is supplied intermittently to the boiler. This is done by fully opening and fully closing a valve in the feedwater line or by starting and stopping the feedwater pump. This action may be initiated by a probe-operated level switch or, more commonly, by a float-operated level switch. The latter has a float that responds to the water level and, through linkage, activates electrical start-stop switches.

Figure 1 shows such a float assembly with a two-wire switch and a three-wire switch.

Figure 1	Float Operated Level Switch

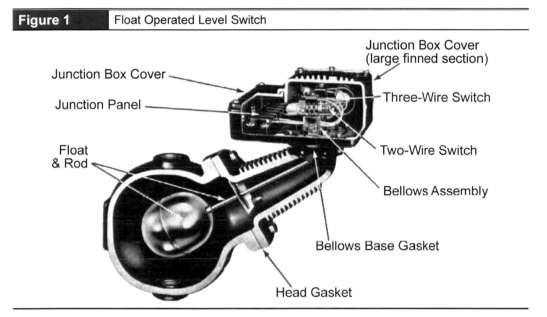

The two-wire switch energizes the boiler feedwater pump and the three-wire switch cuts off the fuel to the boiler if drum level becomes too low. When the boiler water level drops, the float will also drop and, through the rod and linkage, will close the two-wire switch (as shown in Figure 2(a). This will energize the boiler feedwater pump starting circuit. When the water level again rises to a predetermined level in the drum, the float will open the two-wire switch, as in Figure 2(b), and shut down the pump. This on-off cycle between minimum and maximum operating levels repeats continuously.

If the pump fails to start and the water level continues to drop, the 3-wire switch will tilt and open the burner circuit.

Figure 2	Operation of Mercury Switch

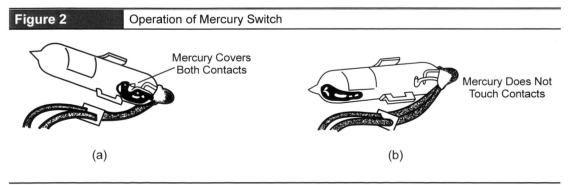

(a)   (b)

SINGLE ELEMENT FEEDWATER CONTROL SYSTEM

Figure 3 illustrates a single element feedwater control system. The control of feedwater to the boiler is based on a single element only, the water level.

Figure 3	Single Element Feedwater Control System

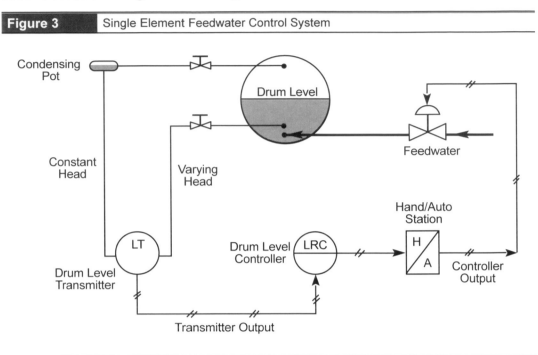

The level in the steam drum is constantly "sensed" by the Drum Level Transmitter (LT). The transmitter has an internal diaphragm or capsule. One side of the diaphragm is exposed to a constant head pressure, while the other side is exposed to a head that varies with the drum level. A change in drum level causes the pressure differential across the diaphragm to change. This differential is proportionate to the actual level in the drum and the corresponding output signal from the level transmitter represents the level.

The output from the transmitter is sent to the Drum Level Controller (LRC), where it is compared with the set point signal. If there is any deviation of level from the set point, the controller output will reposition the feedwater control valve to correct the drum level. This is known as feedback control, as it responds only to changes in boiler water level.

A manual-automatic (ie. Hand/Auto) transfer station allows the operator to start the boiler with the level control on manual. When the boiler is under load and the drum level is stabilized, the operator can transfer the system to automatic control. A recorder may be included in the controller (the "R" in LRC), giving the operator a second, visual indication of drum level.

OBJECTIVE 2

Explain swell and shrinkage in a boiler. Describe the components and operation of a two-element feedwater control system, explaining the interaction of the controllers.

SWELL & SHRINKAGE

In larger watertube boilers, a greater portion of the total water content resides in the boiler tubes, while a smaller portion is in the steam drum. During normal boiler operation, steam bubbles may occupy up to 25% of the total water volume. Moreover, when fuels such as oil, natural gas, or pulverized coal are burned in suspension, there is almost an instantaneous change in combustion heat release in these boilers, which further intensifies the problem of maintaining the correct drum level. As a result, swell and shrinkage become a problem with these boilers.

Swell

Swell is a sudden increase in water level, due to an increase in the steam demand from a boiler. Sudden or rapid increase in boiler load (ie. external steam demand and usage) causes a sudden or rapid increase in steam flow from the boiler. This creates a sudden drop in steam drum pressure, which causes a corresponding drop in the boiling point of the water. The heat energy already in the water causes a larger volume of water to be converted to steam. This increased volume of steam bubbles in the drum and waterwall tubes causes an increase in the drum level (ie. swell).

At the same time, the firing rate of the furnace increases, responding to the increase in steam demand and attempting to restore the boiler pressure to normal. This increases the volume of steam produced in the water space (particularly in the waterwalls), causing a further rise (ie. swell) in the drum level.

Shrinkage

Shrinkage is a sudden decrease in water level, due to a decrease in the steam demand from a boiler. Conversely to swell, a sudden decrease in boiler load causes a sudden increase in drum pressure and boiling point. The pressure increase causes steam bubbles in the drum and waterwalls to begin to collapse, resulting in a decrease in drum level. At the same time the increased boiling point causes less steam to be produced in the waterwalls, which also causes a drop in level.

Control of Swell & Shrinkage

Swell and shrinkage usually last only a short time, until the firing rate of the boiler responds to the change in steam demand. Thereafter the water level should return to normal as quickly and smoothly as possible. Unfortunately, since a single element feedwater control system is sensitive only to drum level, it responds exactly opposite to what is desired during swell and shrinkage.

During swell the increase in steam demand should require a corresponding increase in water to the boiler, to produce the additional steam. Instead the single element control only sees the rise in level and responds by reducing the feedwater flow to the boiler. Likewise, during shrinkage the drop in steam demand should require a corresponding drop in water to the boiler, but the single element control only sees the drop in level and responds by increasing the feedwater flow. In both cases, the result is a fluctuating or unstable drum level, which takes considerable time to stabilize.

For this reason, single element level control is adequate (as described in Objective 1) when the boiler steam drum is large and contains a large percentage of the total boiler water or when load changes are slow and small. Single element systems are generally used on water tube boilers that operate below 1700 kPa pressure and have capacity below 50 000 kilograms per hour with fairly constant load.

To overcome the effects of swell and shrinkage, two-element and three-element feedwater control systems are more effective than a single element control.

TWO-ELEMENT FEEDWATER CONTROL

Figure 4 illustrates the two-element feedwater control system, which improves the single element system by adding a steam flow transmitter. The two control elements are now drum level and steam flow.

Figure 4	Two-Element Feedwater Control

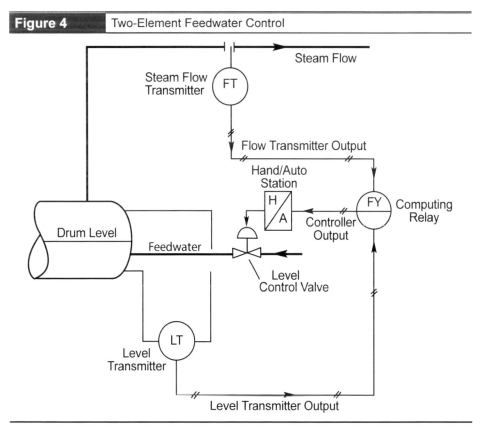

If feedwater pressure and boiler blowdown are constant, the system operates much like a single element control, with the steam flow transmitter having no effect. Variations in drum level due to changes in feedwater pressure or boiler blowdown cause the computing relay to position the feedwater control valve to maintain the level at its set value.

However, if there is a change in steam load from the boiler, the steam flow transmitter immediately senses the change in steam flow. It generates an output signal that is proportional to the steam flow. This signal goes to the computing relay, which acts as a proportional controller and sends a proportional signal to position the feedwater valve.

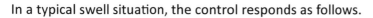

In a typical swell situation, the control responds as follows.

- When steam load suddenly increases, swell begins to occur and the level transmitter output begins to change and in attempt to reduce the feedwater flow.

- However, the steam flow transmitter immediately senses the increased steam flow and sends a corresponding output signal to the computing relay, which overrides (ie. takes precedence over) the drum level signal. This keeps the feedwater control valve in a more open position and allows the water level to stabilize more quickly at the new steam load.

- Once stabilized and the effects of swell no longer exist, the level transmitter signal again takes precedence.

In a typical shrinkage situation, the control responds as follows.

- When steam load suddenly decreases, shrinkage begins to occur and the level transmitter output begins to change and in attempt to increase the feedwater flow.

- However, the steam flow transmitter immediately senses the decreased steam flow and sends a corresponding output signal to the computing relay, which overrides the drum level signal. This keeps the feedwater control valve in a more closed position and allows the water level to stabilize more quickly at the new steam load.

One problem with the system in Figure 4 is the difficulty in restoring the level to the exact setpoint after a load change. The level has some deviation or offset from setpoint at different steam loads. Figure 5 shows an improved version of the two-element system, which addresses this offset problem.

Here, a level recording controller (LRC), is added and the output from this LRC goes to the computing relay. Since the controller is proportional plus integral, it brings the level back to set point after swell or shrinkage are overcome. A two-element control system may be called a feed-forward system, since it anticipates a change in drum level with a change in load and acts accordingly to avoid large level fluctuations.

Figure 5	Two-Element Feedwater Control with Level Controller

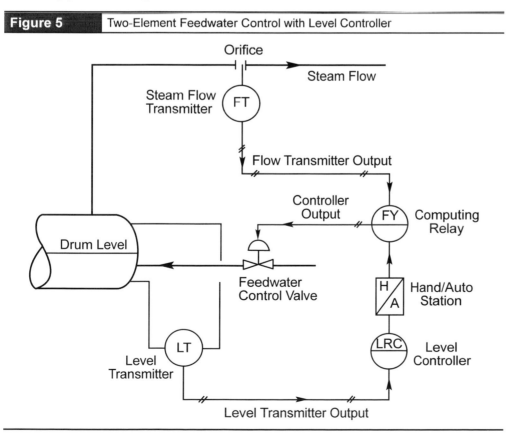

OBJECTIVE 3

Describe the components and operation of a three-element feedwater control system.

THREE-ELEMENT FEEDWATER CONTROL

Three-element feedwater control system is a further improvement over two-element control. It adds water flow as the third element with steam flow and water level. The effects of swell and shrinkage are greatly reduced if not eliminated. The principle of three-element control is that each kg of steam produced requires one kg of water. Therefore, except for internal leakages and blowdowns, the steam flow and water flow should be nearly equal.

Figure 6 shows a three-element control system.

Figure 6	Three-Element Feedwater Control System

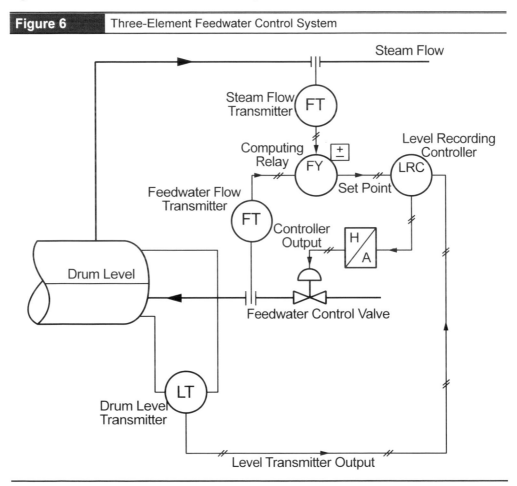

Steam and water flow are both measured. Any change in steam flow is immediately detected and the water flow is adjusted in anticipation of a drop in drum level.

The outputs of the steam and water flow transmitters are compared in the computing relay. Any difference between them causes a change in output from the relay which then becomes the set point signal for the level recording controller (LRC). The relay output, or set point, signal is compared with the drum level transmitter output in the controller, and any deviation of drum level will cause the controller output to reposition the feedwater valve.

- If the steam flow and water flow are equal, the relay output will equal the set point of the LRC.

- If feedwater pressure drops, reducing water flow, the steam flow signal becomes larger than the water flow signal, so the output of the relay increases (as indicated by the '+' sign beside the computing relay, Fig. 6). This causes the controller to open the feedwater valve further

- If feedwater pressure increases (such as when starting a second feedwater pump) water flow will also increase. The water flow signal would now be greater than the steam. The relay output will decrease (as indicated by the '-' sign beside the computing relay, Fig. 6) and cause the controller to reduce the opening of the feedwater valve.

- A sudden increase in steam load causes an increase in the steam flow signal and an increase in the output from the computing relay, which becomes the new set point in the controller. The controller output changes to increase the water flow immediately. When swell subsides, the drum level transmitter will make a correction to the controller output and the feedwater flow.

- With a sudden decrease in load, the steam flow signal will become lower than the feedwater flow signal, causing a decrease in the relay output and the setpoint signal to the controller. The controller output will reduce the feedwater flow. When the effect of shrinkage is overcome, the drum level transmitter will again make final adjustments to the controller output and the feedwater flow.

- If the direct relationship between steam and water flow is interrupted, such as during intermittent or continuous blowdown, the relationship is adjusted automatically by the level controller to maintain the proper drum level.

This system has an automatic/manual transfer station so the boiler can be put into service with the drum level on manual control.

A variation to this three-element control is shown on the next page.

Figure 7 shows a variation of the three-element feedwater control system.

In this design, the output from the drum level transmitter is compared with the set point in the level recording controller, LRC. The output of the LRC is compared with the steam flow transmitter output, at the summing relay. The output of the summing relay then becomes the set point signal for the feedwater flow-recording controller, FRC.

In a potential swell situation, an increase in steam flow increases the set point signal to the feedwater FRC to open the feedwater control valve further. Since this is a proportional plus reset controller, it will keep increasing the water flow until the output of the water flow transmitter is equal to the set point signal. This overcomes the influence of the drum level transmitter and LRC, which is under the effect of swell. As the swell subsides, the drum level transmitter and controller will bring the drum level back to set point.

Figure 7	Three-Element Feedwater Control

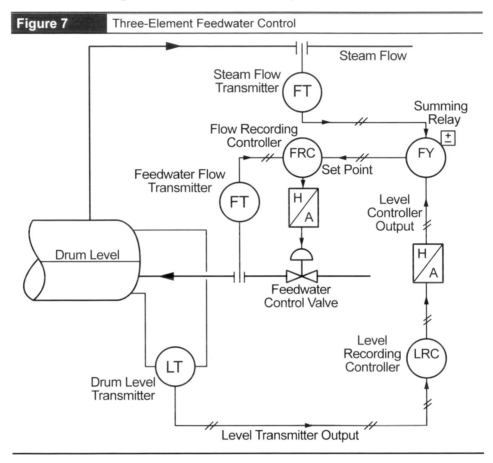

OBJECTIVE 4

Describe the components and operation of a direct combustion control system.

DIRECT PRESSURE OR PARALLEL POSITIONING COMBUSTION CONTROL SYSTEM

This type of combustion control system, as shown in Figure 8, may be used on boilers where the fuel flow is difficult to measure.

Figure 8	Parallel Air-Fuel Combustion Control

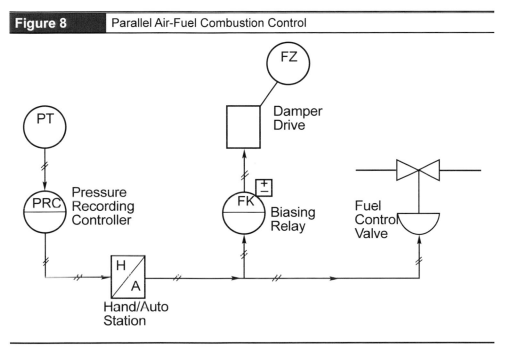

A master steam pressure-recording controller (PRC) regulates the fuel and airflow, simultaneously (ie. in parallel), during changes in boiler load. This one controller positions both the airflow dampers and the fuel flow valve at the same time. Thus, the correct ratio between air and fuel may not be obtained at all loads.

Positioning of the airflow damper and the fuel valve occurs without measuring the actual quantities of air and fuel. The system only measures the boiler pressure (PT) and compares it to a set point. An operator can adjust the biasing relay to achieve the necessary fuel-air ratio and excess air, at different boiler loads.

To ensure the proper amount of excess air is being supplied and the boiler is being operated efficiently, the flue gas is periodically analyzed at different loads. The biasing relay is then calibrated for maximum combustion efficiency. A continuous oxygen analyzer may also be provided to measure the excess oxygen in the flue gas.

OBJECTIVE 5

Describe the components and operation of a 'steam flow – airflow' combustion control system.

STEAM FLOW – AIRFLOW COMBUSTION CONTROL

In boiler combustion, an approximation can be made for the amount of fuel required to produce steam, without actually measuring the fuel. The supporting theory is that since the amount of heat released during combustion determines the amount of steam generated, then the amount of fuel required to produce that heat can be calculated, provided the heating value of the fuel is known.

Also, since each kilogram of fuel burned requires a certain amount of air, there is a definite relationship (ie. ratio) between the steam generated and the air required to burn the fuel and, therefore, to produce the steam. Therefore, it is possible to obtain fairly efficient combustion in a boiler by maintaining a proper ratio between steam flow and air flow.

This form of control is known as steam flow-airflow or semi-metering control. It is used when the fuel flow is difficult or impossible to measure, such as in many coal fired furnaces.

Figure 9 shows the components of a steam flow-air flow control system. It works as follows.

- The steam pressure-recording controller (PRC) sends a control signal simultaneously to the final control element that adjusts the fuel flow and to the forced draft damper drive.

- The signal to the forced draft dampers first passes to a relay, which also receives the output signal from a steam flow-airflow ratio controller (FFRC).

- Steam flow and air flow transmitters supply their respective flow outputs to the FFRC, which compares their ratio to a ratio setpoint, entered by the operator.

- If the ratio does not match the setpoint, the FFRC will modify the relay output to the forced draft damper drive to either increase or decrease the airflow.

If there is also an induced draft fan, the system will include a pressure transmitter, which will measure the furnace pressure. If the pressure varies from the desired set point, the furnace pressure controller will adjust the induced draft dampers to keep the pressure constant at all boiler loads.

Figure 9 Steam Flow-Airflow Combustion Control

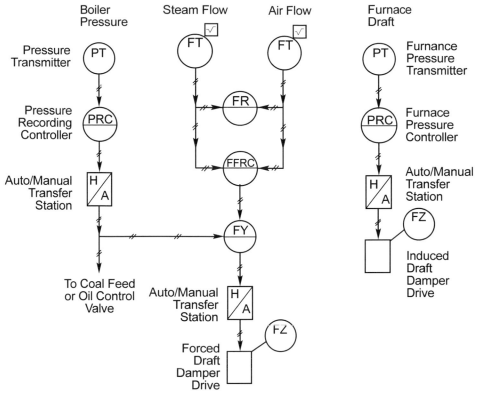

OBJECTIVE 6

Describe the components and operation of a 'fuel flow – air flow' combustion control system.

FUEL FLOW – AIR FLOW COMBUSTION CONTROL SYSTEM

Figure 10 illustrates a fuel flow-air flow system, in which a desired ratio is maintained between the fuel flow and the air flow. When this system is on automatic, the position of the fuel valve is only controlled by the output of the master pressure controller (PRC). The position of the air dampers (which adjust the air flow) is initially determined by the PRC, but then is modified, through a fuel-air ratio controller to achieve the correct fuel-air ratio.

In effect, the fuel flow is the leader and the air flow is the follower, so that a change in airflow follows a change in fuel flow. The reliability of this control system requires that the heating value of the fuel remains constant.

Figure 10	Fuel Flow-Air Flow Combustion Control

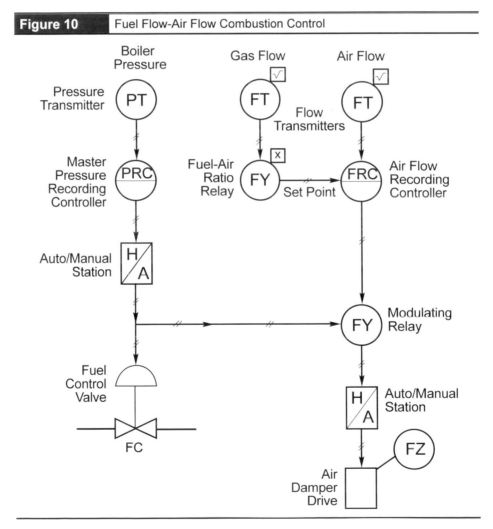

The system operates as follows if steam load increases:

- If steam load increases, the boiler pressure tends to drop. When the pressure transmitter senses the pressure drop, the output signal (from the master pressure controller, PRC) increases simultaneously to the fuel flow control valve and to the air damper drive. The fuel and air flows will increase in response to the PRC.

- Meanwhile, the fuel flow transmitter measures the fuel flow and the output becomes the input to the fuel-air ratio relay. In this relay, the fuel signal is adjusted to obtain the required excess air for complete combustion.

- This adjusted signal becomes the setpoint for the airflow recording controller (FRC), where it is compared with the existing air flow signal from the airflow transmitter. If the initial increase in air flow did not maintain the required excess air, there will be a difference between the set point and the actual air flow. In this case, the air flow controller output will make further adjustments to the modulating relay, which adjusts the airflow to obtain the correct air-fuel ratio.

- Once the pressure returns to the set point, the control system will stabilize the fuel and airflows at the new, increased values to maintain a steady boiler pressure at the new load.

If steam load decreases, the system will respond as follows:

- If steam load decreases, the steam pressure will increase. The master pressure controller will respond by immediately reducing the fuel flow and the input to the modulating relay, causing an initial reduction in fuel flow and air flow.

- Then a reduction in fuel flow controller output will reduce the output signal from the ratio relay and the set point of the air flow controller.

- In turn, the output of the air flow controller will adjust the output of the modulating relay to reduce the airflow and restore the fuel-air ratio to its set value.

- When boiler pressure is back to the setpoint, the fuel and air flows will stabilize at their new, lower values.

It should be noted that, during boiler start-up, the auto-manual station for the air damper drive may be placed on automatic. When the operator adjusts the fuel flow manually, this signal will pass to the input of the modulating relay and the airflow will be automatically adjusted, as well. The auto-manual station downstream of the master PRC is placed on automatic after the boiler is on line and steady.

OBJECTIVE 7

Describe the components and operation of 'air flow – fuel flow' combustion control system.

AIR FLOW – FUEL FLOW COMBUSTION CONTROL SYSTEM

Figure 11 illustrates an air flow-fuel flow system.

This system also maintains a desired fuel-air flow ratio. However, in this system, the position of the air dampers is controlled only by the output of the master pressure controller (PRC). The position of the fuel valve is initially determined by the PRC, but then is modified, through the fuel-air ratio controller to achieve the correct fuel-air ratio.

In this case, the air flow is the leader and the fuel flow is the follower, so that a change in fuel flow follows a change in air flow. [1]

Figure 11	Air Flow-Fuel Flow Combustion Control

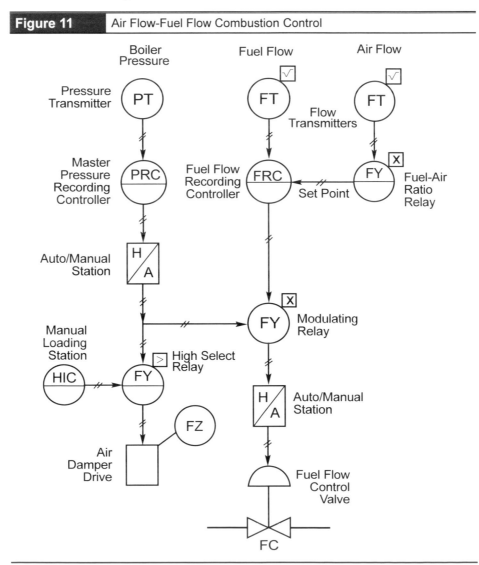

If the steam pressure drops, due to an increase in boiler load, the following occurs.

- The output of the master PRC increases, further opening the air dampers and (through a modulating relay) the fuel valve simultaneously.
- This causes the air and fuel flows to increase, which causes the outputs of their respective flow transmitters to increase.
- The output of the air flow transmitter goes to the fuel-air ratio relay, where the output is modified to obtain the required excess air for efficient combustion.
- This modified output becomes the setpoint for the fuel flow recording controller (FRC), where it is compared with the existing fuel flow signal from the fuel flow transmitter. If there is any deviation between the setpoint and flow the fuel flow controller output will change to correct the output of the modulating relay, resulting in a change in the fuel valve position.

If steam pressure increases, due to a drop in boiler load, the following occurs.

- The output of the master PRC decreases, closing the air dampers and fuel valve further, which causes a reduction in air and fuel flow.
- The decrease in output from the air flow transmitter reduces output/setpoint from the fuel-air ratio relay.
- The fuel flow controller responds to the setpoint change, sending a corresponding signal through the modulating relay to the fuel valve, adjusting it further to maintain the fuel-air ratio.

The control signal to the air damper drive has a **high select relay**, which sends only the highest available signal to the dampers. This safety feature prevents the airflow from decreasing below a minimum, safe value, which is set by the manual loading station. It also prevents a sudden drop in air flow (which could cause too little air in the furnace) during a switch from manual to automatic control.

OBJECTIVE 8

Describe the components and operation of a multi-element combustion control system.

MULTI-ELEMENT COMBUSTION CONTROL SYSTEM

Multi-element combustion control systems use additional control elements, beyond air, gas, steam flows and steam pressure. The purpose is to achieve more precise control, creating more efficient combustion.

There are many, different multi-element systems, some being extremely complex. Each is designed to satisfy the efficiency goals of the operation, the design of the boiler, and the fuel being burned.

Figure 12 shows only one, relatively simple example of a multi-element combustion system. It combines steam pressure, fuel flow (in this case gas), air flow and oxygen (O_2) measurement into a system that ultimately controls the fuel and air to the furnace.

The main components of Figure 12, include:

- Four transmitters, including gas flow, air flow, steam pressure, and flue gas Oxygen (analyzer).
- Four controllers, including master PC, gas FC, air FC, and oxygen AC (for Analyzer Controller).
- Hand/automatic transfer stations (H/A), which allow the operator to switch a controller output between manual and automatic, during startup, shutdown, or to resolve an operating problem.
- Square root extractors (√), which produce an output signal (from flow transmitters) that is directly proportional to the flow.
- Low select relay (<), which selects the lower of two inputs and sends that as the output.
- High select relay (>), which selects the higher of two inputs and sends that as the output.
- Function generator ($F_{(x)}$), which receives an input and does a calculation before sending an output.
- Current to air converter (I/P), which receives an electrical input and converts it to a corresponding pneumatic output.

Figure 12 | Multi-Element Combustion Control

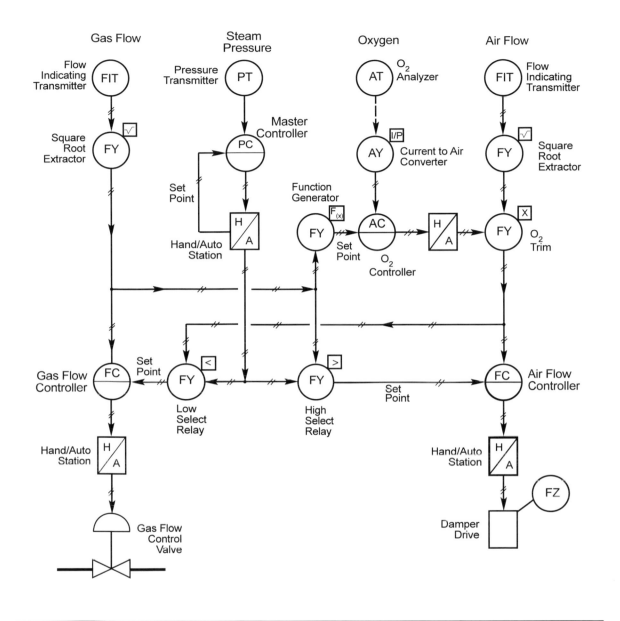

Operation During Load Increase

If load increases, causing steam pressure to drop, the following control actions will occur.

- The output of the pressure transmitter to the master PC will decrease. The master PC output, which goes directly to the high and low select relays, will increase (a reversed control action).

- The high select relay will now see a higher input from the master PC than from the gas flow transmitter. Therefore, the master PC output will also become the output of the high select relay.

- This high select output becomes the setpoint signal to the air flow controller. The increase in setpoint causes the output from the air flow controller to increase and the air dampers to open further, increasing air flow to the boiler.

- Meanwhile, the low select relay sees a higher input from the master PC, than from the air flow O_2 trim relay, so the airflow signal is selected and becomes the setpoint for the gas flow controller. When airflow increases (step 3 above) the setpoint of the gas flow controller increases, opening the fuel valve further to increase the boiler firing rate. The boiler steam pressure will rise. This will return the master pressure to the set point.

- The output of the gas flow transmitter (via square root extractor) goes to the function generator ($F_{(x)}$), which calculates the amount of excess O_2 required for the amount of fuel and produces a corresponding output. The O_2 controller receives this output as its setpoint, which it compares with the actual O_2 from the O_2 analyzer (via the current-to-air converter). The output of the O_2 controller adjusts the output of the O_2 trim relay and, subsequently, the airflow signal to the air FC.

Operation During Load Decrease

- A decrease in boiler load causes an increase in boiler pressure and the output of the master PC will drop.

- The master PC inputs to the low and high select relays will drop.

- Now the master PC output is the lower input to the low select signal relay, while the gas flow is the higher input to the high select relay. This causes a decrease in the set point signal to the gas flow controller, with further closing of the gas valve resulting in reduced gas flow to the burners.

- Since the output of the gas flow square root extractor becomes the set point of the airflow controller, a reduction in gas flow now causes a decrease in output from the airflow controller and a reduction in airflow.

- A decrease in gas flow also reduces the output of the function generator and the set point of the O_2 controller. This controller now adjusts the airflow so the percentage of excess air and O_2 in the flue gas is slightly higher than before.

Notes:

a) When boiler load increases, the air flow is increased before fuel flow to prevent an unsafe combustion condition in the boiler. Also, if air flow fails, the fuel valve will be closed immediately.

b) When boiler load decreases, the fuel flow is decreased before air flow.

c) The function generator, through calculation, changes the O_2 controller setpoint so that excess air and O_2 are less (as a percentage) at higher boiler load and more at lower boiler loads. This increases boiler efficiency.

OBJECTIVE 9

Describe steam temperature control methods and equipment, including attemperation (desuperheating), gas recirculation, gas bypass, and tilting burners.

STEAM TEMPERATURE CONTROL METHODS

To maintain steam turbine efficiency and to avoid fluctuations in the turbine metal temperatures, the temperatures of superheated and reheated steam must be maintained at constant values throughout the operating load range of the turbine. The main variables that affect the steam temperatures from a boiler are:

- Temperature of the furnace
- Temperature and flow of the flue gas through the superheater(s) and reheater
- Cleanliness of the superheaters
- Boiler feedwater temperature

The furnace temperature, flue gas temperature and flue gas flow will all increase when steam load increases, thus tending to cause an increase in steam temperature. The boiler feedwater temperature may also increase with load, particularly if regenerative feed heating is used, but increased feedwater temperature usually means less heat release is required in the furnace (per kg of steam generated) and, therefore, there's a tendency for steam temperature to decrease. The cleanliness of superheaters and reheaters depends upon the type of fuel and can, in some cases, be controlled using soot blowers.

Steam temperatures generally increase with load, since the major portion of superheat and reheat is transferred by convection. A steady steam temperature can only be attained at varying loads if some form of temperature control is employed.

The most common methods for controlling steam temperature are:

- Attemperation (desuperheating)
- Gas recirculation
- Gas bypass
- Tilting burners

ATTEMPERATION (DESUPERHEATING)

Attemperation involves the removal of heat from superheated steam. Two types of attemperators are the surface attemperator, in which the cooling medium is separated from the steam by a tube surface, and the direct contact attemperator, in which the cooling medium directly contacts the steam.

1. Surface Attemperators

There are three types of surface attemperators:

- the condenser type
- the shell type
- the drum type

Condenser Type

A condenser type attemperator consists of a looped tube (or tubes), installed inside the superheater inlet header. A portion of the boiler feedwater passes through these tubes on its way to the steam drum. The feedwater inside the tubes is at a much lower temperature than the saturated steam. Heat transfers to the feedwater, thus cooling and condensing some of the steam. The reduction in steam temperature, plus the increased liquid, entering the superheater results in a lower temperature leaving the superheater. A control valve proportions the correct amount of feedwater passing through the loop tubes, according to superheater outlet temperature.

Shell Type

The shell type attemperator consists of a cylindrical shell, through which boiler water circulates. Superheated steam from the primary superheater passes through a tube bundle within the shell and has its temperature lowered by heat exchange with the boiler water. A control valve directs the necessary proportion of superheated steam through the tubes to achieve the desired final steam temperature.

Drum Type

The drum type attemperator consists of tubes, installed within one of the boiler drums and surrounded by boiler water. Steam temperature is achieved by controlling the amount of superheated steam passing through these looped tubes.

Condenser and shell attemperators have a limited control range. Shell types are costly and difficult to inspect. Drum attemperators have limited capacity and occupy space within the boiler drum. Surface-type attemperators are rare in modern boiler designs.

2. Direct Contact Attemperators

The direct contact attemperator, also referred to as the spray desuperheater, introduces feedwater directly into the superheated steam, through a spray nozzle. The sprayed water vaporizes by absorbing its latent heat from the steam. Loss of this heat reduces the temperature of the superheated steam.

Figure 13 illustrates the arrangement of a direct contact (spray) attemperator.

The water spray nozzle is located at the throat of a venturi section, which causes increased steam velocity and increases the vaporizing and mixing action. A thermal sleeve, incorporated with the venturi section, is located downstream from the spray nozzle. It prevents water droplets from striking the hot surface of the piping, which would cause thermal shock.

The water to a spray desuperheater must be of the highest quality, since any solids carried by the water will enter the steam and cause deposits in superheater tubes and/or on turbine blades. The total solids concentration in the spray water should not exceed 2.5 ppm.

Spray desuperheaters are designed to provide the desired temperature at all boiler loads. Steam temperature is maintained by controlling the amount of spray water.

The direct contact, spray type is fast acting, sensitive and inexpensive. However, it must be supplied with very high quality water.

Figure 13 — Spray Desuperheater

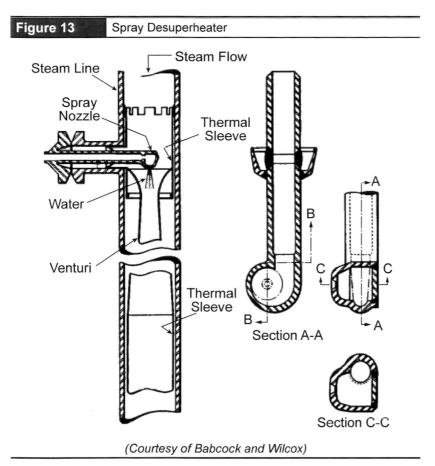

Section A-A

Section C-C

(Courtesy of Babcock and Wilcox)

Figure 14 shows the usual location of a spray attemperator (desuperheater), which is between the primary and secondary stages of the superheater. With this arrangement, the desuperheater is not subjected to excessive superheated steam temperatures, as It would be if located after the secondary superheater.

Figure 14 — Spray Desuperheater Location

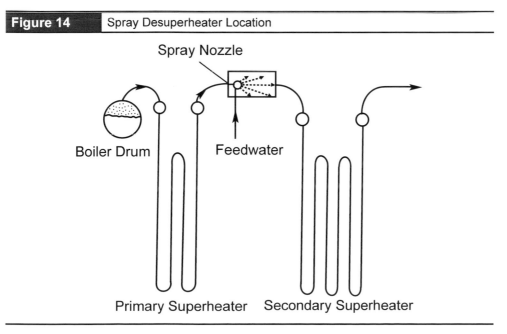

GAS RECIRCULATION

If the superheater (or reheater) is designed to achieve the desired steam temperature at full load, when maximum heat is available from the furnace, then a method must be used to increase the available heat to the superheater or reheater when boiler load is low.

One method, called **Gas Recirculation**, recirculates a portion of the hot flue gases, usually from the economizer outlet, back to the lower part of the furnace. This increases the mass of flue gases to the superheater(s), thereby making more total heat available.

A recirculating fan draws flue gas from the economizer outlet and discharges it into the furnace, in a location that does not interfere with combustion. The recirculated gas mixes with the combustion gas in the furnace, lowers the temperature in the furnace, and thus reduces the heat absorbed by the waterwalls in the furnace. The increased total gas flow, due to the addition of the recirculated gas, causes an increased amount of heat to be carried to the convection surfaces of the unit, including convection superheater.

Figure 15 shows the effect of gas recirculation on the heat absorption in the various sections of a boiler. It shows that as the amount of gas recirculation increases, the heat absorbed in the furnace decreases, while the heat absorbed by the superheaters, reheater and economizer increases.

Figure 15	Effect of Gas Recirculation

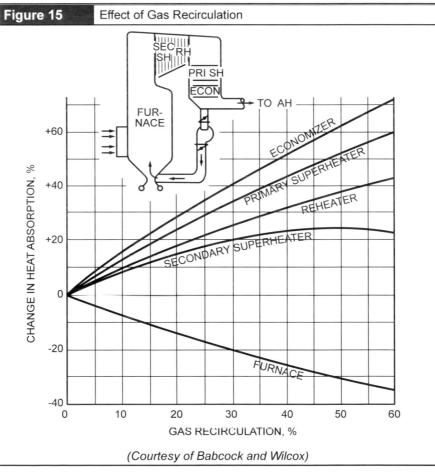

(Courtesy of Babcock and Wilcox)

Gas recirculation does not affect boiler efficiency, although efficiency may be improved if the recirculated gas contains an appreciable amount of unburned fuel particles, which are subsequently burned on their return to the furnace. Extra ductwork, dampers, controls and a recirculating fan are required for gas recirculation, but those costs are rewarded by good temperature regulation over a large load range.

Figure 16 shows the arrangement of the gas recirculating ducts, fan, and control dampers in a central station boiler.

| Figure 16 | Gas Recirculation Arrangement |

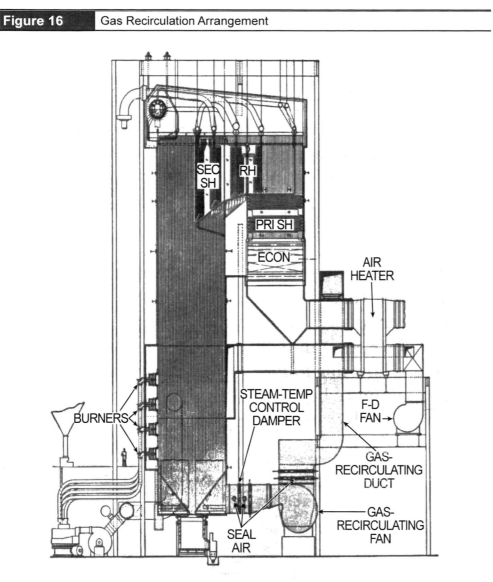

(Courtesy of Babcock and Wilcox)

GAS BYPASS

Gas bypass involves separating the convection section of the boiler into two or more parallel gas passes. In this way, the proportion of combustion gases flowing over the superheater and reheater can be varied, thereby providing a means of steam temperature control.

Figure 17 shows a simple arrangement of a parallel pass design.

The convection reheater is located in a gas pass that is parallel to another gas pass containing the convection superheater. The flow of gas through each parallel section can be varied by control louvers, located at the outlet of each pass.

When the boiler is operating at full load, both sets of louvres are fully open, with 50% of the total gas flowing through each pass. Under these conditions, the superheated steam temperature is higher and spray desuperheating is likely used to control it. Spray desuperheating is generally used when load is between about 40% and 100%. Usually, the 50% gas flow through the reheater is sufficient to maintain the desired reheat temperature.

At lower loads, more gas is passed through the reheater section and less through the superheat section. This allows the reheat temperature to remain constant. The superheated steam temperature still tends to be high even with reduced gas flow through the superheater.

Figure 17	Parallel Gas Bypass

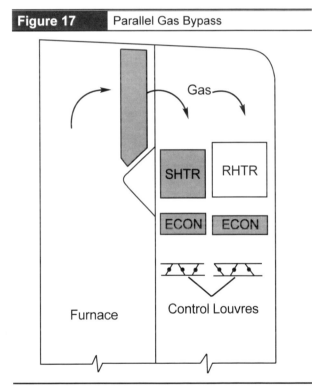

One common problem with gas bypass is the difficulty in maintaining the dampers in good operating condition, due to their exposure to high temperatures. Another problem is the slow response to steam temperature changes.

TILTING BURNERS

Tilting burners provide accurate control and fast response over a wide operating range. They are designed so that the flame can be tilted upward or downward, from the horizontal.

- At high loads, when the steam temperature tends to rise above the desired value, the burners are tilted downwards. This increases the heat absorbed by the waterwalls in the furnace area, thereby decreasing the temperature of the gases leaving the furnace and entering the superheater sections.

- Conversely, at low loads when the steam temperature tends to drop, the burners are tilted upwards, reducing the heat absorption in the furnace and increasing the temperature of the gases entering the superheater sections.

Figure 18 shows the tilting burners in three positions:

a) Tilted downwards to give high heat transfer in the furnace

b) Tilted horizontal to give normal heat transfer in the furnace

c) Tilted upwards to give low heat transfer in the furnace

Figure 18	Tilting Burners

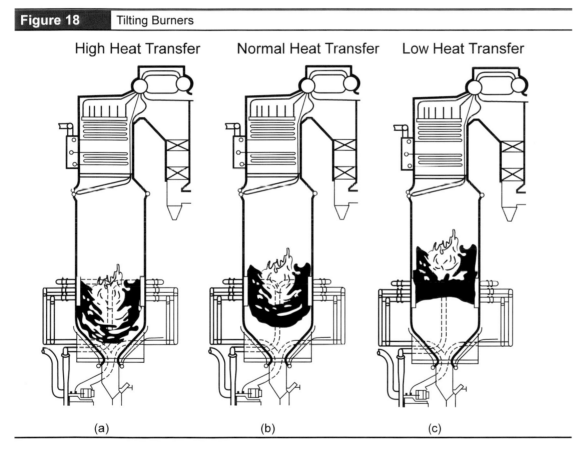

High Heat Transfer   Normal Heat Transfer   Low Heat Transfer

(a)   (b)   (c)

OBJECTIVE 10

Describe the automatic, programmed start-up sequence for a gas-fired boiler.

PROGRAMMING CONTROLS

Small, single burner boilers, equipped with intermittent or interrupted pilots, or with direct spark ignition, require controls that provide correct sequencing (order of operation) of the combustion controls, during start up and shut down. These controls must also ensure that all conditions necessary for proper burner operation are satisfied. This control is called the "programming control" or "programming relay."

Figure 19 shows a diagram of one, simple programming control used on a gas-fired boiler with natural draft.

A manual input by the operator (ie. pushing the start button on the front of the control relay, called "protectoglo" relay in this diagram) causes the system to energize, resulting in the starting of the boiler. The relay automatically programs the ignition system, start up of pilot and main burner, and supervises (watches) the main burner, during its operation.

Figure 19	Programmed Control

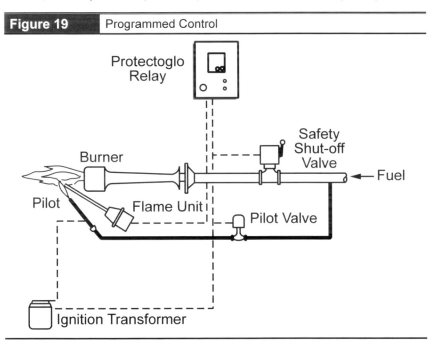

Since most boilers are operated automatically (with no input from the operator), the programming control for these boilers is more complicated. The operation of automatic boilers is controlled by an operating control (space thermostat, pressure or temperature control), which initiates the programming control when heat is required. This control starts the boiler, energizing each component of the firing equipment in the proper order.

Figure 20 shows a programming relay, used on gas and oil fired boilers with either natural or forced draft.

Figure 20	Programming Relay

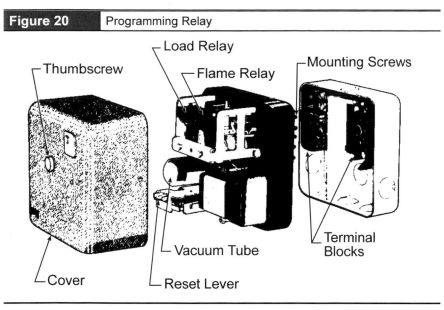

When used on **gas-fired boilers** with natural draft, the sequence of this control is as follows:

- Operating control calls for heat. A switch is closed.
- The load relay of the programming control is energized and pulls in, closing its contacts. Pilot gas valve and ignition transformer are energized.
- Pilot flame is established; the flame detector senses the flame and sends a signal to the programming control.
- This signal is amplified and used to energize the flame relay. This relay pulls in and closes the contacts, and the main gas valve is energized (It opens).
- The pilot flame ignites the main burner.
- Ignition transformer is de-energized. If there is an interrupted pilot (ie. it is off when the main flame is on), the pilot gas valve is also de-energized and closes.
- The control now holds the main gas valve open as long as the operating control calls for heat.
- When the heat demand is satisfied, the operating control opens the switch, causing the load and flame relay of the programming control to open and the main gas valve then closes. The control is now ready again to start the boiler, when heat is required.

The pilot burner may fail to ignite during start-up or, even if the pilot burner does ignite, the main burner may fail to ignite. In either case, after a short trial period of 15 to 30 seconds (from the beginning of the start up depending on the type of control), a lock out switch will be energized, which cuts off power to the ignitor, pilot and main gas valve. The boiler will not be able to start automatically until the operator resets the control. Some controls do allow a second attempt, after a false start, before the control locks out. If the main burner flame fails during operation, the control will be locked out.

When the programming control is used on an **oil fired boiler** (burner not equipped with a pilot) the operation is as follows:

- Operating control calls for heat. A switch is closed.
- The load relay of the programming control closes its contacts. This energizes the ignition transformer, fuel oil valve and burner motor driving the blower and fuel pump.
- Main burner flame ignites.
- The flame detection device (photo cell) senses the flame and its signal causes the flame relay to close.
- Ignition transformer is de-energized.

The control will lock out on ignition failure during start up or flame failure, during operation.

A fully automatic, packaged boiler has a highly sophisticated programming control, which includes one or more timers and several relays. This control serves two primary functions:

1. It programs the operation of the fan or blower, ignition system, fuel valves and modulator system in a proper sequence, which includes suitable purge periods before ignition and after burner shut down.

2. It monitors both pilot and main flame and does not allow the main fuel valve to be energized unless pilot flame has been established and proved. It also de-energizes the fuel valves within 1 to 4 seconds after loss of flame signal.

The programming control includes safe start features. If any part of the starting sequence is not properly completed, it stops the starting sequence and purges the furnace.

Note: Purging a furnace means forcing a flow of air through the furnace for a set period of time. The purpose of purging is to remove any combustible gas that may have collected in the furnace, while the burner is not in operation. An accumulation of combustible gas could cause a furnace explosion, when the pilot is lit again.

PROGRAMMING CONTROL OPERATION SEQUENCE

A simplified schematic diagram of a burner control circuit is shown in Figure 21. The various operating and limit control switches are shown. If any one of these switches opens, it will break the main burner valve circuit and the valve will then close. In this system the scanner supervises both the pilot flame and burner flame. Referring to Figure 21, the operational sequence is as follows:

1. Position of Limit & Control Switches Before Start Up

1. Assuming that the water level in the boiler is normal, then both of the low water cutoff (LWCO) switches (5. and 6.) will be closed.

2. Assuming that the steam pressure is below the cut out point of the operating control, this control switch (2.) will be closed.

3. If the steam pressure is below the operating control it must also be below the high limit control point, so this switch (3.) will be closed.

4. Assuming that the pressure in the fuel supply line is normal, then the low gas pressure control switch (4.) will be closed.

5. The burner valve is closed, since its coil is de-energized, due to the air pressure switch, flame failure switch, and timer-operated switch (T4) being open.

6. If the boiler has been out of operation for some time, the main switch or breaker can now be closed. This energizes the electronic circuit and supplies power to the various control switches

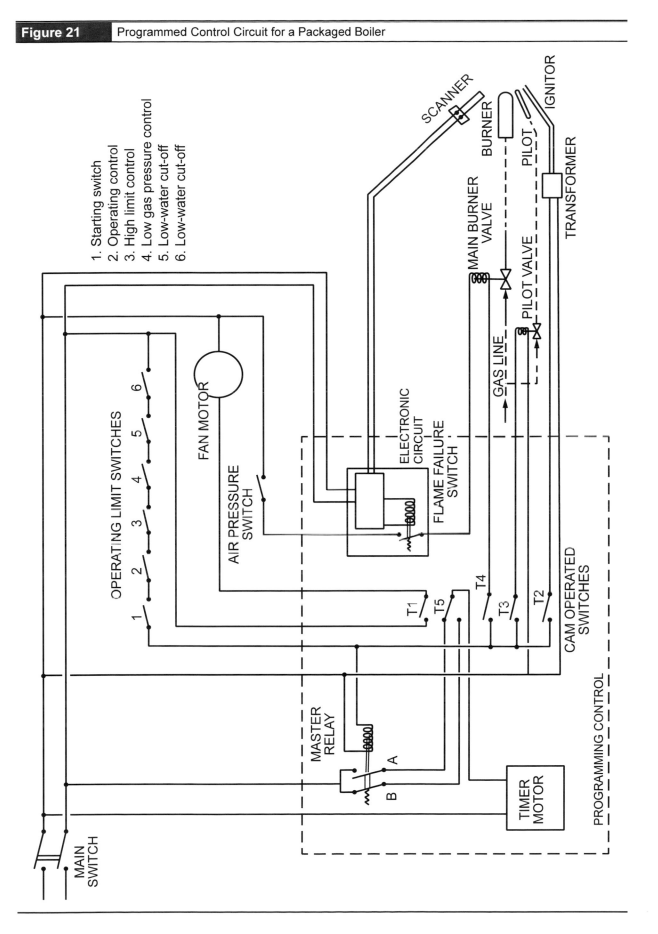

Figure 21   Programmed Control Circuit for a Packaged Boiler

2. Start Up Sequence

1. To start the boiler, close the starting switch (1.). This energizes the master relay, which, in turn, opens switch (B) and closes switch (A). The timer motor is then energized through the switch (T5).

2. The timer starts, immediately closes the fan motor switch (T1) and starts the fan. A few seconds later, the air pressure switch closes, as the air supply to the burner is established.

3. A purge period is now carried out to allow the fan to blow air through the furnace, which will remove any combustible gas, which may have collected there.

4. When the purge period is over, the timer closes switch (T2), which energizes the igniter transformer and causes the igniter to begin sparking.

5. The timer next closes switch (T3), which opens the pilot valve and the pilot flame lights, from the igniter spark.

6. The scanner sees the pilot flame. This completes the scanner electronic circuit, energizes the flame failure switch coil and then closes the flame failure switch.

7. After a short period of time to allow the pilot flame to become well established, the timer closes switch (T4). This completes the burner circuit and energizes the main burner valve coil. The main burner valve opens and the burner lights, from the pilot flame.

8. The timer times out. Switches (T2) and (T3) are opened, shutting off the igniter and the pilot. The scanner is now supervising the main burner flame, only.

9. The timer changes (T5) switch to circuit (B), of the master relay. Since switch (B) of the relay is already open, power to the timer is cut off and it stops.

3. Shut Down Sequence

1. When the steam pressure rises to the cut out point of the pressure control, it will open its switch (2.). This will break the burner circuit, thus de-energizing the coil of the burner valve. As a result, the burner valve closes and the burner flame is extinguished.

2. Since the scanner no longer sees a flame, the electronic circuit is broken and the flame failure switch opens.

3. The opening of the pressure control switch also de-energizes the master relay. As a result, switch (A) opens and switch (B), closes. Since the switch (T5) is closed on circuit (B), the power supply to the timer is re-established and the timer starts up again. It then opens switch (T4).

4. After a few seconds of post purge, the timer will open switch (T1), thus shutting off the fan. At the same time, it switches T5, back to circuit (A). Since the master relay is already de-energized and switch A is open, this will cut off the power supply to the timer and it stops.

5. When the steam pressure drops to the cut-in point of the operating control, the control switch (2.) will close. This energizes the master relay, which starts the timer, and the start up sequence will again proceed. Thus, once the power supply to the boiler has been established and the starting switch has been closed, the operation of the boiler becomes fully automatic.

CHAPTER 8 - QUESTIONS

1. Describe on-off boiler feedwater control.

2. Using a simple sketch, describe single element boiler feedwater control.

3. What are two elements or inputs that could be used in a two-element feedwater control? Make a sketch of this type of control loop.

4. What are the advantages of three-element boiler feedwater control verses two-element boiler feedwater control?

5. Explain what is meant by swell and shrinkage, as related to boiler drum level.

6. What is a direct pressure combustion control system? Make a simple sketch of such a system.

7. Name the inputs (process variables) fed into a multi-element combustion control system. Explain how the airflow and the fuel flow interact during increasing and decreasing boiler steam demand.

8. Sketch and describe a spray type desuperheater arrangement.

9. Describe how tilting burners are used to control steam superheat temperatures.

10. What does purging a furnace mean? What happens if any part of a boiler starting sequence (programmed control) is not properly completed?

ANSWERS: All answers are found within the content of the chapter.

CHAPTER 9

Boiler Procedures

LEARNING OUTCOME

When you complete this chapter you should be able to:

Describe common procedures in the operation and maintenance of high pressure boilers.

LEARNING OBJECTIVES

Here is what you should be able to do when you complete each objective:

1. Explain the steps involved in the commissioning of a new boiler or before starting a boiler after major repairs, including:
   a) hydrostatic test
   b) external and internal inspections
   c) drying out refractory
   d) boiling out
   e) testing shutdowns and safety devices

2. Describe the wet and dry methods when laying up a boiler for an extended time, including nitrogen blanketing.

3. Describe the proper shut down and preparation of a boiler for internal inspection.

4. Describe a thorough inspection of the water and furnace sides of a boiler.

5. Describe typical equipment and procedures for cleaning the water side of a boiler:
   a) mechanically
   b) chemically

6. Explain routine tasks and visual monitoring that the operator must perform on a large operating boiler.

7. Explain the procedures and precautions that an operator must exercise to avoid furnace and pressure-side explosions.

8. Describe sootblowing systems and describe the procedures for operating sootblowers.

OBJECTIVE 1

Explain the steps involved in the commissioning of a new boiler or before restarting a boiler after major repairs, including:
  a) hydrostatic test
  b) external and internal inspections
  c) drying out refractory
  d) boiling out
  e) testing shutdowns and safety devices

BOILER COMMISSIONING STEPS

Before a new or repaired boiler is to be put into service, it will require several preparatory steps to be taken. These will include the following:

- Inspection of the external and internal equipment
- Hydrostatic testing
- Drying out the new or repaired refractory
- Boiling out the internal waterside heating surfaces
- Testing shutdowns and safety devices

These steps ensure the safety of the operations personnel, the equipment, the public, and the environment.

This section deals with commissioning a new boiler, as the steps for commissioning a boiler after major repairs, are very similar.

External Inspection

An external inspection of the new unit must be carried out to ensure that nothing has been overlooked, during the construction of the unit, which would impede the commissioning process. This includes the following:

- Any missing or open valves
- Any safety valve connections that are blinded off
- Open ended boiler piping
- Provisions for expansion provided, as the boiler expands when the temperatures and pressures are increased
- All temporary braces and hangers, used during construction, are removed
- All hot surfaces have restricted access and insulated, for personnel protection
- Checking for any potential air or flue gas leaks, by running the forced draft fan
- All safety and relief valve discharge outlets are piped to a safe location to prevent personnel and property being hurt and damaged
- All instrumentation controls installed, operational and calibrated for their normal use
- The furnace and flue gas passages are inspected to ensure all debris has been removed as well as ladders, tools, and scaffolding
- Fans, dampers, fuel burning equipment and the necessary controls are checked before the access openings to the furnace and breeches are closed

Internal Inspection

An internal inspection of the boiler must also be carried out to ensure:

- No tools or other material have become lodged in any of the tubes or headers
- Straight tubes can be sighted through with a portable light
- Bent tubes can be proven clear of obstruction, by passing a wooden ball through. Compressed air can be used to blow the ball through the tubes
- The headers and drums have been cleaned so the boiler can be closed in preparation for the hydrostatic pressure test

Hydrostatic Test

The purpose of this test is to prove the boiler is tight, under an internal pressure that is applied to the boiler. The boiler manufacturer, or the repair agency in the case of a boiler repair, carries out this test. The authorized person is a provincial government or an insurance company boiler inspector, or a qualified employee of the company purchasing the boiler, depending upon the law in the jurisdiction, concerned.

Access to the external parts of the boiler must be made possible, at the time of the hydrostatic test. This requires that the boiler casing, insulation and brickwork, if any, be left off. Drum internals are usually left out because it may be necessary to access the tube ends in the drum in the event of a fault in this area.

Where possible, the pressure relief valves should be removed and the connections blinded to avoid any sediment or dirt entering the valves. If this is not possible, they must be gagged or clamped closed to prevent them opening under such high pressure.

In the case of a repaired boiler, some of the instrumentation associated with the waterside of the boiler must be isolated to prevent damage during the hydrostatic test.

The water used for the hydrostatic test should be clean and "not less than ambient temperature, but in no case less than 20°C (as per ASME, Section I, PG-99).   Also, the metal temperature must not exceed 50°C during the close examination (as per ASME, Section I, PG-99.2). If the boiler is completely filled with water and a part should fail during the test, then the pressure will be instantly released, without hazard.

Care must be taken to ensure that all available high point vents are open, to release any air from the boiler as it is being filled. Once the boiler is completely filled with water, the vents are closed and a special test pump used to gradually apply pressure.

(from PG-99.1) "Hydrostatic pressure tests shall be applied by raising the pressure gradually to not less than 1 1/2 times the maximum allowable working pressure as shown on the data report to be stamped on the boiler". This is the primary membrane test pressure. Then (from PG-99.2) "the hydrostatic test pressure may then be reduced to the maximum allowable working pressure, as shown on the Data report to be stamped on the boiler, and maintained at this pressure while the boiler is carefully examined."   If the pressure does not maintain there is likely a boiler leak.

On successful completion of the hydrostatic test, the pressure is released and the boiler is drained. The vents are opened to aid in the draining.

The drum internals are installed, and the pressure relief valves fitted. After installation of the drum internals, the drums are inspected again for debris. If there is any possibility that something fell into one of the tubes, then all the tubes must be proved clear using the methods mentioned earlier. After inspection of the drums, the manhole covers are replaced using new gaskets.

Drying Out the Refractory

The refractory and insulation are now applied to the boiler and the casing is put into place. Some expansion of the boiler may take place during the hydrostatic test. After the insulation has been applied, ensure that there is adequate clearance for further expansion, once heat is applied to the boiler.

New, and recently repaired, boilers must have the moisture removed slowly from the refractory, to prevent it from cracking.

At the beginning of this commissioning step, the first thing that should be done is to ensure that the low water level shutdown alarm is on, indicating a low water level condition. Open the drum vent and begin slowly filling the boiler with clean water in preparation for the refractory dry-out. The first thing is to ensure the gauge glass is in service. This gauge glass should be a temporary glass, as the chemicals for the drying and boiling out period, produce a caustic solution in the water, which will damage the gauge glass.

Continue to raise the drum water level, and as the level rises, the feedwater controllers can be commissioned. Add water until the drum level is about one-third of the gauge glass, and then add approximately 25% of the chemicals to be used for the boil out.

The superheater drains must be opened fully and left throughout the drying process to allow the superheater tubes to circulate steam vapour and stay cool. The drum vents are also left open to allow air to escape.

After purging the furnace, the fans are run on minimum output and a low flame is started in the furnace. Depending upon the amount of refractory, the fire is maintained for several hours or several days to control the boiler so that it only produces a vapour from the superheater drains and drum vents. The refractory manufacturer supplies a set of guidelines that indicates how fast the refractory temperature should rise each hour.

Once the drying out of the refractory is complete, the remainder of the chemicals are mixed with the boiler water.

Boiling Out

The purpose of the boil out is to remove any oil, grease, or other contaminating materials from the internal surfaces of the waterside of the boiler. This is completed by adding chemicals to the boiler water and then raising and maintaining a steam pressure in the boiler, for a predetermined period of time. This will dissolve any deposits present on the drum and tube surfaces.

One suggested treatment is to add the following, for each 45 000 L of boiler water content:

- 18 kg trisodium phosphate
- 2.25 kg caustic soda
- 2.25 kg sodium silicate
- 22.5 kg soda ash

Often these chemicals are pumped as a solution, into the boiler drum with a chemical feed pump. If this is not possible, then the chemical solution may be added through a steam drum manhole.

Make sure the superheater drains are wide open, unless otherwise specified by the manufacturer. When the pressure reaches 170 kPa, the drum vents are closed. The firing rate of the boiler is now increased in order to raise the pressure, in stages, to approximately one half the design working pressure.

As the firing is increased in the boiler, check to see that the supporting structure does not interfere with the expansion of the boiler. During the boiling out period, the blow-off valves are operated, at intervals of two to four hours, in order to blowout sludge and sediment from the mud drums and headers. After each blow off, the water level is brought up to the normal level in the steam drum. Additional chemicals are added as required.

The boil-out is complete when samples from the blow-off show that the water is clear. At this point, the burners are shut down and the pressure is allowed to drop. At approximately 170 kPa, the drum vents are opened to allow air in to prevent creating a vacuum in the boiler. After the boiler has cooled, all blow-off valves are opened and the boiler is drained. After draining, the manhole and handhole covers are removed and the boiler thoroughly flushed out with high-pressure water. All surfaces are then inspected for cleanliness. If any oil or grease remains on the surfaces, it will be necessary to boil-out the unit again.

Testing Shutdowns & Safety Devices

If the boil-out has satisfactorily cleaned the internal surfaces, the boiler may be closed up and the permanent gauge glasses installed. The blow-off valves are shut, and the steam drum is refilled to slightly below its normal level. After the furnace has been thoroughly purged, the burners are lit off and the steam drum pressure is slowly increased.

While the boiler is still at a low firing rate and not yet up to normal operating steam flow, it is recommended that the major safety devices be tested. The low water fuel cutoff should be tested by closing the feedwater valve and allowing the water level to drop, carefully observing at what level in the gauge glass the cutoff activates and closes the fuel valve. An alternative method is to open the bottom blowoff valve and lower the water level slowly until the cutoff activates.

Low and high fuel pressure shutdowns may also be tested while on low fire by artificially creating the shutdown conditions, using the isolating valves upstream or downstream of the pressure switches to manipulate the pressures.

Although pressure relief valves are generally bench tested after an overhaul, it is a good idea to test them again under hot, operating conditions. With minimum load on the boiler, close the outlet non-return valve and allow the pressure to slowly rise until the safety valve pops open. Note the pressure. Then slowly open the non-return valve, allowing the boiler pressure to drop. Note the pressure at which the pressure relief valve closes. If either the opening pressure or the blowdown are outside acceptable limits, arrange for adjustment and retesting before the boiler is brought into full service.

OBJECTIVE 2

Describe the wet and dry methods when laying up a boiler for an extended time, including nitrogen blanketing.

BOILER LAYUP

When a boiler is taken out of service for an extended period of time, it should be cooled, drained, cleaned internally and externally, and inspected. The inspection will determine what repair work is necessary and what mechanical and chemical cleaning should be done.

Wet and dry storage are two methods used to lay up a boiler. Which method is used depends upon the length of time the boiler is laid up.

Dry Storage

Dry storage is preferable for boilers that are out of service for an extended period of time or in locations where freezing temperatures, during the standby are expected. The cleaned boiler should be thoroughly dried, because any moisture left on the metal surfaces will promote corrosion. The drum, superheater, economizer and other waterside vents are opened to drain the boiler completely. A small flame is used to evaporate any water left in the boiler. The vapours, at the drum vent, are analyzed for moisture content. The analysis of these vapours is used as an indication of the boiler waterside being moisture free. The flue gas temperature in the stack should not exceed 200°C, or the temperature recommended by the boiler manufacture.

After drying, precautions must be taken to preclude the entry of any moisture or air.

- A moisture absorbing material, such as silica gel, should be placed on trays inside the drums. This material will absorb moisture from the air.

- The manholes should then be closed and all connections on the boiler should be tightly blanked.

- If available, a supply of an inert gas, such as nitrogen, can be connected to the drum vent to provide a positive pressure. The nitrogen pressure should be maintained at approximately 35 kPa.

- Warning signs and tags must be attached, noting that the boiler is stored under nitrogen pressure.

- The effectiveness of the materials and need of their renewal should be determined through regular, internal boiler inspections.

Wet Storage

Wet storage is used for a boiler that is placed in a stand-by condition. Wet storage is used if the stand by boiler may be required for service at short notice, or if it is impractical to employ the dry storage procedure. This method is not generally employed for reheaters or for boilers that may be subjected to freezing temperatures.

Two different methods of wet storage are described as follows:

Boiler Completely Filled

The clean, empty boiler is closed and filled with softened, deaerated feedwater. While filling, chemicals should be added to prevent corrosion during the layup period. These include an oxygen scavenger, such as sulphite (or other proprietory scavenging chemicals) and an alkalinity (ie. pH) control, such as caustic soda. A residual of oxygen scavenger is maintained to absorb any oxygen present in the feedwater. Caustic soda (or equivalent) is added in sufficient quantity to ensure the pH of the water is at least 10.0, which is the recommended minimum pH.

The chemicals should be added in such a way that they become evenly distributed throughout the water. If possible, fill non-drainable superheaters with demineralized water or condensate. Water pressure, slightly above atmospheric, must be maintained within the boiler during the storage period. A head tank or a temporary water line may be connected to the highest boiler vent to maintain a slight head pressure.

Boiler Partially Filled

Another method used for a short lay up is to fill the boiler with treated feedwater to the normal working level. The space above the water is then filled with an inert gas, such as nitrogen, that is maintained at approximately 35 kPa. In this way, the water will not be exposed to oxygen and corrosion will be prevented.

OBJECTIVE 3

Describe the proper shut down and preparation of a boiler for internal inspection.

BOILER SHUTDOWN

Boilers must be taken out of service at regular intervals, for cleaning, inspection and repair. The maintenance program will determine these intervals.

The firing rate is reduced to a minimum and the combustion controls are switched from automatic, to manual.

If the boiler is connected to a common header with other boilers when the fuel supply is shut off, the boiler pressure will drop below the header pressure. The stop-and-check (non-return) valve on the shutdown boiler will close. The stem of the stop-and-check valve closed and locked. The header valve may now be closed and locked. The drain between the stop-and-check valve and the header valve can be opened.

Fuel supply valves are to be isolated.

Lock out the draft fan and the feedwater pump motor breakers. Close and lockout the feedwater supply valves.

The boiler and boiler setting should be allowed to cool slowly with the air dampers shut. When the pressure in the boiler steam drum drops to 170 kPa, the drum vents are to be opened to avoid the formation of a vacuum within the boiler. Do not drain the boiler until it is cool enough to prevent any sludge present from being baked on the surfaces. After the boiler is drained, close and lock out the blowdown valves as well as the continuous blowdown valves. Open the drum manholes.

Fireside Cleaning

The fireside of the boiler is cleaned of all dust and soot by washing with a hot alkaline solution of water. The alkaline water is to prevent acid corrosion, which occurs when the fuel deposits contain sulphur. The fireside can now be inspected.

Waterside Cleaning

The waterside of the boiler is not washed until the inspector has examined and determined the amount of sludge and scale present. This will indicate if the boiler water and feedwater treatment is adequate. After the inspector is finished with his inspection the waterside of the boiler is washed down with high-pressure water. This water wash will remove the sludge and some of the scale.

During the high-pressure flush, the blowdown valves should be disconnected, if possible, to prevent them from getting plugged with scale. Any remaining scale will be removed by mechanical or chemical cleaning. After completion of the mechanical or chemical cleaning, the waterside is ready for surface inspection.

OBJECTIVE 4

Describe a thorough inspection of the water and furnace sides of a boiler.

WATER SIDE INSPECTION

When examining the waterside surfaces, the inspector looks for signs of corrosion, pitting, and cracking of the metal. Cracks may appear in ligaments between tube holes. Drum internals must be checked for looseness and cracking at the fastened ends. Particular attention is paid to drum connections such as pressure relief valve and steam outlet connections. Manhole and handhole openings and drum welds are examined closely.

Internal corrosion usually appears in one or more of the following three forms:

- Pitting along the water surface line
- Broad areas of pitting above the water surface line
- Local pitting in the tubes and headers below the water level

This pitting is the result of dissolved air or oxygen in the feedwater. The boiler tubes must be carefully inspected for the build-up of scale. Any scale found in the tubes must be removed by mechanical or chemical means before the boiler is put back in service.

FURNACE SIDE INSPECTION

When inspecting the fire side of the boiler, the inspector may require removal of sections of refractory or insulation in order to facilitate inspection of tube or drum surfaces. The surfaces are examined for bulges or blisters, which indicate overheating.

Refractory and brickwork of the burners, baffles, and furnace walls are checked for deterioration. In a fire tube boiler, the ends of fire tubes are checked for signs of leakage and tube sheet ligaments are checked for any cracking.

The dampers and air registers are checked for warpage and to ensure they move freely. Burners should be examined for signs of carbon buildup and overheating blisters.

OBJECTIVE 5

Describe typical equipment and procedures for cleaning the water side of a boiler:
  a) mechanically
  b) chemically

MECHANICAL CLEANING

The removal of scale from boiler surfaces by mechanical means involves the use of power driven tools, which either cut or knock the scale from the surfaces.

In a fire tube boiler, the scale will form on the outside surfaces of the tubes and may be removed by passing a vibrating hammer or "rattler" through the tubes. This loosens and dislodges the scale from the outside of the tube.

In a water tube boiler, the scale forms on the inside surfaces of the tubes. Rotary wire brushes, scrapers, cutters and drill heads are used to remove the scale.

These mechanical cleaning tools may be driven by water, compressed air, steam or in some cases, electricity. The following illustrations, Figures 1 to 4, show various types of cleaning tools and driving motors.

If a cutter head is used, a stream of water is introduced into the tube to provide cooling for the cutter heads, and to wash the scale out of the tube.

Figure 1	Wire Brush Cleaners

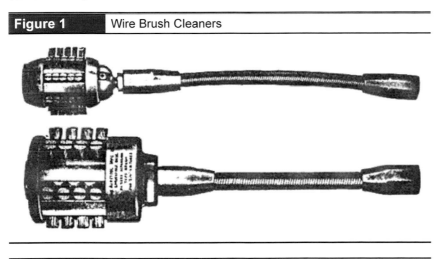

Figure 2	Scale Cutting Head with Water Driven Motor

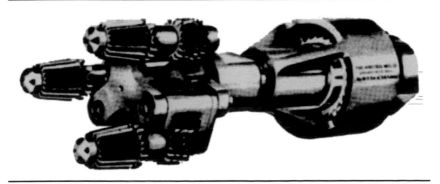

| **Figure 3** | Scale Cutting Head with Air Driven Motor |

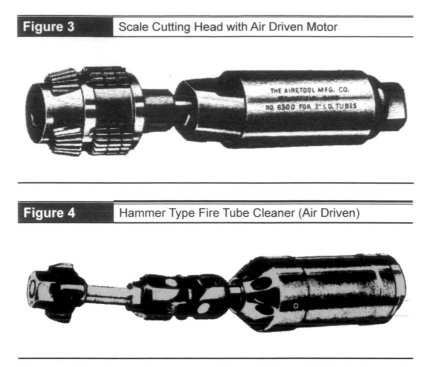

| **Figure 4** | Hammer Type Fire Tube Cleaner (Air Driven) |

After the mechanical cleaning is done, the tubes are flushed with high-pressure water to get rid of all the scale that was removed from the tube sidewalls.

Mechanical cleaning methods are used mostly on firetube and small watertube boilers. In terms of time and manpower, mechanical cleaning of large boilers is often very expensive, and does not always assure clean surfaces.

CHEMICAL CLEANING

Many of the internal surfaces of boilers cannot be cleaned properly by mechanical means. Chemical cleaning is used in these cases. This process is the quickest, cheapest, and the most efficient method of cleaning the internal surfaces of boilers of all sizes and designs. It has the following advantages compared to the mechanical cleaning method:

- Less time and maintenance personnel are required. Even a large unit can be cleaned in less than 36 hours.
- Inaccessible areas can be cleaned more thoroughly than mechanical cleaning.
- With chemical cleaning in mind, boilers can be designed without special provisions for mechanical cleaning accessibility.

Chemical cleaning involves washing the boiler internal surfaces with an acid solvent and then flushing with clean water. The unit is then treated with a neutralizing solution and flushed with clean water.

In preparing the boiler for the cleaning process, all parts, which are not to be cleaned, are isolated. All brass or bronze fittings must be replaced with steel. Adequate venting must be provided to prevent formation of acid vapors, which cause corrosion.

The acid solution may be applied by one of the following two methods:

- Circulation
- Soaking

1. Circulation Method

An arrangement for the chemical cleaning of a "once-through" boiler, by the circulation method, is shown in Figure 5.

- After the unit is removed from service, it is cooled and drained.

- The superheater section is filled with demineralized water and pressurized with nitrogen.

- The boiler proper is then filled with demineralized water through the filling connection, #1. While the filling is taking place, all air is vented through the vents, #2.

- The water is now circulated through the unit, using the chemical cleaning pump. Low-pressure steam is admitted through connection #3 in order to raise the temperature of the circulating water to 95°C.

- The chemical solutions are admitted through connection #4 to give the desired concentration in the circulating water. During cleaning, the temperature must be maintained at 95°C and the vents must be opened, frequently, to remove any hydrogen gas accumulations. Samples of the circulating solution are taken (at valve 10) every half hour and analyzed.

- When it has been determined by sample analysis that the cleaning is complete, the cleaning pump is stopped. The solution is removed from the unit by closing valve #5 and opening valve #6, while demineralized water is admitted through valve #1.

Figure 5	Chemical Cleaning - Circulation Method

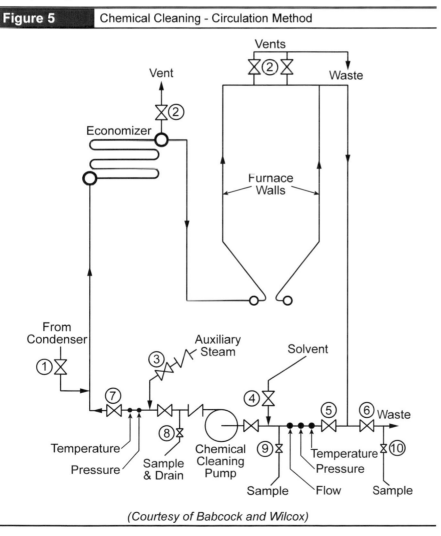

(Courtesy of Babcock and Wilcox)

- When the cleaning solution has been displaced, the demineralized water is circulated by the chemical cleaning pump and ammonia and hydrazine are added to provide a neutralizing solution, which should be heated to 95°C. This neutralizing solution should be circulated for two hours and all vents, drains, superheater piping and dead end piping should be flushed out. The neutralizing solution is then displaced by demineralized water.

- The final step is to add more ammonia and hydrazine and recirculate the solution.

2. Soak Method

An arrangement for the chemical cleaning of a conventional type boiler by the soak method is shown in Figure 6.

To prepare the boiler for soaking, thermocouples must be installed at the steam drum, at the centre of each furnace wall, and at one of the lower furnace wall headers.

- The boiler is then filled with demineralized water and brought up to a temperature of 77°C to 82°C, by means of the pilot burners, or light firing of the main burner. The firing is stopped and the boiler is then drained.

- The superheater is backfilled with treated condensate, or demineralized water, to prevent chemical vapors from entering during the cleaning.

- The drum gauge glass is replaced with a plastic tube.

- The vents #5 and valve #1 are opened and the filling pump started. Steam is admitted through valve #6 to keep the water flowing to the boiler at 77°C to 82°C and the inhibited chemical or solvent is admitted through valve #7. The amount of chemical entering is adjusted to give the desired solution strength, as sampled at valve #9.

- When the boiler is at normal operating level, the filling pump, heating system, and chemical feed are stopped. Valves #2 and #8 are closed and the drum vents #5 are left open. The boiler is then allowed to soak for a required period of time. The time is usually determined beforehand, by testing a sample of deposit from the boiler. The time normally ranges from 4 to 8 hours

- After the required soak time, the boiler is completely drained under nitrogen pressure of about 35 kPa by closing the vents #5 and opening valves #2, #3, and #4.

- When the boiler is completely drained, valves #3 and #4 are closed and valves #1, #5, and #8 are opened. The boiler is filled with demineralized water with the filling pump, until a level appears in the water gauge. Demineralized water is flushed into the boiler through the feedwater line until the drum level rises. This prevents any chemical from entering the feedwater system.

- Similarly, the superheater should be back flushed with demineralized water until a level increase is observed in the drum. Then the boiler is completely filled using the filling pump until water overflows through the vents #5. This is to ensure the removal of any chemical vapors from the drum.

- The boiler is now drained under nitrogen pressure and the fill and flushing step, is repeated. The boiler is again drained under nitrogen pressure and the pH of the rinse water is tested. If the pH is below 5, the fill and flushing step must be repeated.

- If the pH is satisfactory, then the next step is to neutralize the surfaces. The temporary gauge glass is replaced by the regular drum level gauge and the boiler is filled to slightly below operating level, with a solution of 10 kg of soda ash per 100 kg of water.

- The boiler is fired and boiled out for 4 to 6 hours. For boilers operating at 1400 kPa or less, the boil out pressure is operating pressure. For boilers operating at above 1400 kPa, the boil out pressure is the higher of 1400 kPa, or one half the operating pressure, although it is not necessary to exceed 4200 kPa.

- After the boil out, the boiler is shut down and drained without using nitrogen.

- While the boiler is still hot, it is filled with demineralized water containing 0.5% sodium nitrite (to prevent rusting) until the drum vents overflow. The boiler is drained after one hour. If there is any evidence of loose deposits remaining in the boiler, then the headers and tubes should be thoroughly flushed out.

Figure 6	Chemical Cleaning - Soaking Method

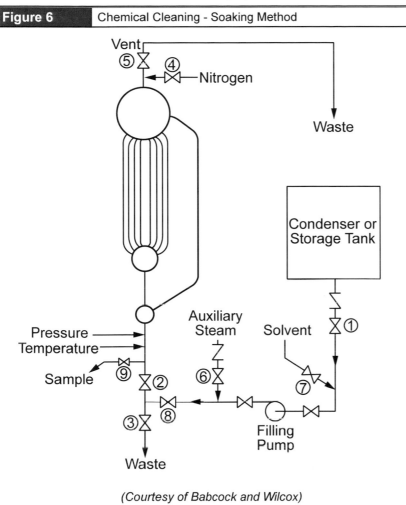

(Courtesy of Babcock and Wilcox)

Due to the careful chemical control required and the potential dangers involved in dealing with corrosive solutions, possible explosive and toxic products of the cleaning process, the chemical cleaning must be supervised by personnel specially qualified in this highly technical field.

A specialty company usually performs the acid cleaning. During the procedure, smoking or bare light bulbs must not be permitted in the vicinity, due to the possibility of hydrogen gas being produced from the chemical reactions. Other safety precautions include protective clothing for personnel, such as goggles, gloves and aprons. After opening the unit for inspection, air should be circulated through to remove any hydrogen gas, which may pass off from the metal. This is done before any personnel are allowed to enter the boiler. All solutions must be neutralized before discharging to sewers, rivers, and lakes.

OBJECTIVE 6

Explain routine tasks and visual monitoring that must be performed by the operator on a large operating boiler.

ROUTINE OPERATION

The main concern of the power engineer is to operate the boiler safely and efficiently. To do this, the boiler water level must be maintained at the correct point and the steam pressure at the required pressure. The furnace must be operated as efficiently as possible to obtain maximum benefit from the fuel.

Heating surfaces must be clean to ensure maximum heat transfer to the water and steam in the boiler. The condition of the water in the boiler is of prime importance. Therefore, the water pretreatment and internal treatment programs must be diligently observed, including correct testing of residuals, injection of chemicals, and maintaining the boiler blowdown schedule.

The boiler auxiliaries, controls and fittings must be regularly checked for proper functioning. These are discussed in the following sections.

Water Level Indicators

In order for the gauge glass to show the correct level, all connections to the gauge glass and the water column, must be blown down to ensure they are clear and free from obstructions. If the gauge glasses are of the flat or round glass mica-protected types, the manufacturer's instructions regarding blowing down, should be followed. Excessive blowing down will damage the glasses, due to corrosion.

If the water column is fitted with high and low water alarms, then their operation is checked as well.

Feed Pumps

Close attention must be paid to the operation of the boiler feed pump with discharge and suction pressures logged. Bearing temperatures should be checked, frequently, and proper lubrication of the pump and its driver must be maintained. The boiler operators must be familiar with the procedure for starting up the standby feed pump and stopping the in service pump. This should be done at regular intervals in order that both pumps have approximately equal time in operation. A supply of feedwater must always be available for the feed pump. Correct operation of the feedwater regulator, or the level control system, must be checked and tested.

Feedwater Supply

In order to avoid scale formation and corrosion in the boiler, the make-up water for the feedwater supply must be properly treated. In addition to this, testing of the boiler water itself must be carried out. This will enable the required amount of chemical treatment to be determined and will help set the continuous blowdown rate. The boiler water is tested regularly.

Combustion Process

The admission of fuel and air to the furnace, in conjunction with boiler load changes, is done by means of an automatic combustion control system. The operator must be familiar with manual operation of the control system, in case of a system failure.

Special attention must be paid to the combustion process that occurs in the furnace. An analysis of the flue gas must be taken regularly to ensure the boiler is firing at the most efficient standard possible. Visual examination of the fire in the furnace is also helpful as the flame color and the amount of smoke or haze are indications of the completeness of combustion.

Fuel burning and draft equipment must be checked for proper operation. Burners must be cleaned, when necessary, and there must be an adequate supply of fuel available at all times. When burning heavy oil, the temperature of the fuel must be maintained at the recommended value. If the fuel burned is pulverized coal, the temperature of the air supplied to the pulverizers must be kept at the recommended value. In the case of natural gas, oil fuel or pulverized coal, care must be taken, at low firing rates, to see that a stable flame is maintained at the burners.

Ash Removal

If coal is the fuel used in the boiler, the removal of ashes will be one of the routine duties of the operator. In smaller and medium sized coal burning plants, dumping grates are often used. These are operated intermittently, as ash builds up and interferes with the airflow. In larger plants, continuous ash discharge is provided by means of travelling grate stokers. With this type, the operator must take care that unburned fuel is not discharged from the end of the grate, together with the ash.

When pulverized coal is burned in the furnace, the ash may be removed in the solid or liquid state from the bottom of the furnace. In some types, molten ash is allowed to run continuously from the furnace into a tank of water.

Whenever ash is being removed, the personnel involved in the operation must wear safety goggles, gloves and other protective clothing.

Where dust collectors are installed, it is important that these be emptied, frequently, otherwise the dust may build up and plug the outlet from the collector. An excessive amount of dust or ash may cause a fire in the collector hopper. Ash and dust removal is carried out at least once a shift and more often, if necessary.

Boiler Blow-Off (Blowdown)

All boilers should be bottom blown, at least once a day. This is done to remove sludge that has accumulated in the bottom drum. The proper procedure must be used to blowdown the boiler.

Additional Duties

In addition to the items discussed in the previous sections, the operator should make a general inspection of the entire plant every two hours.

Any changes to any part of the plant should be entered on a log sheet or in a log book. Any usual or unusual occurrence must also be logged clearly.

OBJECTIVE 7

Explain the procedures and precautions that an operator must exercise to avoid furnace and pressure-side explosions.

BOILER EXPLOSIONS

Boiler or furnace explosions could result in injury to personnel, expensive repairs and loss of production. If an explosion does occur, then the person in charge of the boiler or pressure vessel must notify the proper authorities. Boiler explosions can be considered under two general classifications:

- Furnace explosions, which occur when an accumulation of combustible gases ignite and explode within the furnace, or gas passes of the boiler.
- Pressure explosions, which occur when a pressure part of the boiler, such as the steam drum, fails due to steam pressure, or a structural weakening of the metal.

Causes of Furnace Explosions

The most common causes of furnace explosions are as follows:

- Failure to purge the furnace adequately before start-up. There may be an accumulation of combustible gases within the furnace of an idle boiler and, when an attempt is made to light a burner in the furnace, this gas could explode unless the furnace has been thoroughly purged.
- Admission of fuel to main burner before pilot flame or other ignition source is established. This will result in a flow of raw fuel into the furnace, which could explode when ignition is provided.
- The main flame in the furnace may get blown out. This could be caused by a momentary interruption of fuel or air supply, or the burner flame may be blown out by a higher than normal air flow particularly if the furnace is still cold. Another cause of flame interruption could be some water in the fuel, as in the case of oil or gas.
- Attempting to light one burner off other burners, in operation. This causes a concentration of fuel adjacent to the burner, which will ignite from the other burner flames and could result in an explosion.
- Incorrect amount of air supplied to the burner can resulting in incomplete combustion. This will also result in an accumulation of combustibles within the furnace and a possible explosion.

Prevention of Furnace Explosions

Furnace explosions may be prevented by:

- Instructing all employees on the proper lighting procedures and the minimum stable loads.
- Maintaining efficient igniters and pilots.
- Setting a limit on the number of ignition trials.
- Purging the furnace with at least 50% of the fan capacity, for five minutes after each ignition attempt.
- Ensure that all combustion controls and auxiliaries have been checked and are ready for service.
- Ensure all interlocks for the combustion control system are working properly.
- Routinely verify that all flow indicators are working properly to avoid an accumulation of combustibles in the furnace.
- Keep the fuel gas supply lines purged of water and all other contaminants.

Causes of Pressure Explosions

A failure of a pressure part of the boiler may be due to any of the following:

- Pressure in excess of that for which the boiler was designed. This occurs if the safety valves fails to operate and the firing rate was greater than that required by the boiler load.
- Weakening of the material to an extent that the pressure part fails, at normal working pressure. This may be due to any, or all, of the following:
    a) Overstressing of material due to too rapid heating up of the boiler during start-up.
    b) Overheating of the material due to low water level in the boiler.
    c) Overheating of the material due to build up of scale, sludge, or oil on the heating surfaces.
    d) Overheating of the material due to faulty water circulation within the boiler.
    e) Weakening of the material due to corrosion.

Prevention of Pressure Explosions

Pressure explosions may be prevented by:

- Testing safety valves on a regular basis.
- Following proper boiler start-up procedures.
- Ensuring all operating personnel are familiar with boiler operating procedures, routine and emergency.
- Follow all recommended water treatment guidelines for your particular operation.
- Ensuring proper positioning of all sootblowers. This should be done during the boiler commissioning stage.

OBJECTIVE 8

Describe sootblowing systems and describe the procedures for operating sootblowers.

SOOTBLOWERS

During the operation of some boilers (particularly coal fired and some oil fired boilers) the heating surfaces exposed to the combustion gases become coated with soot and ash. The soot and ash act as an insulator, which reduces the heat transfer through the surfaces. This lowers both the efficiency and capacity of the boiler. The deposits may also obstruct the passage of the combustion gases, which in turn increases the power requirements for the draft fan.

The most common method for removing soot and ash deposits is to blast them with jets of steam or compressed air from stationary or movable sootblowers. These sootblowers are located at various points within the path of the flue gas. Depending on the application, they may be of the fixed or retractable type.

Sootblowers located in the high temperature zones of the boiler, such as the furnace walls and secondary superheater and reheater sections, are the retractable type. This allows the sootblowers to be withdrawn from the boiler when not in use, thus protecting them from the high temperatures.

Figure 7 shows a type of retractable soot blower. It consists of a short-stroke lance that penetrates the wall by 3 to 5 cm. The sootblower, supported by wall boxes welded to the furnace tubes, move up and down with the tubes as they heat and cool. A single nozzle at the tip directs a jet of superheated steam or compressed air at the tube face to dislodge the deposit. The lance rotates through 360° and cleans a radius of approximately 1.5 metres.

Figure 7	Typical Retractable Furnace Wall Sootblower

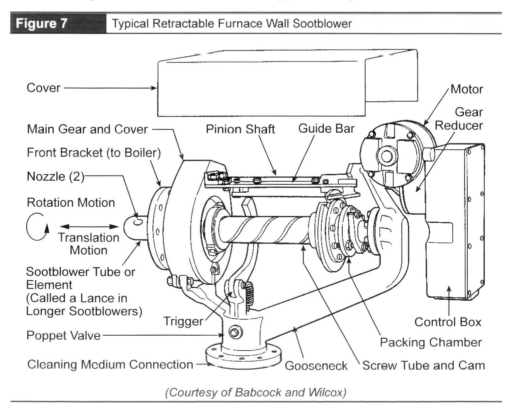

(Courtesy of Babcock and Wilcox)

Figure 8 is a diagram of the soot-blower arrangement in a large coal fired boiler.

The long retractable sootblowers are located in the convection section, which contains the superheater, reheater and economizer banks of coils. The wall sootblowers are located in the radiant section of the boiler.

Figure 8	Retractable Sootblowers Locations

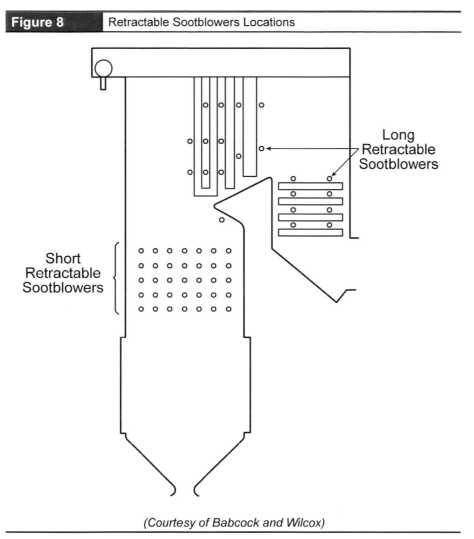

Long Retractable Sootblowers

Short Retractable Sootblowers

(Courtesy of Babcock and Wilcox)

It is important that soot blowers be adjusted so that they do not impinge directly upon tubes or baffles, otherwise erosion of these parts will occur. Erosion will be accelerated if the blowing medium contains any moisture. If the blowing medium is air, it must be dry. If steam, it must be dry and preferably superheated.

The factors that determine when the sootblowers should be operated include:

- High draft losses
- Low superheater steam outlet temperature
- High furnace gas outlet temperature

These indicate that the various banks of boiler tubes are becoming coated with soot, thus reducing their heat transfer capability.

Figure 9 shows a long retractable sootblower used on a chemical recovery boiler. A lance, containing a series of cleaning nozzles, extends into the boiler to clean the various banks of tubes. This design has a travel range of 1 to 17 metres.

Figure 9	Long Retractable Sootblower

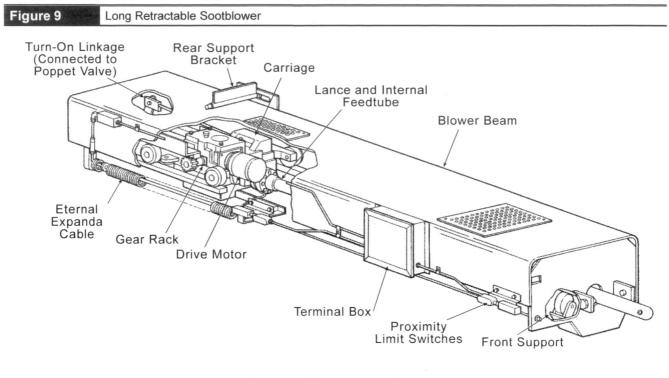

(Courtesy of Babcock and Wilcox)

Figure 10 shows a type of fixed, non-retractable sootblower that is used to remove dusty or lightly sintered ash from tube banks or duct systems. The fixed type is usually more economical to install and operate than the retractable type, but can only be used where lower gas temperature area permit and where high mass energy from large nozzles is not required. Nozzle sizes range from 6 mm to 10 mm, in diameter.

Figure 10	Nonretractable Type Sootblower

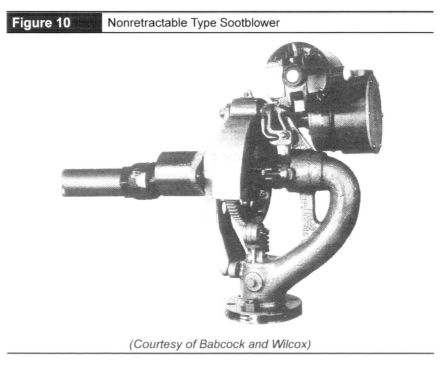

(Courtesy of Babcock and Wilcox)

Sootblower Operation

The following is a procedure for a manual soot-blowing operation:

- Ensure that the boiler load is at 50% capacity or higher. This ensures sufficient flue gas flow to allow the dust particles, which can form an explosive mixture, to be rapidly removed from the furnace.
- Increase induced draft until the furnace pressure is approximately 7 mm water gauge above the normal value. Then close the isolating cocks on furnace draft indicators and CO_2 sampling points.
- Clear all dust and ash hoppers.
- Crack open the drain valve on the main steam supply header to remove any condensate.
- Crack open the main-steam supply header isolation valve.
- When all the water has been discharged from the main steam supply header, close the drain valve and fully open the isolation valve.
- Close all the boiler inspection windows.
- Operate each sootblower individually, commencing with those nearest the bottom of the furnace and working systematically towards the rear of the boiler.
- Make sure that the retractable sootblowers are fully traversed into the gas pass (or furnace) before opening the steam stop valve. Also ensure they are fully withdrawn immediately after use.
- Do not allow steam to discharge from retractable sootblowers except when fully advanced in their blowing positions.
- Do not allow rotating or traversing sootblowers to remain in one position while discharging steam. Their motion should be slow, but continuous.
- When the soot blowing cycle has been completed, close the main steam header isolation valve.
- Maintain induced draft until the normal furnace draft conditions, are established.
- Clear all dust and ash hoppers.
- Open isolating cocks for draft and CO_2.

Soot blowing on steam generators is usually controlled remotely by the control room operator. The unit operator's responsibility is to visually observe the operation of the soot blowers and report any problems.

CHAPTER 9 - QUESTIONS

1. a) What is the purpose of a hydrostatic test on a boiler?

   b) Describe in detail how to prepare a new boiler for a hydrostatic test, and how you would carry out this test.

2. Describe briefly the purpose and the procedure for the following:

   a) Drying out.

   b) Boiling out.

3. Describe the wet and dry methods of laying up a boiler and list advantages and disadvantages of each.

4. Describe how to properly shut down a boiler, isolate and prepare it, for an internal inspection.

5. Describe a waterside side inspection of a boiler.

6. Describe mechanical cleaning of the waterside of a boiler.

7. Discuss the following:

   a) List two methods used to chemically clean the waterside of a boiler.

   b) What are the advantages of chemically cleaning the waterside of a boiler compared to mechanical cleaning?

   c) Describe one of the methods used to chemically clean the waterside of a boiler.

8. Make a list of the routine duties that a Power Engineer should carry out when on shift.

9. List four causes of a boiler furnace explosion.

10. What are some reasons why a pressure explosion may occur at normal operating pressures?

11. What precautions are necessary when using sootblowers?

ANSWERS: All answers are found within the content of the chapter.

Internal Water Treatment for Boilers

LEARNING OUTCOME

When you complete this chapter you should be able to:

Discuss internal water treatment methods and systems for the control of scale, corrosion, and carryover and explain testing and monitoring strategies.

LEARNING OBJECTIVES

Here is what you should be able to do when you complete each objective:

1. Explain the causes and effects of boiler scale; explain the most common internal methods of scale control, including phosphate treatment, chelate treatment, sludge conditioning and dispersion.

2. Explain the causes and effects of boiler and condensate return line corrosion; explain treatment methods for acidic, caustic, oxygen, and carbon dioxide corrosion, including sulphite, hydrazine, and amine treatment.

3. Explain the mechanical and chemical causes, effects and types of carryover; explain methods of carryover control, including the use of antifoam and blowdown.

4. Describe the design and explain the operation of simple blowdown, heat recovery, and automatic blowdown systems.

5. Explain, in general terms, the sampling and testing strategies for boiler internal conditions; describe typical sampling and automatic monitoring equipment.

6. Describe typical chemical feed systems, including pot feeders, continuous feed with day tanks, and continuous feed with pump tanks.

OBJECTIVE 1

Explain the causes and effects of boiler scale; explain the most common internal methods of scale control, including phosphate treatment, chelate treatment, sludge conditioning and dispersion.

CAUSES OF BOILER SCALE

Boiler scale is a relatively hard layer of mineral deposit that forms on the water side of boiler metal. Scale formation usually occurs in the hotter areas of the boiler, particularly in the steam generating sections, but is not restricted to these areas. Most susceptible are the generating tubes, including those in the generating banks of risers and in the waterwall sections of watertube boilers.

Firetube boilers are not exempt, since scale can form on the water side of the firetubes and of the internal combustion chamber.

The primary **cause** of boiler scale is the presence of undesirable minerals in the boiler water. The chief culprits are calcium and magnesium, since they generally exist in relatively large quantities, compared to other Impurities, and they deposit quite readily from the water. Other deposits of concern include iron, copper, aluminum and silica.

EFFECTS OF BOILER SCALE

A porous scale forms on the waterside of heating surfaces when the water boils, leaving mineral deposits behind. The chief **effects** of this scale deposition are as follows:

a) Scale restricts heat transfer and causes metal to overheat:

On the water side of a heating surface the scale acts as an insulator that restricts the transfer of heat from the furnace or combustion gases to the water. This results in a reduction in the cooling effect that the water has on the metal, causing the temperature of the metal to increase.

If the scale is allowed to progressively thicken, the metal temperature may become high enough to reduce the strength of metal. This can weaken the metal to the point that it can no longer withstand the internal pressure of the boiler. At this point, rupture of the metal will likely occur.

b) Scale traps water beneath it and encourages corrosion:

When scale forms, there may be voids or pockets created between the scale and the tube surface. Water can be trapped in these pockets and when this trapped water boils, steam escapes and the remaining water becomes highly concentrated and often has a high pH. This can lead to a condition called **caustic gouging** or **underdeposit corrosion**, which is possible in all boilers, but more frequently in high-pressure boilers.

Scale-induced corrosion is visually undetectable and can cause sufficient loss of metal to eventually result in tube failure.

c) Scale sloughs off and causes flow restrictions:

When a boiler is shut down and restarted, the extreme temperature changes in the metal can cause some of the scale to fall, or slough, off and drop to the bottom of the tubes or headers. After several such occurrences, significant piles of scale can accumulate in low spots, such as horizontal waterwall headers, and restrict the flow of water through some of the tubes.

Restricted water flow reduces the cooling in a tube and, if restriction is sufficient or if it persists for a long time, the tube may become overheated and weakened to the point of rupture.

INTERNAL METHODS FOR CONTROLLING BOILER SCALE

The first line of attack in preventing boiler scale is to remove the scale-forming minerals before they enter the boiler, through various pre-treatment systems. However, such systems are not 100% efficient, so the remainder of treatment must occur internally (that is, within the boiler itself).

There are two main methods, or strategies, used to control scale formation through internal treatment of boiler water.

The first method involves precipitating the scale-forming solids from the water, by chemical means, and then discharging them from the boiler. This program uses **phosphate** as the primary treatment chemical and is useful in all boilers, regardless of operating pressure. The basic steps in this method include:

a) Through chemical reaction the scale-forming minerals remain in solution, but as less harmful solids. These solids are kept suspended in the boiler water and do not deposit on the metal surfaces. In this form the impurities are commonly referred to as **suspended solids**.

b) These suspended solids will not stick to the boiler metal, leaving them free to fall to the bottom of the boiler water space (usually into the mud drum) or to remain dispersed throughout the water.

c) Finally, remove these excess suspended solids from the boiler by **blowdown**.

The second common method involves the use of a special chemical, called a chelate, which reacts with the scale-forming minerals and actually prevents them from coming out of solution with the boiler water. This method is used only on boilers that operate below 4000 kPa.

Phosphate Treatment

When sodium phosphate compounds are injected into boiler water, they react chemically with the calcium and magnesium compounds that are already in the water. These reactions cause the calcium and magnesium carbonates to combine with the phosphate and to precipitate out (that is, fall out) of solution.

Calcium and magnesium phosphates are produced by the reactions and these compounds are virtually insoluble in water, so they come out of solution. Sodium carbonate is also produced, but it does not form a hard scale and can be removed by **blowdown**.

The most common chemicals used are **orthophosphates**, including monosodium, disodium, and **trisodium phosphates** (so named because of the number of Na ions in the chemical) and more complex polyphosphates. In all cases, upon entering the boiler water, the chemical converts to trisodium phosphate (Na_3PO_4) and then enters into a reaction with calcium and magnesium. Simple examples of such reactions are as follows:

Reaction 1

$$3CaCO_3 \quad + \quad 2Na_3PO_4 \quad \rightarrow \quad Ca_3(PO_4)_2 \quad + \quad 3Na_2CO_3$$

calcium	trisodium	tricalcium	sodium
carbonate	phosphate	phosphate	carbonate

Reaction 2

$$3MgCO_3 \quad + \quad 2Na_3PO_4 \quad \rightarrow \quad Mg_3(PO_4)_2 \quad + \quad 3Na_2CO_3$$

magnesium	trisodium	trimagnesium	sodium
carbonate	phosphate	phosphate	carbonate

Note: Reaction 2 is actually an undesirable reaction, since magnesium phosphate is a very sticky, adherent precipitate. However, if silica is also present in the water, the magnesium usually precipitates as magnesium silicate, which is much less sticky.

The success of a phosphate program depends on the **alkalinity** of the boiler water being sufficiently high. Best results are obtained when the pH is between 11.0 and 12.0. Below a pH of 9.5 the calcium will not precipitate efficiently. Sufficient alkalinity can be obtained by having feedwater that contains alkalinity and/or by adding caustic soda (sodium hydroxide) to the boiler water, if necessary. The reaction that occurs with sodium hydroxide is as follows:

Reaction 3

$$MgCO_3 \quad + \quad 2NaOH \quad \rightarrow \quad Mg(OH)_2 \quad + \quad Na_2CO_3$$

magnesium	sodium	magnesium	sodium
carbonate	hydroxide	hydroxide	carbonate

The presence of sodium hydroxide in the water is preferred because the magnesium hydroxide precipitate is much less sticky than the magnesium phosphate precipitate. Also, if hydroxide is present, the precipitate formed in Reaction 1 above will actually become a mixed phosphate/hydroxide compound, $Ca_{10}(OH)_2(PO_4)_6$, which is also much less sticky than the tricalcium phosphate shown.

Phosphate is controlled in a boiler by injecting sufficient chemical to maintain a slight residual of excess phosphate. As long as the excess exists there is virtually no chance of scale formation since the excess suggests that all calcium and magnesium have been reacted with. The excess must be kept to a minimum, however, since large excesses will, over time, create a phosphate sludge or soft scale in the boiler.

If a loss of a phosphate residual occurs in the boiler, there will be an opportunity for scale to begin forming. The loss of residual may occur due to underfeeding phosphate chemical, a sudden breakthrough of excess hardness from the pretreatment system, or contamination in the condensate return system.

Chelate Treatment

Chelate treatment uses chemicals, called **chelants** (or chelating agents), to hold scale-forming impurities in solution, not allowing them to precipitate out of the boiler water. It could be considered the opposite of phosphate treatment, which relies on precipitation.

The principle by which chelants act is often called **solubilization**. Calcium and magnesium hardness, plus iron, are kept soluble in the water and thus prevented from forming scale and sludge.

Chelants are weak, organic acids, which have been neutralized into sodium-based salts (compounds which contain sodium). The two most common chelating agents are:

EDTA is a tetrasodium salt of ethylenediaminetetraacetic acid. NTA is a trisodium salt of nitrilotriacetic acid.

When chelants enter the boiler water, they hydrolyze into strong organic ions. These ions then attract the ions of calcium, magnesium and iron that already exist in the water. In this way, the chelant absorbs these ions into itself. Once absorbed, the calcium, magnesium and iron will no longer form a deposit and can be removed from the boiler by blowdown.

Advantages & Disadvantages of Chelate Treatment

One advantage of chelants is that they can be used to remove existing scale from a boiler without removing the boiler from service, although this practice is discouraged for heavily scaled boilers. If a carefully controlled amount of excess chelant is injected, the chemical will absorb calcium, magnesium and iron, not only from the water, but also from the existing scale. Great care must be taken to not remove scale too quickly as it can lead to sloughing and collecting of the sludge into locations that can restrict water circulation.

Extreme overfeeding of chelant can result in the loss of protective magnetite layers on the boiler metal and, in even more extreme cases, can result in corrosion of boiler metal. If the free chelate in the water is in excess of about 100 ppm, metal attack can occur.

By comparison to conventional phosphate treatment, chelants require closer control, due to the potential corrosion hazard. Complete oxygen removal is mandatory, since oxygen seriously hampers the effectiveness of chelation.

Chelant feed systems must also be designed with non-corrosive materials, usually stainless steel, for tanks, injection pumps, lines, and nozzles.

Chelates are more expensive and may be uneconomical if the feedwater hardness exceeds 2 ppm. However, chelants do remove metal ions and have the ability to remove existing scale. The latter may save the considerable cost of boiler downtime and off-line cleaning.

Chelates are also more forgiving with changing feedwater conditions and can handle sudden hardness breakthroughs either directly or by subsequent absorption of resulting scale.

Sludge Conditioning & Dispersion

The sludge (or precipitate) that is produced in the precipitation reactions must be conditioned so it will stay well dispersed and will not adhere to the boiler surfaces. This is accomplished by using special chemicals, **called sludge conditioners** or **dispersants**. These chemicals are injected into the boiler water, either separately or in mixture with the other treatment chemicals.

Modern sludge conditioners consist of synthetic **polymers**, the most common being sulphonated and carboxylated polymers. A polymer is a substance that contains large molecules, formed by the joining of several smaller molecules into chain-like structures. The polymer contains an ionic, negative charge, which has the ability to attract positively charged ions from the water.

When a polymeric dispersant is added to boiler water, it attracts the particles of suspended sludge, due to a weak positive charge that exists on the surface of the sludge. In this way the sludge particles are prevented from attracting to each other to form larger particles and from attracting to the metal surfaces of the boiler. This causes them to remain dispersed in the water and to then be discharged through boiler blowoff.

Polymers also have the ability to condition the sludge by changing its structure in such a way that is becomes more crystalline. This results in the sludge being much less sticky and having much less ability to adhere to boiler surfaces.

A good chelate program uses a dispersant that is designed specifically for **iron**. Also, since precipitation of scale-forming ions does not occur in a chelate program, the suspended solids in the boiler are reduced. Therefore, the polymers will be more effective in keeping iron and copper in suspension because there is very little, if any, calcium and magnesium sludge being generated and the polymer can concentrate more on other suspended solids, like the iron and copper.

OBJECTIVE 2

Explain the causes and effects of boiler and condensate return line corrosion; explain treatment methods for acidic, caustic, oxygen, and carbon dioxide corrosion, including sulphite, hydrazine and amine treatment.

CAUSES & EFFECTS OF BOILER SYSTEM CORROSION

Corrosion is the loss of metal due to chemical interaction between the metal, the water and certain impurities in the water. More specifically, it is the loss of iron from the metal, which produces two undesirable effects.

- It thins and weakens the boiler metal, often to the point where internal pressure cannot be contained and rupture occurs.
- It results in the re-deposition of the iron onto metal surfaces in hotter areas of the boiler, which can result in restriction of heat transfer and overheating of the boiler metal.

Two Areas of Concern

When speaking of corrosion in a **boiler system** it is necessary to consider two main areas:

- The primary area of concern is inside the boiler itself where both of the above effects can occur with disastrous consequences.
- The second area of concern is the condensate system, which returns condensate to the boiler as feedwater. Corrosion here not only weakens the condensate piping, but also results in iron being transported into the boiler where it can then be deposited as harmful scale.

There is one **desirable corrosion** activity in a boiler, which is the formation of a protective **magnetite layer** on the boiler surfaces.

Boiler Magnetite Layer Formation

There is a natural corrosion reaction that occurs between water and mild steel, even without the presence of other corrosion factors. On new, freshly cleaned or exposed boiler metal this reaction takes iron from the metal and creates a very thin layer of **magnetite**, which becomes a protective layer against other corrosion. The forming reaction allows this layer to reach a sufficient thickness (approximately 15 to 100 microns (0.015 to 0.010 mm), at which point the water can no longer react with the boiler metal. However, since the magnetite layer is composed of iron it is itself susceptible to corrosion from other sources. The magnetite layer is formed by the following reaction.

$$3Fe \quad + \quad 4H_2O \quad \longrightarrow \quad Fe_3O_4 \quad + \quad 4H_2$$

Iron Water $\longrightarrow$ Magnetite Hydrogen

Four Proponents of Corrosion

There are four main proponents of corrosion in a boiler system. These include:

1. Low boiler water pH (acid corrosion)
2. High boiler water pH (caustic corrosion)
3. Oxygen corrosion
4. Carbon Dioxide corrosion

1. Low Boiler Water pH (Acidic Corrosion)

Boiler water is generally corrosive to metal when the pH is outside the range of 8.5 to 12.7. When the pH is less than 8.5 acidic corrosion can occur and this corrosion is accelerated as the pH gets lower.

Low pH is commonly referred to as **acidity**. Acids are known to be very corrosive to most materials, including metals. In a boiler, continuous operation at low pH can result first in loss of the magnetite layer and then in a general thinning of the metal and/or localized thinning in areas of high stress.

During normal operation, low pH may occur when the feedwater (particularly the returning condensate) becomes contaminated with process substances of low pH. Another cause may be improper operation of pretreatment demineralizers, which use acid as a regenerant, allowing low pH water into the boiler.

Prevention of low pH is best achieved by carefully monitoring the pH of make-up water and condensate returns to detect and correct any contamination. The boiler water itself must also be monitored for pH. If other means of correction are not effective and the pH level is persistently low or experiences a temporary low excursion, a caustic solution may be injected to raise the pH. In some cases, lower pressure boilers may require a continuous, controlled feed of caustic.

2. High Boiler Water pH (Caustic Corrosion)

The opposite of acidity is alkalinity. A high boiler water alkalinity, above a pH of 12.7, can be very corrosive to boiler metal. Since alkalinity is generally a result of caustic substances (that is, sodium hydroxide, NaOH) in the water, this type of corrosion is also called **caustic corrosion**. It takes the form of deep, irregular, localized gouges in the metal surface.

In high-pressure boilers, caustic corrosion can occur in two main ways:

- General (that is, wide-spread) corrosion may occur throughout the boiler due to caustic entering with the treated water from a demineralization system. A common contaminant from the demineralizer process is sodium hydroxide (caustic).

- A more frequent cause is the accumulation of caustic between scale or iron deposits and the boiler surface. When boiler water, containing caustic, flows into voids beneath the scale, it encounters high heat and vaporizes into steam. The steam leaves the void and is replaced by water and this continuous process results in a high concentration of caustic beneath the scale. The caustic dissolves the magnetite layer. With the protective layer gone, the boiler water reacts with the boiler metal to restore the layer, taking iron from the metal to do so.

Preventing Caustic Corrosion

In lower pressure boilers caustic corrosion is rare and can best be prevented by a good scale prevention program, such as phosphate or chelate, which eliminates the ability of the caustic to concentrate.

In more critical, high-pressure boilers the most common internal treatment, in addition to scale prevention, involves the use of a phosphate program. There are three such programs, called **coordinated phosphate**, **congruent phosphate** and **equilibrium phosphate**.

Coordinated Phosphate Program

This program involves the injection of disodium phosphate, which reacts with the caustic (NaOH) in the water to produce trisodium phosphate and to simultaneously control the pH. The simple form of this reaction is as follows.

$$Na_2HPO_4 \quad + \quad NaOH \quad \rightarrow \quad Na_3PO_4 \quad + \quad H_2O$$

| disodium phosphate | sodium hydroxide | trisodium phosphate | water |

The key to this program is to keep the ratio of sodium to phosphate (that is, Na/PO_4) in the boiler water at 3.0. This prevents the formation of free sodium hydroxide (NaOH) in the water.

Congruent Phosphate Program

This is an improvement over the coordinated phosphate program because it further reduces the risk of free caustic (NaOH) in the boiler water. In this program the Na/PO_3 ratio is kept lower, at less than 2.6. The ratio is usually increased by adding caustic soda (sodium hydroxide, NaOH) or trisodium phosphate (Na_3PO_4) and the ratio is decreased by adding disodium phosphate.

A serious problem that can occur with this program is the **hideout** of phosphate. In larger boilers with tube areas subjected to high heat, and perhaps reduced circulation, some of the phosphate may actually precipitate out of the boiler water and "hide out" on the tube surfaces. During load changes this precipitate may then go back into solution, causing confusion in the control of the phosphate program and causing spikes in NaOH. In effect the phosphate program has caused an opportunity for corrosion in some boilers.

In both the coordinated and the congruent phosphate programs there is a tendency to inject more phosphate chemical into the boiler than is necessary, thus maintaining a residual amount that can be determined by testing. It is difficult to maintain steady conditions when boiler load changes.

Equilibrium Phosphate Program:

This program operates with a phosphate concentration at which the phosphate, the pH and the Na/PO_4 ratio will remain stable even when the load on the boiler changes. It requires determination, by testing, of the "perfect" amount of phosphate to be injected to a particular boiler under operating conditions (no two boilers may be exactly alike). From this the optimum residuals of phosphate can be determined, at which the problems of phosphate hideout and excess NaOH will not occur, regardless of boiler load.

Note: The use of phosphate to control pH is not to be confused with the use of phosphate to control scale formation. In low pressure boilers the primary purpose of injecting phosphate is for scale control; in high pressure boilers that use demineralized water the primary purpose is pH control. They are two separate programs.

Caustic Embrittlement

Caustic embrittlement is a form of caustic corrosion. This form of corrosion has become less common, with improvements in the control of free caustic in boiler water. It occurs when the caustic in the water accumulates at a boiler leak, in an area of high metal stress. The leak creates a build-up of caustic, which reacts with the highly stressed metal, changing the crystalline structure of the metal and making it brittle. In this state the metal is severely weakened and unable to withstand the pressure, often leading to sudden rupture or cracking.

In order for embrittlement to occur, three conditions must exist:

- a mechanism to concentrate the boiler water (such as a leak) must be present
- the boiler metal must be under high stress
- the boiler water must have an embrittling characteristic (that is, a high concentration of free sodium hydroxide)

Embrittlement locations included rivets, tube sheets, any boiler part subject to stress and leakage, even external leaks such as gauge glasses and columns. The treatment to prevent embrittlement is to maintain water that is relatively free of caustic (NaOH), such as in a phosphate program. In low-pressure boilers, sodium nitrate may be injected to combat embrittlement.

3. Oxygen Corrosion

When oxygen is present in hot water, even in very small concentrations, it is extremely corrosive to any surrounding metal. The maximum acceptable concentration of oxygen in boiler water is in the range of 5 to 7 ppb (parts per billion).

In a boiler system, oxygen may be introduced through make-up water, through leakage into condensate return pumps, and leaking cooling or sealing water on transfer pumps. If the oxygen is allowed to get past the pretreatment deaeration equipment and reach the boiler, much of it will be released with the steam, but some of it will directly attack the boiler metal.

The most vulnerable spots are the feedwater injection pipe, the steam drum (particularly at the water level), and the downcomers. If the boiler has an economizer, the majority of corrosion will usually occur in the economizer tubes, since this is the first area of exposure to increased temperature. Oxygen that gets through the boiler and exits with the steam then becomes very corrosive to the condensate system or anywhere that the steam condenses.

Oxygen corrosion takes the form of small, but potentially deep **pits** in the metal. The pattern of pitting may be quite random, and can cover a very localized area or a wide area. In either case, oxygen pitting can progress very rapidly and result in rapid failure of the metal.

The corrosion reactions are complex and electrochemical in nature. The reaction involves the combination of oxygen with iron to produce iron oxides. This chemical removal of iron from the boiler surface is oxygen corrosion.

$$\text{Fe} \quad + \quad \tfrac{1}{2}\,O_2 \quad + \quad H_2O \quad \rightarrow \quad Fe(OH)_2$$

Iron   oxygen   water   iron hydroxide

Preventing Oxygen Corrosion

Internal treatment for oxygen involves the addition of a chemical to the boiler water, which reacts with the free oxygen and eliminates it from the water. The chemical is added upstream of the boiler, usually in the storage area of the deaerator or at the suction of the feedwater pumps. This allows protection of the feedwater piping and the economizer.

The chemical most commonly used is sodium sulphite. It reacts with oxygen to produce sodium sulphate, which can then be removed from the boiler by blowdown. The basic chemical reaction is as follows:

$$2Na_2SO_3 \quad + \quad O_2 \quad \rightarrow \quad 2Na_2SO_4$$

sodium   oxygen   sodium
sulphite   sulphate

The sulphite is fed continuously to the feedwater in quantities sufficient to maintain a specified residual of sulphite in the boiler water. Usually a sulphite residual of 10-15 ppm is sufficient to handle any swings in the amount of oxygen entering the boiler.

There are two disadvantages of the sodium suphite program:

- First is the formation of the sulphate, which increases the dissolved solids in the water. This necessitates additional boiler blowdown.
- Second, in boilers (over 6000 kPa) with a sulphite residual greater than 15 ppm, the sulphate can further break down into sulphur dioxide and hydrogen sulphide. These will carry over with the steam and contribute to condensate return line corrosion.

An **alternate method** of oxygen removal is the injection of chemicals, other than sulphite, commonly referred to as **oxygen scavengers**. These are volatile chemicals, which means they partially vaporize due to the heat. One advantage, in addition to the chemical reaction in the boiler, the vaporized chemical carries over with the steam and provides some corrosion protection for condensate return lines. Another advantage is the oxygen scavenger does not add to the dissolved solids in the boiler. One such chemical, although it is no longer popular due to its toxic properties, is **hydrazine**. The following reaction occurs for hydrazine.

$$N_2H_4 \quad + \quad O_2 \quad \rightarrow \quad H_2O \quad + \quad N_2$$

hydrazine   oxygen   water   nitrogen

Hydrazine has largely been replaced with other organic scavengers, which work in similar ways and have similar advantages.

4. Carbon Dioxide Corrosion

Carbon dioxide is created inside a boiler when the carbonate and bicarbonate impurities in the water decompose and carry out with the steam as carbon dioxide. Inside the boiler itself the carbon dioxide is not a problem, but when the steam condenses in the external condensate system the CO_2 combines with condensate to produce **carbonic acid**. The acid attacks metal in a generalized corrosion pattern, identified by grooves in the metal.

Preventing Carbon Dioxide Corrosion

There are two effective methods for preventing CO_2 corrosion. Both involve the injection of volatile chemicals into the boiler water. The chemicals vaporize, carry out with the steam and then condense wherever the steam condenses. One group of chemicals acts to chemically neutralize the acidity of carbonic acid, while the other group creates a protective film on the surface of the metal.

Neutralizing Amines are amine-based chemicals that have the ability to react with and neutralize acidity. The most common amines are morpholine, cyclohexylamine, diethylaminoethanol (DEAE) and dimethylpropanolamine (DMPA). The amount of chemical injected into the boiler water is usually adjusted to raise and maintain the pH of the returning condensate above 8.0 (usually in a range of 8.0 to 9.0). This is an indication that sufficient neutralization is occurring.

Neutralizing amines are not effective against oxygen corrosion (pitting) in return lines. Also, if boiler make-up water has a high 'M' alkalinity (carbonates and bicarbonates) the corresponding quantity of neutralizing amine that is required may be very expensive.

Note: Ammonia is an alternative chemical for CO_2 neutralization. However, its use is restricted since it is corrosive to copper and zinc in condensate systems.

Filming Amines provide corrosion protection by establishing a continuous, physical barrier between the metal and the corrosive condensate. This barrier consists of a thin chemical film that bonds to the metal surface. Some common filming amines include octadecylamine, hexadecylamine and dioctadecylamine.

Filming amines protect against oxygen corrosion as well as CO_2 corrosion. They can be injected at a fixed feed rate, independent of the amount of 'M' alkalinity in the feedwater. Fixed feed rate makes a filming program generally less expensive than a neutralizing program.

In practice, it is quite common to inject a combination of both neutralizing and filming amines, thus affording dual protection against corrosion. This may be two separate chemicals or a blend of amines into one chemical that has both filming and neutralizing capabilities.

OBJECTIVE 3

Explain the mechanical and chemical causes, effects and types of carryover; explain methods of carryover control, including the use of antifoam and blowdown.

WHAT IS CARRYOVER?

Carryover can be defined as any solid, liquid or vaporous contaminants that leave the boiler with the steam. The steam carries these contaminants out of the boiler steam drum(s).

The term **steam purity** is often used in reference to carryover, such that steam with high purity contains very little carryover. It is virtually impossible to obtain zero carryover (that is, 100% pure steam), but it must be minimized due to its harmful effects on boiler and external equipment.

EFFECTS OF CARRYOVER

When boiler water carries over with the steam it takes with it any **dissolved** or **suspended solids**, which are contained in it. When the water contacts heating surfaces or other surfaces in piping and equipment external to the boiler the solids will tend to deposit out of the water. This creates problems in several key areas, as follows:

- If the boiler has a superheater, the entrained water will be heated and some of it will boil while passing through the superheater. Solids will deposit from the water onto the superheater tubes and a scale will form that restricts heat transfer. The tubes may overheat, be weakened and may eventually rupture. Corrosion activity may also develop under the scale, causing metal loss and eventual tube failure.
- Steam turbine blades will become fouled as solids in the water deposit on them. **Silica** is particularly harmful as it forms a very hard deposit on turbine blades. Water may cause erosion of turbine blades. This will result in turbine imbalance and loss of efficiency and capacity. Deposits may also affect the operation of governor and stop valves.
- Large slugs of water may cause thermal shock on piping and equipment, with subsequent damage.
- Loss of production may occur due to downtime for carryover repairs.

CAUSES OF CARRYOVER

The causes of carryover can be divided into two broad categories, mechanical and chemical.

Mechanical Causes include the following:

- Poorly designed steam drum internals, with inefficient steam/water separation components and/or insufficient steam space to allow for adequate separation time.
- Operating with an excessively high water level, so that steam space and separation time are reduced.
- Operating at higher than design steam rates so that steam production and velocities are increased.
- **Priming**, is a sudden slug of water entrained with the steam, due to a sudden, drastic increase in the firing rate of a boiler. The increase causes the boiler water level to swell and the steam flow to increase. The combined effect "lifts" slugs of water out with the steam. Drum separators are not designed for such slugs.
- **Misting**, is a fog-like mist caused by tiny water particles being thrown off by the water as steam bubbles burst on the surface.

Chemical Cause is primarily due to one thing:

- **Foaming**, which is a condition characterized by the formation of bubbles (ie. foam or froth) on the surface of the boiler water. The foam is lighter than water and is easily carried by the steam, through the separators and scrubbers, out of the boiler.

  Boiler water conditions that contribute to foaming include the presence of highly organic substances and the presence of a high concentration of dissolved and suspended solids. The organic substances, such as oil, combine with the alkalinity in the boiler water to produce a soap-like substance. The solids strengthen the steam bubbles at the surface of the water, preventing them from bursting, and causing them to accumulate as foam. Besides contributing to carryover, this foam can cause inaccurate indication of boiler water level.

PREVENTION OF CARRYOVER

Mechanical carryover can be prevented by careful boiler design and by operating the boiler within the design parameters for water level and firing rates. Large and sudden swings in boiler load should be avoided. Careful inspection and maintenance of steam separation equipment must be undertaken during boiler overhauls.

Chemical carryover can be prevented, or minimized, in three main ways:

- Eliminate all sources of oil and other high organics that might contaminate the feedwater. Oil is almost impossible to correct once it enters the boiler, so the best control is in the pretreatment system.
- Inject **antifoam agent** into the boiler water. These chemicals do not eliminate the cause of the foam, but they act upon the foam itself to weaken the bubble film and cause the bubbles to burst more easily. Some antifoam agents cause fewer, but larger, steam bubbles to form and these larger bubbles collapse readily on the surface of the water. Antifoam agents are not generally used unless foaming is a chronic, repeating problem. Also, some phosphate programs tend to stabilize foam, thus requiring an antifoam agent to counteract this stabilization.
- Use **blowdown** to control the concentration of solids in the boiler water. This involves removing concentrated boiler water so that the accumulation of solids cannot reach a level that contributes to carryover. Solids include those that are brought into the boiler by the feedwater and those that are produced as a result of scale-preventing and corrosion-preventing chemical reactions (ie. phosphate, chelate and sulphite reactions).

- **Continuous blowdown** removes a continuous flow of highly concentrated (with dissolved solids) water from the steam drum, while **intermittent blowdown** removes suspended solids by regular, manual blowdown of water from the mud drum and/or lower water headers.

- The amount of blowdown is usually determined by taking regular tests of the solids concentration and then adjusting blowdown to keep the concentration within a specified range, or below a specified maximum. Although each location will have its own specific guidelines, an example of standard guidelines for the maximum solids in a boiler, to help prevent carryover, are given in Table 1. Note that, as operating pressure increases, the tendency to carryover increases so the dissolved solids will be less.

Table 1	Sample Maximum Solids Guidelines
Operating Pressure (kPa)	**Max. Boiler Water Conductance (μmhos)**
0-2000	**3500**
2000-3000	**3000**
3000-4000	**2500**
4000-5000	**2000**
5000-6000	**1500**
6000-7000	**1000**
7000-10000	**150**
10000-14000 +	**100**

OBJECTIVE 4

Describe the design and explain the operation of simple, heat recovery, and automatic blowdown systems.

IMPORTANCE OF EFFICIENT BLOWDOWN

Efficient control of boiler blowdown is an important objective in the operation of most boilers. Since very hot water is discharged from the boiler and this water contains significant quantities of heat, a failure to reduce the heat loss results in a reduction in operating efficiency.

This is particularly true for continuous blowdown, where water and heat are being removed continuously, 24 hours per day. Although the instantaneous flow may be relatively small in comparison to intermittent (manual) blowdown, the total loss over a 24 hour period will be significantly higher. Efficiency can be maximized if the amount of blowdown can be reduced and if heat can be recovered from the blowdown water.

SIMPLE BLOWDOWN SYSTEM

A simple blowdown system involves control that is totally reliant on the operator. Both the continuous and manual blowdowns are set by the operator and all heat in the blowdown water is lost from the system.

Figure 1 shows a simple system. In this system, the manual and continuous blowdown lines discharge into a common blowdown tank (also called a "blowoff" tank). The pressure of the water drops to almost atmospheric in the tank and part of the water flashes into steam. The steam vents to atmosphere, while the water drains to sewer, thus releasing all the heat into the environment.

Figure 1	Simple Blowdown System

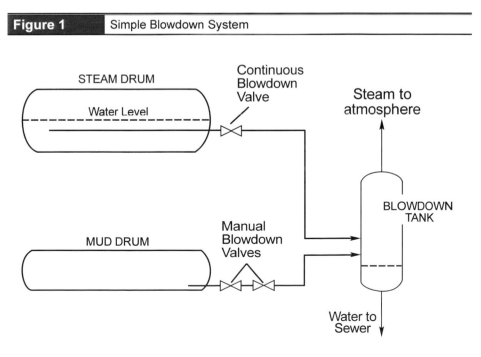

Control of the continuous blowdown flow, is manually adjusted by the operator. Once or twice a day, depending on the results of conductivity tests, the operator will adjust the opening of a valve on the continuous blowdown line. If conductivity (that is, dissolved solids) are high, the operator opens the valve further to increase blowdown. If conductivity is low, the valve is closed more to reduce blowdown. The problem with this system is the ease by which the conductivity limits can be overshot, particularly if feedwater conditions change and boiler solids fluctuate. It is very easy to have excessive blowdown, which is very inefficient.

Another problem with wide fluctuations in blowdown rates and conductivity levels is the effect on internal treatment chemical programs. Erratic solids levels in the boiler result in erratic residuals of phosphate, sulphite, and so on, which leads to confusion over the amounts of chemicals that should be added on a daily basis.

HEAT RECOVERY BLOWDOWN SYSTEM

A significant improvement in efficiency can be accomplished by recovering heat from the blowdown water and from its flash steam. Figure 2 shows such an arrangement.

In this system the continuous blowdown line, still with an operator-adjusted flow valve, is directed into a flash tank. The flashed steam is removed from the top and sent back to the deaerator, thus reducing the amount of make-up steam that is required from the steam system into the deaerator. The blowdown water from the flash tank is drained, via a level control, through a heat exchanger and then to sewer. Condensate, returning to the deaerator, passes through the heat exchanger where it absorbs heat from the blowdown water, thus cooling the blowdown considerably.

In some cases, the manual blowdown may also be directed through the flash tank. However, because manual blowdown is short-duration and high-flow, it is usually directed through a normal blowdown (blowoff) tank.

Figure 2	Heat Recovery Blowdown System

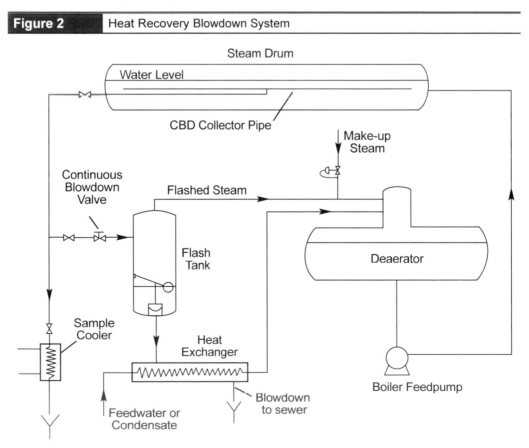

AUTOMATIC BLOWDOWN SYSTEM

The adjustment of continuous blowdown can be taken out of the operators' hands and controlled automatically. This provides for a very steady concentration of dissolved solids, even if feedwater quality changes during the day. It makes internal treatment programs much easier to control and, when combined with heat recovery, is far the most efficient blowdown system.

Figure 3 shows the main components of an automatic blowdown system.

Figure 3	Automatic Blowdown System

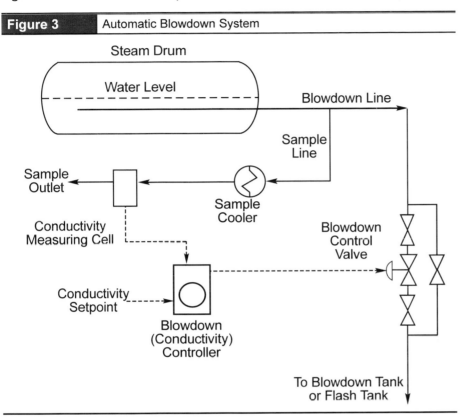

The continuous blowdown line is fitted with a modulating control valve. A sample of boiler water is continuously drawn off, upstream of the control valve, and is sent through a sample cooler. It then enters a measuring cell where the conductivity of the water is continuously detected and the result transmitted to a conductivity controller.

The controller may be mounted locally or in the control room. In either case, an operator enters the desired conductivity as the setpoint for the controller. The controller continuously compares the cell reading to the setpoint and makes an adjustment to the position of the automatic blowdown valve, if required. For example, if the setpoint is 3000 µmhos and the cell indicates 2800 µmhos, the controller will close the valve further, reducing blowdown flow.

This system, if well maintained, results in a very steady conductivity reading.

OBJECTIVE 5

Explain, in general terms, the sampling and testing strategies for boiler internal conditions; describe typical sampling and automatic monitoring equipment.

INTRODUCTION

This objective is not intended to create water chemists out of power engineers. It does not attempt to cover every testing and monitoring strategy in existence, since the huge variety of boilers and treatment programs available would make that task immense.

Also, to a non-chemist, the complexity of many of the chemical concepts and reactions can be overwhelming, and in most cases is beyond the knowledge level required to perform daily operational duties. The objective does attempt to give an overview of the more common approaches to sampling and testing, so that the operator charged with performing some of these duties will have a basic understanding of their purpose and function.

> *An operator must become totally familiar, through in-company training, with the specific testing programs and procedures at his/her place of employment.*

Units of Measure for Water Testing & Analysis

The measurement of a water sample and the results of the test are generally indicated in metric units. For example, a test may require that a very specific amount (for example, 100 millilitres, mL) of the boiler water that is being tested be added to a dish (crucible). If the correct amount is not tested, then the results will be inaccurate. The test may also require that a titration take place, in which a certain titration chemical is added to the measured sample. The amount of chemical used from the burette to reach the final endpoint of the test is read from the burette scale, which is also indicated in millilitres.

Parts Per Million (ppm)

One common expression of the amount of a certain, tested substance within a sample of water is parts per million, or ppm. When a test is conducted, multiplication factors are generally applied to the result and the result can be expressed as ppm.

For example, the sulphite content in a boiler sample might be found, by testing, to be 5.0 ppm. This simply means that in every one million parts of water, there are five parts of sulphite. That is, in every 1 000 000 kilograms of water there are 5 kilograms of sulphite.

Note: To avoid extremely small numbers when reporting results for some substances, it is often more convenient to use smaller units. For example, oxygen in water is usually expressed in parts per billion, or ppb. 1.0 ppb = 0.001 ppm.

Milligrams per Litre (mg/L)

This unit, mg/L, is even more common than ppm, having largely replaced ppm as the recognized reporting unit for water analysis. In fact, there is a direct relationship between ppm and mg/L. That is:

$$ppm \times \text{solution density} = mg/L$$

Since the solution we are dealing with is water, and since the density of water is generally taken as 1.0, it can be realized that, for water only, test results may be interchangeably expressed, as:

$$ppm = mg/L$$

Note: parts per billion, ppb = micrograms/L = $\mu g/L$

GUIDELINES FOR MONITORING & TESTING OF BOILER WATER

The nature of the raw water, the type of pretreatment, the operating pressures and designs of the boilers, and the condition of the returning condensate are typical factors that will determine the type of internal treatment that is required. However, regardless of the specific programs in place, there are general guidelines that should be applied for effective monitoring, testing and control of any treatment program. These include, but may not be limited to:

- identified, critical points in the boiler and system from which samples must be taken and tested
- a time schedule for each of the required samples and tests
- a clear, detailed procedure and interpretation for each test
- established acceptable limits, or targets, for each tested parameter
- comparison of test results against the acceptable limits or targets
- guidelines/instructions to maintain each tested parameter within its acceptable range or target, including actions to be taken if a parameter is outside of its range or target
- schedules and procedures for injection of control chemicals
- acceptable training for those charged with daily monitoring and control of the treatment
- a regular reporting procedure of results
- forecasting steam production and corresponding make-up requirements
- emergency troubleshooting procedures for severe excursions (for example, pH very low)

TYPICALLY MONITORED PARAMETERS

The following descriptions are given for the more common internal treatment parameters which are tested, either on a daily basis or on a more-frequent schedule. The exact details of each test are avoided, but a general overview of the test, its purpose, interpretation and control are given.

Phosphate

Phosphate, in its various forms, can be a complex chemical component in boiler water and can be measured in a number of ways. The most common method, used on a daily or shift basis by a power plant operator is a method that determines the **ortho-phosphate** residual in the water, as explained in Objective 1. A slight residual of phosphate is maintained in the boiler water to ensure that any calcium and/or magnesium hardness can be reacted with.

Regardless of the type of phosphate program being used (ie. coordinated, congruent, or equilibrium) the general approach is to maintain a residual that is appropriate to the particular program, by testing for the residual on a regular basis and adjusting the feed of phosphate chemical to remain within the phosphate range.

Phosphate test results are expressed in **mg/L** or in **ppm**. The acceptable residual may vary from as low as 2.0 mg/L (for the more complex equilibrium program) to 20 or 30 mg/L (for the coordinated program). In any case, the operator will have specific guidelines to follow and will be expected to keep the phosphate reading within a desired range (for example, between 20 and 30 ppm).

The ortho-phosphate test, performed by the operator, involves mixing a measured amount of filtered boiler water, in a tube, with specific amounts of reagents (one being molybdate). The water will turn a blue color, with the depth of color corresponding to the amount of phosphate in the water. The tube color is then compared against standard colored tubes, which are each marked to represent a specific mg/L or ppm of phosphate.

More sophisticated and complete determination of all phosphate components can be made, in lab conditions, using a spectrophotometer.

Sulphite

When sodium sulphite is used to remove dissolved oxygen from boiler water, it is fed to the water on a continuous basis and a residual of sulphite is maintained in the boiler water. The feed point for sulphite is usually into the deaerator or between the deaerator and the boiler (quite often at the suction of the feedwater pumps), since this allows protection of the feedwater lines and the economizer. The sulphite test result is given in **mg/L**, and a typical sulphite residual will be in the 10-20 mg/L range.

The sulphite test requires a fresh sample of boiler water, which has had as little contact with air as possible and is cooled to room temperature. Phenolphthalein indicator is added to the water, turning it red. Then sulphite indicator is added until the water becomes clear, indicating an acceptable pH. Finally the sample is titrated with potassium iodide-iodate solution until a faint permanent blue color appears. The millilitres of titrant used are multiplied by a factor to give a sulphite residual in mg/L.

Alkalinity

As discussed in Objective 2, alkalinity in boiler water is due to the presence of carbonate, bicarbonate and hydroxide ions. Excessively high boiler water alkalinity can lead to the release of corrosive carbon dioxide into the steam and condensate, causing steam contamination, caustic corrosion, and embrittlement. At the same time, excessively low alkalinity will not protect against acid corrosion (low pH) and will not assist in the precipitation of scale-forming salts from the water, as intended.

Complete alkalinity chemistry is somewhat complicated, but the operator should at least be aware of three alkalinity tests and their significance. The results of all alkalinity tests are given in **mg/L** as **CaCO₃**.

> **P Alkalinity:** The "P" stands for Phenolphthalein, which is a titrating indicator that changes color at a pH of 8.3 and is used to indicate half of the carbonates plus all hydroxides in the water.
>
> **M Alkalinity:** The "M" stands for Methyl, which is a titration indicator that changes color at a pH of 4.3 and is used to indicate the TOTAL amount of alkalinity (ie. carbonates + hydroxides + bicarbonates) in the water.
>
> **OH Alkalinity:** The "OH" stands for Hydroxide and is a calculated alkalinity, based on the P and M tests. It is found from the calculation "2P - M = OH", giving only the amount of hydroxide alkalinity in the water. This is often referred to as the caustic alkalinity.

Generally, the total (M) alkalinity is the reading used for control. The operator will have a range, within which the M Alkalinity must be kept. Since a phosphate program also affects the alkalinity, it may be necessary to adjust the feed of phosphate, or caustic soda may be added, or in extreme cases, boiler blowdown may be used to reduce the alkalinity. The acceptable limits of total alkalinity in boilers, is a function of operating pressure, with the limit decreasing as pressure increases. For example, limits range from <350 mg/L for boilers operating at 0-2 MPa (0-300 psi) to <100 mg/L for boilers operating at 7-10 MPa (900-1000 psi).

The alkalinity test requires adding phenolphthalein indicator to a boiler sample, which turns the sample red, then titrating with sulphuric acid until the sample becomes clear. This is the endpoint for P alkalinity. Then add methyl orange to the same sample, which turns the sample yellow, and continue titrating with sulphuric acid until the sample turns red. This is the end point for M alkalinity.

Total Dissolved Solids, Specific Conductance, Conductivity

The dissolved solids in boiler water must be kept below certain limits, as explained in Objective 3, primarily to prevent carryover from the boiler. The concentration of dissolved solids increases when the water boils and leaves the solids behind.

Water that contains dissolved solids will conduct electricity. The amount of electricity that can be conducted will be directly related to the amount of solids. The ability of water to conduct an electric current is called its **conductivity.** When the exact amount can be measured for a particular sample, it is referred to as the **specific conductance**, and these two terms are often used interchangeably. If the opportunity is presented for a small electric current to pass through a water sample, then the amount of current that actually passes through will be a measure of the specific conductance, and therefore an indication of the **total dissolved solids** in the water.

The units of specific conductance are micro-mhos per cm (**μ mhos/cm**). The equivalent SI unit is micro-siemens (**μ S/cm**). An approximate relationship between the specific conductance and the actual total dissolved solids (TDS) in the water is:

1.0 μmho/cm of conductivity = 0.9 mg/L of dissolved solids

In practice, the specific conductance (or total dissolved solids) of the boiler water is monitored on a regular basis and the results are used to adjust the continuous blowdown. The conductivity must be maintained within a specified range for each boiler (see Objective 3).

To perform the conductivity test, a measured amount of filtered boiler water is placed in a flask and then a probe from a conductivity meter is placed into the water. The meter passes a current between electrodes in the probe and then measures and indicates the current on a display that is calibrated to read in μmhos. Alternatively, some meters have a dish built into the meter, into which the sample is poured, thus eliminating the probe. Also, some meters may be calibrated to indicate the total dissolved solids directly as mg/L.

pH Measurement

pH is a measure of the relative acidity or alkalinity of boiler water. Its value as a monitoring parameter is largely as a back-up when alkalinity is used for control. Normally, with a phosphate program in place, the alkalinity and pH fall into line. However, since control of corrosion, plus the effectiveness of scale-reducing reactions are so pH dependent, regular pH tests are often prescribed. The acceptable pH ranges for boilers up to 6 MPa (900 psi) is 7.5 to 10.0, and for higher pressure the range is 9.0 to 9.6. While alkalinity testing is prominent on boiler water, pH testing is very important in feedwater and condensate return lines.

A pH test uses a special pH meter, with a probe and electronic circuitry that displays a direct pH readout. Calibration of the meter is first required, using a neutral buffer liquid. **Remember**: the pH reading has no units. A pH of 7.0 is neutral, a pH of less than 7.0 is acidic, and a pH of greater than 7.0 is alkaline (caustic).

Chloride

Calcium chloride, magnesium chloride, sodium chloride, and iron chloride often exist in boiler water. However, these compounds do not precipitate out of the water. That is, they remain in solution and are, in effect, harmless except that they increase the dissolved solids. This means that there is a relationship between the chlorides in the boiler feedwater and the chlorides in the internal boiler water that can always be measured. In cases where the chloride concentration is high enough, this relationship can be used to determine and control the amount of blowdown required from the boiler, as follows:

$$\frac{\text{chloride in feedwater}}{\text{chloride in boiler water}} = \% \text{ blowdown}$$

The chloride test involves titration. A sample of boiler water is added to a flask and phenolphthalein indicator is added, turning the sample red. Sulphuric acid is added until the sample turns clear, indicating a pH of 8.3. Then potassium chromate is added to the sample, followed by titration with silver nitrate until the sample turns a rusty color. This is the end point, from which the chloride is calculated, in **mg/L**.

Iron

Occasional testing for iron in the boiler water is an important monitoring parameter. By taking iron tests at different locations in the system it is possible to determine the source of the iron, whether it is due to the water supply or to corrosion within the system. That corrosion may be occurring inside the boiler itself, or in the feedwater or condensate systems that supply the boiler. Iron that is present in the feedwater or condensate may end up precipitating on the boiler surfaces as hard iron scale. So, the monitoring of iron is important in the control of scale and corrosion.

The iron test is performed by a lab technician, since it requires special equipment. A sample of boiler water has an iron reagent added to it, developing an orange color if iron is present. The sample is placed in a spectrophotometer where the absorbency of the sample is measured. The reading is transferred to a calculation, which gives the iron content in **µg/L** or **ppb**.

Dissolved Oxygen

This test is done occasionally, usually as a check on the efficiency of deaeration equipment, to determine the amount of dissolved oxygen that may be getting into the boiler. Methods range from titration, for concentrations in mg/L amounts, to very specialize instruments, such as on-line analyzers for amounts measured in micrograms/litre. These tests are generally done by lab technicians or by consultants.

Steam Purity

Steam purity refers to the amount of solids that are carried over with the steam, from the boiler into the external steam header and ultimately into steam users, such as steam turbines. Determination and minimization of impurities in steam is important to the integrity of superheaters and downstream equipment. Deposits left on superheaters cause them to overheat and possibly rupture. Deposits left on turbine blades cause loss of efficiency and even severe damage due to unbalancing of blades.

Tests may be done occasionally to determine the effectiveness of carryover prevention efforts. The general procedure is to collect and condense a sample of steam taken from the outlet of the boiler, upstream of the superheater. The sample is subjected to various testing techniques to determine the solids content, often down to parts per billion. The procedures range from a relatively simple conductivity (specific conductance) test, to sodium tracer (in which the sodium in the steam is compared to the sodium in the boiler water) and anion analyzer tests (using chromatography). Such procedures are beyond the scope of the operator, due to the equipment and accuracy involved, and are performed by a lab tech or a consultant.

Sampling

Obtaining a boiler water sample requires care to ensure accurate results. In most cases the sample is run through a cooler to reduce it to ambient temperature. Most tests require the lower temperature for accuracy. Sample bottles must be well rinsed and flushed with the new sample to avoid interference from previous samples. A sample line must be run for several minutes before a sample is taken, to avoid contamination from sitting idle.

In many plants, the sample lines from each location are run into a testing lab, or close proximity to, and the samples are kept flowing slowly at all times. This ensures the sample is current. Sample coolers are placed in the lines between the source and the lab.

AUTOMATIC MONITORING

In more sophisticated installations, particularly with higher pressure, higher capacity boilers where the internal treatment is so critical, there may be automatic analyzers for some of the crucial parameters. These provide continuous readings to a central location, including computer control systems, and relieve the testing responsibility from the operator, although occasional manual checks may be required. Some of these analyzers may even be tied into control loops, such as an automatic blowdown system. Examples of automatic monitors include:

- specific conductance meters
- corrosion rate analyzers
- hardness analyzers
- fouling and corrosion monitors
- pH meters
- dissolved oxygen analyzers
- turbidity analyzers

OBJECTIVE 6

Describe typical chemical feed systems, including pot feeders, continuous feed with day tanks, and continuous feed with pump tanks.

SHOT & POT FEEDERS

This method of chemical feed is described briefly, only because it may still be used in a few older and smaller systems. Even most older installations have upgraded from this method, due to the difficulty in maintaining steady, consistent chemical residuals and to the discontinuing of older forms of chemical.

Shot feeding involves the injection of chemicals over a relatively short period of time. Using a shot feeder assembly, usually in the form of a closed pot attached to the feedwater line, the chemical is transported into the boiler by exposure to the feedwater. The rate at which the chemical enters is somewhat controllable. Two common arrangements are illustrated in Figure 4.

Figure 4	Typical Chemical Pot Feeders

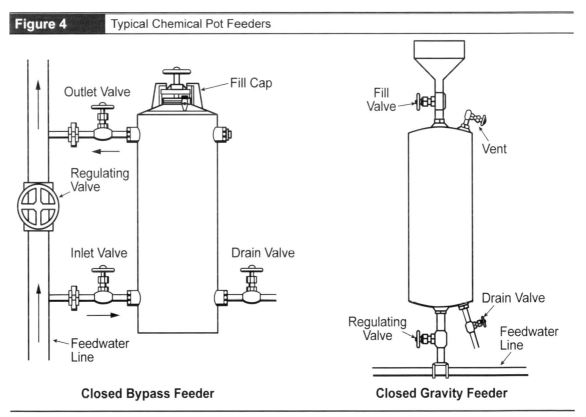

Closed Bypass Feeder   **Closed Gravity Feeder**

In the closed bypass feeder, the chemicals, in solid briquette form, are placed inside the pot and then feedwater flow is directed through the pot, dissolving the chemical and carrying it to the boiler. The rate of injection can be crudely controlled using the regulating valve on the feedwater line. This restricts flow, forcing more flow through the pot as desired.

The closed gravity feeder would be used more for liquid chemicals. The chemicals are poured into the pot and then the regulating outlet valve will determine how fast the chemicals feed, by gravity, into the feedwater line.

CONTINUOUS FEED SYSTEM (USING DAY TANKS)

A large majority of industrial boilers in operation today are supplied with chemicals by a continuous feed system. This involves feeding the chemicals to the boiler system at the most efficient injection points and at a steady and continuous rate. Advantages of continuous feed include:

- greater flexibility in controlling residuals and less chance of losing positive residuals, thus less chance of scale and corrosion
- a reduction in large swings in residuals and boiler solids, making blowdown control much easier and improving overall efficiencies
- safer handling of chemicals

Figure 5 shows an example of a typical continuous feed system, using **day tanks** for each chemical. The tanks are usually stainless steel, rubber lined or made of special plastic or fiberglass materials.

The chemicals, in either powder or liquid form, are added to their respective day tanks by the operator. The remainder of the tank is then filled with water. A mixer on each tank is used to ensure a complete and consistent mixture is achieved. Each tank has one or two dedicated pumps, complete with pressure gauges, isolating valves and check valves.

Figure 5	Continuous Feed System with Day Tanks

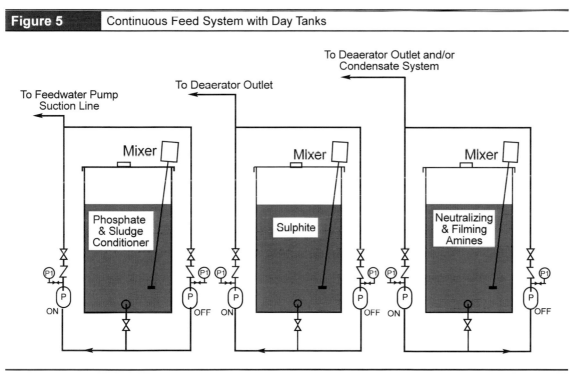

With this system, the normal practice is to mix one batch of chemical per day (hence the term "day tank") in each tank, attempting to maintain a constant concentration of chemical in the tank. The pump can then be adjusted to deliver the correct flow required to keep the corresponding boiler residual within its control range.

One disadvantage of this system is the difficulty in maintaining a consistent concentration in each tank. For example, if a residual is high and the operator adjusts the pump flow downwards, the tank will not draw down as much during that day. Then, if the same amount of chemical is added to the tank, the concentration will become stronger. If pump flow is not reduced, the pump will deliver more chemical to the boiler and residual may rise too high. This type of residual-cycling scenario is common and creates confusion between chemical addition and pump flow, particularly when several different operators are involved.

One method of reducing this confusion is to prepare chemical batches using a table of tank level vs. chemical addition. In effect, the higher the level in the tank, the less chemical would be added to it. In this way the chemical concentration remains more consistent and the pump flow has more direct effect on the boiler residual.

CONTINUOUS FEED SYSTEM (USING PUMP TANKS)

An improvement on the day tank system is shown in Figure 6. In this arrangement, each chemical is pumped to its required location in pure form, not diluted with water.

| Figure 6 | Continuous Feed with Pump Tanks |

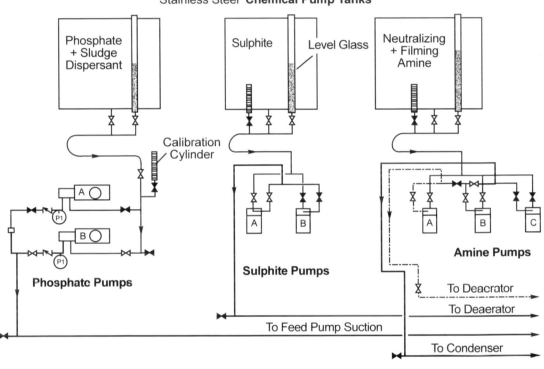

Each chemical is kept in a stainless steel pump tank from which the pump takes direct suction. A gauge glass on the pump tank allows the operator to ensure there is always a level in the tank and to initiate refilling the tank, when necessary, from a supply tank.

Depending on the complexity of the steam system being served, each tank has at least two pumps. Residual control is much improved, since the operator need only adjust the pump flow, without also being concerned about chemical concentration.

Chemical Pumps

The two most common designs of chemical feed pumps are the reciprocating, plunger-type and the electronic impulse-type. They both allow for fine control of chemical flow.

Plunger pumps consist of one or more reciprocating plungers, driven by an electric motor through an adjustable control box, with the ability to change the length of the pump stroke. An adjustment knob on the pump control box has a graduated scale that allows the operator to set the stroke up or down to vary the amount of chemical delivered. Increasing the stroke increases the flow.

Because plunger pumps are positive displacement, they are useful at all pressures, but especially when injecting chemical directly into a boiler (such as phosphate, sludge dispersant and chelate pumps). The operator will normally have a table of "flow vs. stroke settings" for reference when making adjustments.

Electronic impulse pumps use a moving diaphragm to push the chemical into the feed line. They are limited to low discharge pressures, so are useful only when chemicals are pumped into the deaerator or into low-pressure steam and condensate piping.

Impulse pumps can be adjusted for both speed and length of stroke. While their capacities are lower, their flow regulation is finer. A table of "flow vs stroke vs speed" can be used when making adjustments.

CHAPTER 10 - QUESTIONS

1. a) Explain three effects of scale in a high-pressure boiler.

   b) What are the three main steps by which a precipitation program prevents scale?

2. Explain the difference between a phosphate program and a chelate program. State two advantages and two disadvantages of a chelate program.

3. What is meant by sludge dispersion and how does it occur?

4. Describe two ways that caustic corrosion can occur in a boiler.

5. What is caustic embrittlement and what conditions must exist for it to occur?

6. Explain the differences in cause, location, appearance, and prevention of oxygen and CO_2 corrosion.

7. State three forms of carryover and explain how carryover can be prevented.

8. Sketch and explain the operation of an automatic blowdown system.

9. Explain the purpose, importance, and units for each of the following tests:
   a) specific conductance
   b) iron
   c) phosphate
   d) total alkalinity

   ANSWERS: All answers are found within the content of the chapter.

Boiler Water Pretreatment

LEARNING OUTCOME

When you complete this chapter you should be able to:

Explain the purpose, principles, equipment, and monitoring of boiler water pretreatment processes.

LEARNING OBJECTIVES

Here is what you should be able to do when you complete each objective:

1. *Describe the design and explain the terms, purpose and operation of a clarifier, using coagulation, flocculation, and subsidence.*

2. *Describe the design and explain the terms, purpose and operation of gravity and pressure filters.*

3. *Describe the design and explain the terms, purpose and operation, including chemical reactions for a cold lime softener.*

4. *Describe the design and explain the terms, purpose and operation of a hot lime softener.*

5. *Explain the principles of ion exchange softening in general, identifying the common anions and cations in untreated water.*

6. *Describe the design, components, and operation of a sodium zeolite softening system including chemical reactions.*

7. *Describe the design, components, and operation of a hydrogen zeolite softening system including chemical reactions.*

8. *Describe the design, components, and operation of a dealkalization system including chemical reactions.*

9. *Describe the design, components, and operation of a demineralizer system, including mixed bed and degasification.*

10. *Explain the principle and operation of a reverse osmosis system.*

11. *Describe the design, principle, and operation controls of a typical deaerator.*

OBJECTIVE 1

Describe the design and explain the terms, purpose and operation of a clarifier, using coagulation, flocculation, and subsidence.

WATER CLARIFICATION

Turbid water is water that contains suspended solids (i.e particles). Often, these particles are so small that they are not individually visible, but collectively they may be noticeable as a darker color to the water. In any case, the particles must be removed before the water enters a boiler, where the particles would potentially settle out as a harmful sludge. **Water clarification** is a process that uses a "clarifier" to remove these suspended particles from the raw water.

When the suspended particles are relatively large or heavy, a simple process of **subsidence** (also called settling or sedimentation) may be sufficient. The turbid water is allowed to stand in a simple tank and the particles (often called sediment) are allowed to settle to the bottom, while the clarified water is drawn off the top. The settled solids are removed from the bottom and the tank is then ready for another cycle. This is intermittent, batch settling.

Continuous, rather than batch, subsidence is more common, particularly when large volumes of water are involved. The turbid water continuously flows through an open vessel (tank) in which the reduced water velocity and the retention time allow the solids to settle to the bottom. Clarified water leaves from an overflow at the top of the tank. Mechanically operated rakes or scrapers continuously remove the settled solids from the bottom of the tank. The solids may also be removed by periodically flushing with high-pressure water jets.

When the suspended particles are very small or very light, they cannot be effectively or quickly removed by simple settling, as described above. In this case, a clarification process is used, which has three stages of clarification: coagulation, flocculation, and subsidence.

- **COAGULATION:** Tiny particles are so light that they have difficulty settling in water. Also, these particles have the same ionic, electrical charge, so they repel each other. The purpose of coagulation is to bring these tiny particles together (i.e to coagulate them), forming larger particles that can then settle. To do this, a chemical, called a **COAGULANT**, is added to the water to neutralize the electrical charges on the particles. The particles no longer repel each other; they join together to form larger, heavier particles. During coagulation, the water is vigorously agitated, creating turbulence which improves the dispersion of the coagulant and promotes contact between the particles. The heavier particles created are called **FLOC**.

- **FLOCCULATION:** While coagulation creates the initial floc, the settling rate of this floc can be further improved by bringing the floc pieces together to enlarge and form even heavier floc. This second process is called flocculation. It uses another chemical, called a **flocculant** (also called a **coagulant aid**), which causes the small floc pieces to quickly join together into a larger, heavier and more cohesive, sticky floc, which can settle more rapidly. Flocculation is aided by more gentle agitation of the water, which promotes floc contact, but without disturbing cohesion.

- **SUBSIDENCE:** As described above, subsidence is the final settling of the heavy floc toward the bottom of the clarifier, from which it can be removed.

Although chemicals are used in this process, it is still considered to be a mechanical (physical) process. The chemicals only aid in the settling of the small particles.

The most common coagulants are aluminum sulphate (alum), $Al_2(SO_4)_3$, aluminum hydroxide, $Al(OH)_3$, and sodium aluminate, $Na_2Al_2O_4$.

Coagulation is most effective at moderate temperatures and with a pH that is controlled between 5.5 and 8.0, to prevent dissolving the floc.

Figure 1 shows a typical **water clarifier,** which is designed to allow coagulation, flocculation, and settling of suspended solids from water.

The raw water enters at the top. The coagulant is also introduced at the top, through the chemical feed pipe. The water and chemicals (including coagulant and flocculant, in this case) are mixed together by mechanically driven agitators and travel down the central zone of the clarifier. By the time the water reaches the bottom of the mixing zone, particles have coagulated. Below that further flocculation occurs and the coagulated particles form a sludge blanket in the bottom portion of the upflow zone. This sludge blanket acts as a filter for the upflowing water, attracting and holding any free particles. The clarified water is drawn off, through a submerged collector pipe at the top of the upflow zone. The coagulated particles (sludge) collect in the conical section at the bottom and are periodically removed through the desludging valve.

Figure 1	Water Clarifier

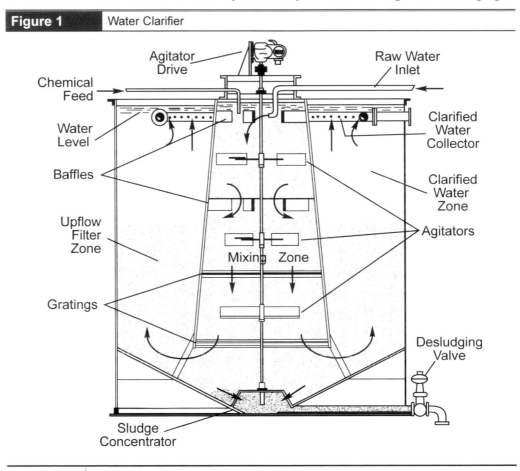

FILTERS

A filter consists of a bed of porous material through which the water is passed, either by gravity or under pressure. The porous material will trap suspended matter from the water, clarifying the water. The usual filter medium is either sand or anthracite. When the filtered water will become boiler feedwater, sand is rarely used, since the water may absorb silica, which could deposit as scale in the boiler.

After a filter has been in service for a period of time, the filter bed becomes "plugged" with the suspended matter from the water. The filter must be backwashed to remove this matter. Backwashing consists of reversing the direction of flow through the filter, thus freeing the trapped material from the bed and washing it to waste.

GRAVITY FILTERS

Figure 2 shows a simple gravity filter, using sand as the filter media.

Figure 2	Gravity Filter

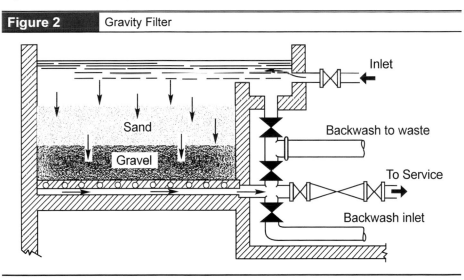

This filter has a rectangular, reinforced concrete shell. In some cases, the shell is made of wood or steel and may be circular in shape. The bed of sand, usually 40 cm to 80 cm deep, rests on a gravel support bed that is 30 cm to 60 cm deep. The gravel prevents loss of sand. The water enters at the top and flows downward through the filter bed to the outlet at the bottom. When backwashing is required, the flow is reversed, entering at the bottom and discharging from the top, to waste.

Figure 3 shows a gravity filter that is designed to automatically backwash when the bed becomes sufficiently plugged. This design works as follows.

- The inlet water normally passes downward through the filter bed and up through the outlet pipe.

- As impurities accumulate in the filter bed, the water has a difficult time getting through the bed and the level in the backwash pipe rises until it eventually flows over the loop at the top.

- The backwash pipe then begins to siphon the water from the space above the bed. This causes the backwash storage water to flow from the storage space through a pipe to the underside of the bed. It then passes upward through the bed to waste, thus backwashing the bed.

- When the storage water level drops below the end of the siphon breaker pipe, the backwashing will stop and normal flow through the filter bed will resume, first filling the backwash storage space and then passing through the outlet to service.

- The filling of the backwash storage space provides a rinsing period before the filter returns to service.

Figure 3	Gravity Filter - Filtering and Backwash Flows

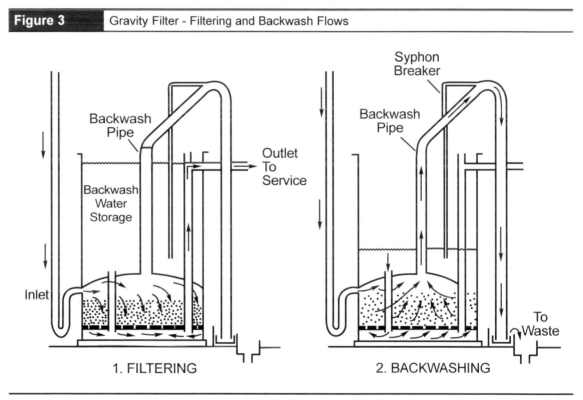

PRESSURE FILTERS

Figure 4 shows a pressure filter.

The steel shell contains a bed of anthracite, which is supported on a strainer plate. Water, containing suspended solids, is pumped under pressure through the filter. It enters at the top and passes down through the filter bed, then through stainless steel strainers located below the bed and into the bottom outlet.

Pressure gauges (not shown in the figure) are installed on the inlet and outlet lines and when the pressure difference between them reaches a certain value, usually from 35 to 55 kPa, it means that the filter media is becoming plugged and backwashing is required.

During the backwashing period, a rotary surface washer may be used to loosen material from the surface of the bed. The water leaves the nozzles of the rotary washer at high velocity, which causes the washer arm to revolve.

Frequently, filters are used in conjunction with settling tanks and coagulation. The sequence is to first coagulate and settle the impurities in a settling tank and then pass the water through filters, for final clarification.

If filters are used on their own, a coagulant is often fed to the filter so that finer particles will combine into larger particles that can be more easily trapped by the filter bed.

Figure 4	Pressure Filter

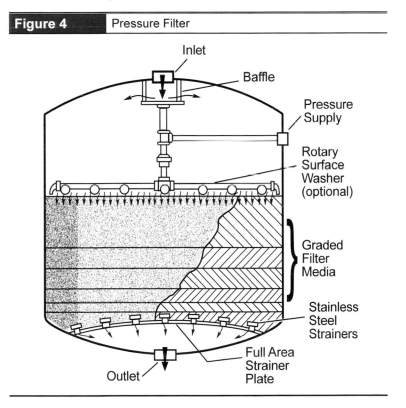

OBJECTIVE 3

Describe the design and explain the terms, purpose and operation, including chemical reactions for a cold lime softener.

INTRODUCTION

In the chemical methods of water treatment, chemicals are used in one way or another to react with the dissolved solids of the water. This reaction will soften the water by changing the dissolved solids to highly soluble dissolved solids, which do not easily form scale. The dissolved solids can also be made insoluble so that they come out of solution and separate from the water in the softener.

COLD LIME-SODA SOFTENING

Figure 5 shows a typical cold lime-soda softener.

In the cold lime-soda softening process, raw water (at room temperature), softening chemicals (calcium hydroxide and sodium carbonate) and a coagulant, are all mixed together in a central mixing zone by motor driven agitators. Insoluble compounds, $CaCO_3$ and $Mg(OH)_2$, are produced when the softening chemicals react with the scale forming materials, $Ca(HCO_3)_2$, $Mg(HCO_3)_2$, $CaSO_4$, $MgSO_4$, $CaCl_2$, and $MgCl_2$, in the water. The insoluble compounds, with the aid of the coagulant, form a sludge, which can be discharged from the bottom of the softener. However, part of the sludge is kept in suspension by the action of the agitators and the flow of the water, forming a sludge blanket through which the water passes as it flows upwards toward the outlet. The sludge blanket aids in the removal of any suspended impurities not already settled from the water.

Figure 5	Cold Lime-Soda Softener

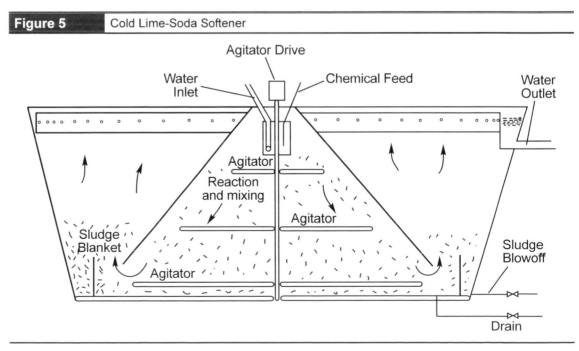

Chemical Reactions

Hydrated lime, $Ca(OH)_2$, produced from unslaked lime (CaO) and water, is used to chemically precipitate the carbonate (temporary) hardness in the water as follows:

1) $Ca(HCO_3)_2$ + $Ca(OH)_2$ → $2CaCO_3$ + $2H_2O$

   Calcium   Calcium   Calcium

   Bicarbonate + Hydroxide → Carbonate + Water

and

2) $Mg(HCO_3)_2$ + $2Ca(OH)_2$ → $Mg(OH)_2$ + $2CaCO_3$ + $2H_2O$

   Magnesium   Calcium   Magnesium   Calcium

   Bicarbonate + Hydroxide → Hydroxide + Carbonate + Water

The hydrated lime also reacts to precipitate the sulphate and chloride (permanent) hardness, in accordance with the following:

3) $MgSO_4$ + $Ca(OH)_2$ → $Mg(OH)_2$ + $CaSO_4$

   Magnesium   Calcium   Magnesium   Calcium

   Sulphate + Hydroxide → Hydroxide + Sulphate

and

4) $MgCl_2$ + $Ca(OH)_2$ → $Mg(OH)_2$ + $CaCl_2$

   Magnesium   Calcium   Magnesium   Calcium

   Chloride + Hydroxide → Hydroxide + Chloride

The calcium sulphate and calcium chloride, resulting from these reactions together with that naturally present in the water, then reacts with the soda ash (sodium carbonate), as follows:

5) $CaSO_4$ + Na_2CO_3 → $CaCO_3$ + Na_2SO_4

   Calcium   Sodium   Calcium   Sodium

   Sulphate + Carbonate → Carbonate + Sulphate

and

6) $CaCl_2$ + Na_2CO_3 → $CaCO_3$ + $2NaCl$

   Calcium   Sodium   Calcium   Sodium

   Chloride + Carbonate → Carbonate + Chloride

It can be seen, from the above reactions, that conversions have been made from calcium sulphate and magnesium sulphate to calcium carbonate and magnesium hydroxide. The first objective of these conversions is the complete precipitation of all calcium and magnesium salts.

The second objective is that, in the event some of these salts do enter the boiler, they should be in the form of calcium carbonate (rather than calcium sulphate) and magnesium hydroxide (rather than magnesium sulphate). This is important because sulphates generally form hard scale in a boiler, while calcium carbonate and magnesium hydroxide from soft sludges, which can usually be removed by blowdown.

OBJECTIVE 4

Describe the design and explain the terms, purpose and operation of a hot lime softener. Describe the components of a complete system.

HOT LIME-SODA SOFTENING

In the hot lime-soda softener, steam is used to heat the incoming water to above 100°C. Chemical reactions are the same as the cold process, but they are almost instantaneous and produce softer water. The hot lime soda softener may combine, in one unit, the functions of softening (reducing hardness to 10 to 30 ppm), silica removal, deaeration and filtration. This process is most suitable for softening water with high hardness.

Figure 6 shows a hot process softener system, including pressure filters, which are usually necessary to filter out any carryover of sludge particles from the softener. A chemical tank and pump, with an arrangement for proportioning the chemical to the raw water flow, a sludge recirculating pump and a filter backwash pump, complete the essential equipment.

- Raw water enters the top through a series of sprays, with the amount being controlled by the level in the softener.
- Steam enters at the top, where it heats and deaerates the incoming water. The steam pressure maintained inside the tank governs the temperature of the process.
- Chemicals enter at the top and are thoroughly contacted by the water sprays. The chemical reactions occur almost instantly, forming calcium carbonate and magnesium hydroxide. These compounds come out of solution and form sludge.
- The large diameter of the softener causes slow velocity and it takes about one hour for the water to flow downward and to the treated water outlet (ie. there is a one hour retention time).
- At the inverted cone the water turns upwards, while the sludge drops to the cone chamber below, forming a sludge bed.
- Some of the bottom sludge is periodically discharged to waste to control the sludge level. Some sludge is continuously recirculated to the top of the softener, which promotes coagulation and reduces the amount of chemicals required.
- The softened water leaves the outlet and goes to the pressure filters. The filters are backwashed with water from the softener; the backwash water returns to the softener after leaving the filters.

Control of lime soda softening requires frequent testing and control adjustments. Extra care is required to ensure sludge carryover with the treated water is kept to a minimum. Otherwise the filters will plug up very quickly. Also, the chemical feed system requires constant attention, since lime tends to settle out on the inside of the piping and the pumps.

Figure 6   Hot Lime-Soda Softener

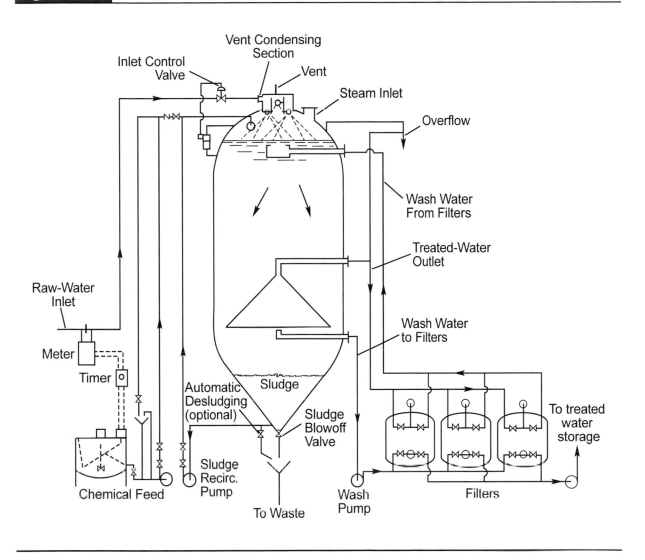

OBJECTIVE 5

Explain the principles of ion exchange softening in general, identifying the common anions and cations in untreated water.

ANIONS & CATIONS IN WATER

Natural, untreated water contains dissolved mineral salts, which exist in the water as compounds composed of negatively and positively charged particles, called ions. The negative ions are termed anions, with some common examples being sulphates (SO_4^{2-}), nitrates (NO_3^-) and bicarbonates (HCO_3^-). The positive ions are termed cations and common examples of these are calcium (Ca^{2+}), magnesium (Mg^{2+}) and sodium (Na^+).

Mineral compounds are formed in the water when anions and cations unite chemically. For example, the above ions unite to form the following compounds:

$CaSO_4$	Calcium sulphate
$Ca(NO_3)_2$	Calcium nitrate
$Ca(HCO_3)_2$	Calcium bicarbonate
$MgSO_4$	Magnesium sulphate
$Mg(NO_3)_2$	Magnesium nitrate
$Mg(HCO_3)_2$	Magnesium bicarbonate
Na_2SO_4	Sodium sulphate
$NaNO_3$	Sodium nitrate
$NaHCO_3$	Sodium bicarbonate

The presence of these compounds in boiler water is harmful because their ions contribute to sludge deposits, scaling, corrosion, and carryover, as explained in the previous chapter. Therefore, effective water treatment involves the removal of these harmful anions and cations before the water enters the boilers or other critical process equipment.

For example, if water contains the scale-forming salt, calcium sulphate ($CaSO_4$) it will be in the form of calcium (Ca^{2+}) cations and sulphate (SO_4^-) anions. If the calcium (Ca^{2+}) cations could be exchanged for sodium (Na^+) cations, then the salt would now be sodium sulphate (Na_2SO_4) and, since this salt is extremely soluble, it would not produce scale in a boiler. The same would hold true if the cations of the other scale producing salts could be exchanged for sodium cations.

If, the water also contains the scale forming salt, magnesium bicarbonate ($Mg(HCO_3)_2$) then this salt will be in the form of magnesium (Mg^{2+}) cations and bicarbonate (HCO_3^-) anions. If the Mg^{2+} cations are exchanged for Na^+ cations, then the salt will now be sodium bicarbonate ($NaHCO_3$) and, since this salt is extremely soluble, like most sodium compounds, it will not produce scale in a boiler.

OBJECTIVE 6

Describe the design, components, and operation of a sodium zeolite softening system including chemical reactions.

SODIUM ZEOLITE SOFTENING

Sodium zeolite softening uses the principle of ion exchange to convert scale-forming salts into non-scale forming salts. The softener contains a granular material, called zeolite, which has the ability to remove the calcium and magnesium cations from water and to replace them with sodium cations. The Ca^{2+} and Mg^{2+} cations are then held by the zeolite material, which has given up Na^+ cations in exchange for them.

When the zeolite material has given up all of its Na^+ cations in exchange for Ca^{2+} and Mg^{2+} cations, it must be regenerated before it can resume the softening process. Regeneration involves removing the zeolite softener from service and filling it with a solution of brine (sodium chloride, NaCl). The zeolite then absorbs the Na^+ cations from the brine and discards the Ca^{2+} and Mg^{2+} cations to the brine. The brine, now containing the Ca^{2+} and Mg^{2+} cations, is flushed to sewer. The softener, now recharged with sodium, is rinsed with water and returned to service until regeneration is again necessary.

There are many zeolite materials. Examples are natural green sand, synthetic gel, sulphonated coal and styrene resin. Zeolite is usually referred to by the simple chemical formula, Na_2Z.

Figure 7 shows a single zeolite softener, along with a regenerant (brine) tank. The zeolite material is supported on a bed of gravel or anthracite and is contained in a steel pressure tank. The raw, unsoftened water passes through a meter, an inlet valve, and into the top of the softener. It travels downward through the bed of zeolite, where the ion exchange occurs, before leaving the bottom as softened water.

Figure 7	Sodium Zeolite Softener

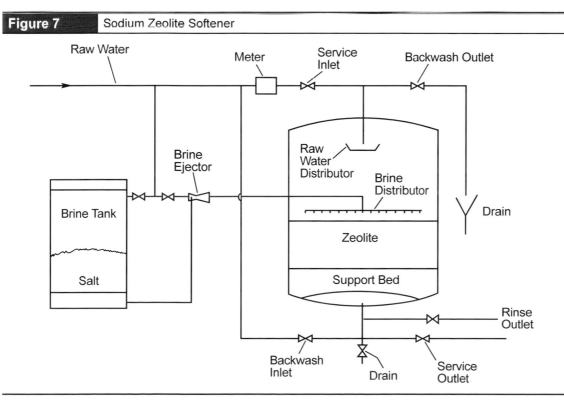

When the zeolite becomes exhausted of sodium, the softener is taken out of service and regenerated.

- The first step is backwashing, which loosens the bed and removes any solid deposits. Valves are manipulated and raw water enters at the bottom, flows upward through the bed, and through the backwash outlet to sewer.

- After backwashing for a specific time, the injection cycle (often called the "exchange cycle") occurs. A salt solution (sodium chloride, brine) is passed through the zeolite bed, using an ejector. Raw water flows through the ejector, producing a vacuum, which draws brine out of the brine tank. The brine enters the softener just above the zeolite bed and flows down through the zeolite, where it exchanges its sodium for the calcium and magnesium ions in the zeolite. Now loaded with calcium ions (calcium chloride) and magnesium ions (magnesium chloride), the water leaves the bottom of the softener and goes to sewer. When all brine has been injected the zeolite should now be free of calcium and magnesium and re-charged with sodium.

- After the injection cycle, the softener is rinsed. This rinse cycle may occur in two stages. First, the injection water is maintained (minus the brine) for a slow rinse, which ensures time for all brine to move down through the bed to achieve maximum exchange. Then, a fast rinse ensures all excess brine, containing calcium and magnesium are rinsed away. The fast rinse uses raw water through the normal inlet and at normal flow rates, but discharges to the sewer. The rinse cycle also re-compacts the bed. When the rinse is complete, the softener is returned to service.

The softening reaction in sodium zeolite softening is as follows (using calcium as an example):

$$Ca^{++} \quad + \quad Na_2Z \quad \rightarrow \quad CaZ \quad + \quad 2Na^+$$

Calcium Ion	Sodium Zeolite	Calcium Zeolite	Sodium Ion

Regeneration is accomplished by reaction with sodium chloride solution. The reaction for calcium is as follows:

$$CaZ \quad + \quad 2NaCl \quad \rightarrow \quad Na_2Z \quad + \quad CaCl_2$$

Calcium Zeolite	Sodium Chloride	Sodium Zeolite	Calcium Chloride

Note: In each of the above reactions, replacing the Ca^{2+} cation with Mg^{2+} will show the parallel reactions that occur for magnesium exchange.

Figure 8 shows, in more detail, the piping connections for a zeolite softener. Rather than several valves to change flows during backwash, injection, and rinse, this unit has a single, master valve that connects the appropriate piping for each cycle.

Figure 8	Zeolite Softener Details

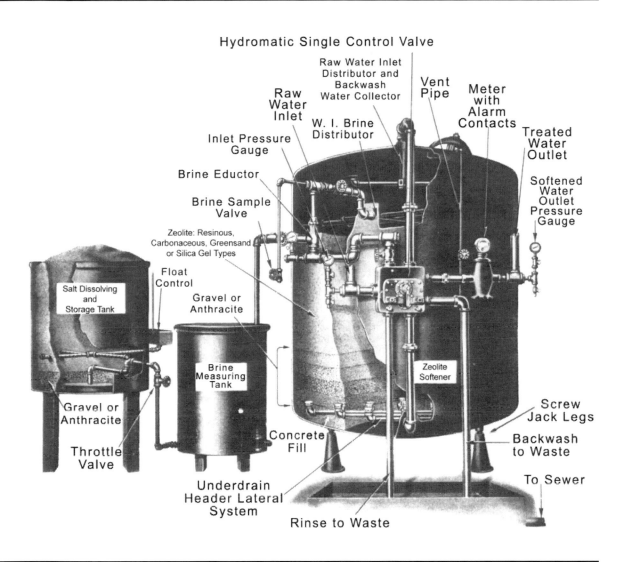

OBJECTIVE 7

Describe the design, components, and operation of a hydrogen zeolite softening system including chemical reactions.

HYDROGEN ZEOLITE SOFTENING (HYDROGEN CATION EXCHANGE

In sodium zeolite softeners the salts of calcium and magnesium are replaced with salts of sodium. While this method does get rid of the scale forming calcium and magnesium, it does not reduce the total amount of salts dissolved in the water, since sodium salts replace the calcium and magnesium salts. Unfortunately, one of the sodium salts, sodium bicarbonate, will decompose in the boiler, forming sodium carbonate, sodium hydroxide and carbon dioxide. Each of these is harmful in some way. The sodium hydroxide may cause embrittlement of the boiler metal. The carbon dioxide will be carried over with the steam and form corrosive carbonic acid in the return lines. Sodium bicarbonate promotes foaming of the boiler water.

A hydrogen zeolite softener removes scale forming salts, without forming sodium bicarbonate. Hydrogen zeolite material may be composed of lignite, sulphonated coal, coke, or synthetic resin.

Hydrogen zeolite removes calcium, magnesium and sodium cations from the salts in the water and replaces them with hydrogen ions. The mineral salts are converted into acids, which are then neutralized using an alkali or base, such as caustic soda (NaOH). In some cases, the acidic effluent water from the hydrogen zeolite softener may be neutralized by mixing it with the effluent water from a sodium zeolite softener.

The softening reactions in a hydrogen zeolite softener are as follows:

$CaSO_4$	+	H_2Z	→	H_2SO_4	+	CaZ
Calcium Sulphate		Hydrogen Zeolite		Sulphuric Acid		Calcium Zeolite

Na_2CL_2	+	H_2Z	→	$2HCL$	+	Na_2Z
Sodium Chloride		Hydrogen Zeolite		Hydrochloric Acid		Sodium Zeolite

$Ca(HCO_3)_2$	+	H_2Z	→	$2H_2CO_3$	+	CaZ
Calcium Carbonate		Hydrogen Zeolite		Carbonic Acid		Calcium Zeolite

$Mg(NO_3)_2$	+	H_2Z	→	$2HNO_3$	+	MgZ
Magnesium Nitrate		Hydrogen Zeolite		Nitric Acid		Magnesium Zeolite

When the zeolite becomes exhausted of hydrogen ions, it is regenerated. Sulphuric acid is passed through the zeolite, where it exchanges its hydrogen ions (H) for the Ca, Mg and Na ions in the zeolite. The reactions produce sulphates, which are then rinsed to sewer. The following reactions represent this regeneration.

$$CaZ \quad + \quad H_2SO_4 \quad \longrightarrow \quad H_2Z \quad + \quad CaSO_4$$

$$MgZ \quad + \quad H_2SO_4 \quad \longrightarrow \quad H_2Z \quad + \quad MgSO_4$$

$$NaZ \quad + \quad H_2SO_4 \quad \longrightarrow \quad H_2Z \quad + \quad NaSO_4$$

Calcium, Magnesium, Sodium Zeolites	Sulphuric Acid	Hydrogen Zeolite	Calcium, Magnesium, Sodium Sulphates

Figure 9 shows a hydrogen zeolite softener in parallel with a sodium zeolite softener. The effluent from the hydrogen zeolite unit mixes with the effluent from a sodium zeolite unit in order to neutralize the sulphuric and hydrochloric acids produced during hydrogen ion exchange. Blending valves are used to regulate the mixing to achieve an acceptable pH.

Another important component of this system is the de-gassifier. Its purpose is to remove carbonic acid (H_2CO_3), which easily breaks down into water and carbon dioxide.

$$H_2CO_3 \quad \longrightarrow \quad H_2O \quad + \quad CO_2$$

Carbonic acid	Water	Carbon Dioxide

In the degassifier the water from the zeolite exchangers flows downward over trays, where it is scrubbed by upward flowing air, from a blower. The air carries the released CO_2 to atmosphere, while the water collects in the bottom and is removed by a transfer pump to storage.

Figure 9   Hydrogen and Sodium Zeolite Softeners

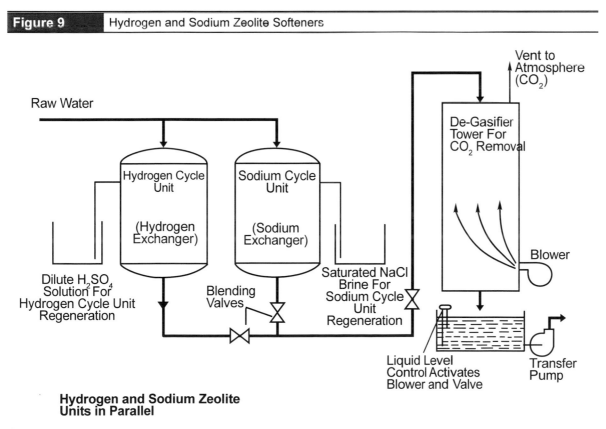

Hydrogen and Sodium Zeolite Units in Parallel

OBJECTIVE 8

Describe the design, components, and operation of a dealkalization system including chemical reactions.

DEALKALIZATION SYSTEM

In addition to hardness removal, most boiler operations also require the reduction of alkalinity, which zeolite softening does not accomplish. Dealkalization processes must be used to reduce alkalinity, caused primarily by carbonate and bicarbonate anions.

Figure 10 shows one type of dealkalization unit, featuring a hydrogen zeolite unit that contains a special weak acid cation resin (zeolite). A weak acid cation dealkalizer removes not only the carbonate and bicarbonate ions associated with alkalinity, but also the calcium and magnesium ions associated with hardness.

This system consists of the following:

- A pressure tank partially filled with weak acid cation exchange resin (Hydrogen Zeolite Unit)
- A concentrated acid measuring tank
- A system for the dilution of the acid to provide the hydrogen ions for regenerating the resin
- A degasifier to remove the carbon dioxide generated by the ion exchange process
- An alkaline neutralizer system, containing an alkali, such as sodium hydroxide (NaOH), to neutralize the acidic effluent from the hydrogen zeolite unit

| **Figure 10** | Hydrogen Zeolite with Alkaline Neutralizer (Dealkalizer System) |

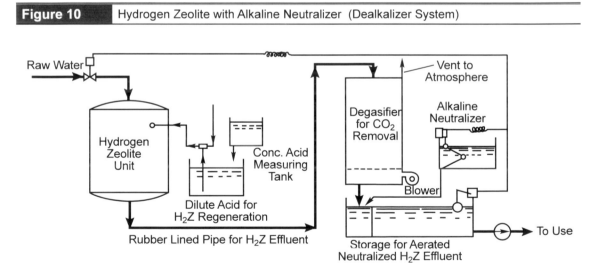

When water that contains alkaline anions, such as HCO_3 (bicarbonate), associated with hardness cations, such as Ca (calcium), passes through the hydrogen zeolite resin, the resin exchanges its hydrogen cations for the hardness cations in the water. The alkalinity ions combine with the hydrogen on the zeolite to form carbonic acid.

$Ca(HCO_3)_2$	+	$2 Z H$	$\rightarrow$	$2 Z Ca$	+	$2H_2CO_3$
Calcium Bicarbonate		Hydrogen Zeolite		Calcium Zeolite		Carbonic Acid

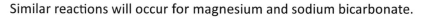
Similar reactions will occur for magnesium and sodium bicarbonate.

The water from the weak acid cation dealkalizer contains residual (non-exchanged) hardness cations plus acidic compounds. This water goes to the degasifier, where carbonic acid is reduced to carbon dioxide, by cascading the water over a packed bed of plastic saddles, causing it to break up into tiny droplets. Air, supplied by the blower, flows upward and carries the released carbon dioxide to atmosphere.

Since there may be additional, softening reactions that occur in the hydrogen zeolite exchanger, as shown in Objective 7, there may be additional acidic compounds formed. In this case, an alkaline neutralizer, NaOH, is added to the degasifier effluent to neutralize the acidity. The neutralization reactions are as follows:

1. H_2SO_4 + $2NaOH$ $\rightarrow$ Na_2SO_4 + $2H_2O$

      Sulphuric Acid   Sodium Hydroxide   Sodium Sulphate   Water

2. HCl + $NaOH$ $\rightarrow$ $NaCl$ + H_2O

      Hydrochloric Acid   Sodium Hydroxide   Sodium Chloride   Water

3. H_2SiO_3 + $2NaOH$ $\rightarrow$ Na_2SiO_3 + $2H_2O$

      Silicic Acid   Sodium Hydroxide   Sodium Silicate   Water

The sodium sulphate and sodium chloride contained in the neutralized water are very soluble and do not tend to produce scale in the boiler. The sodium silicate, however, will produce extremely hard scale in the boiler and must be removed by some other method.

The regeneration process, and the associated chemical reactions, are similar to that of a hydrogen zeolite softener. The unit is first backwashed. Then concentrated acid from a measuring tank is diluted to the proper concentration and passed down through the resin bed. The hydrogen ions from the regenerant reoccupy the zeolite. Finally, slow and fast rinses flush spent acid and ions from the resin.

OBJECTIVE 9

Describe the design, components, and operation of a demineralizer system, including mixed bed and degasification.

DEMINERALIZATION SYSTEMS

Demineralization is the removal of all mineral salts from water. A demineralization system is an arrangement of cation and anion exchange beds, usually in series. Upon leaving the system, the water has had all cations replaced with hydrogen ions (H^+) and all anions replaced with hydroxyl (OH^-) ions. The result is water that is virtually free of dissolved minerals.

There are many possible demineralization arrangements, composed of multiple exchangers. They are designed according to:

- The properties of the raw water
- The desired properties of the treated water
- Equipment costs
- Regeneration costs
- Ease of operation and control

Figure 11 is a table that shows nine different demineralizer arrangements. Information is included for each system with regard to:

Application: type of raw water handled and special requirements for the treated water.

Typical Effluent: expected limits of specific conductance and silica in the treated water.

Advantages and Disadvantages of each system.

Note: The conductance of water is directly related to the amount of dissolved solids it contains. The lower the conductance, the less dissolved solids are in the water.

As Figure 11 shows, demineralization systems consist of at least one cation exchanger and one anion exchanger. Combinations of these are used to achieve the best results, but in all cases the anion exchangers follow the cation exchangers. Larger systems have more than one of each type of exchanger.

Some systems include both weak and strong cation exchangers, which require more equipment, but have lower chemical costs than a single strong cation unit. The reason for this is that a weak cation exchanger has a higher regeneration efficiency and requires a lower concentration of acid regenerant. If it precedes the strong acid cation exchanger, it will remove most of the calcium and magnesium ions from the water and only the few that are left must be removed in the strong cation exchanger. Therefore, the strong cation exchanger requires less frequent regenerations, with a corresponding saving in chemical costs.

This also explains the use of weak and strong anion exchangers, in the same system. Strong anion exchangers are required for silica removal, but are expensive to regenerate. Weak anion units remove most other anions and are cheaper to regenerate. Preceding the strong anion exchanger, with a weak anion exchanger, results in less frequent regeneration of the strong anion unit and a saving in chemical costs.

Figure 11   Demineralizer Systems

DEMINERALIZER SYSTEM	APPLICATION	TYPICAL EFFLUENT	ADVANTAGES AND DISADVANTAGES
SA → WB	Silica and CO_2 are not objectionable.	Specific conductance 10-30 micromhos. Silica unchanged.	Low equipment and regenerant costs.
SA → WB → D	Silica is not objectionable but CO_2 removal is required.	Specific conductance 10-20 micromhos. Silica unchanged.	Low regenerant costs, but requires repumping.
SA → SB	Low alkalinity, raw water, silica removal required.	Specific conductance 5-15 micromhos. Silica 0.02 to 0.10 ppm.	Low equipment costs, repumping not required, high chemical costs.
SA → D → SB	High alkalinity, raw water silica removal required.	Specific conductance 5-15 micromhos. Silica 0.02 to 0.10 ppm.	Low chemical costs, repumping is required.
SA → WB → D → SB	High alkalinity, sulfate and chloride raw water. Silica removal required.	Specific conductance 5-15 micromhos. Silica 0.02 to 0.10 ppm.	Low chemical costs, high equipment costs, repumping required.
WA → SA → D → WB → SB	High hardness, alkalinity, sulfate and chloride raw water. Silica removal required.	Specific conductance 5-15 micromhos. Silica 0.02 to 0.10 ppm.	Lowest chemical cost, high equipment cost, repumping required.
SA → D → SB → SA → SB	High alkalinity, high sodium raw water, high purity treated water required.	Specific conductance 1-5 micromhos. Silica 0.01 to 0.05 ppm.	Low chemical cost, high equipment costs, repumping required.
MB	Low solids, raw water, high purity treated water required.	Specific conductance is less than 1 micromho. Silica 0.01 to 0.05 ppm.	Low equipment costs, high chemical cost.
SA → D → SB → MB	High alkalinity and dissolved solids raw water, high purity treated water required.	Specific conductance is less than 1 micromho. Silica 0.01 to 0.05 ppm.	Lower chemical cost, higher equipment cost, requires repumping.

KEY

SA	STRONGLY ACIDIC HYDROGEN CATION	WA	WEAKLY ACIDIC HYDROGEN CATION	WB	WEAK BASE ANION
SB	STRONG BASE ANION	D	DECARBONATOR OR VACUUM DEAERATOR	MB	MIXED BED

Figure 12 shows a simple flow diagram for a high capacity demineralization system that includes seven cation exchangers, six anion exchangers and five mixed-bed exchangers. Such an arrangement allows individual exchangers to be removed from service for regeneration, without interrupting system production.

Figure 12	Large Demineralization Plant

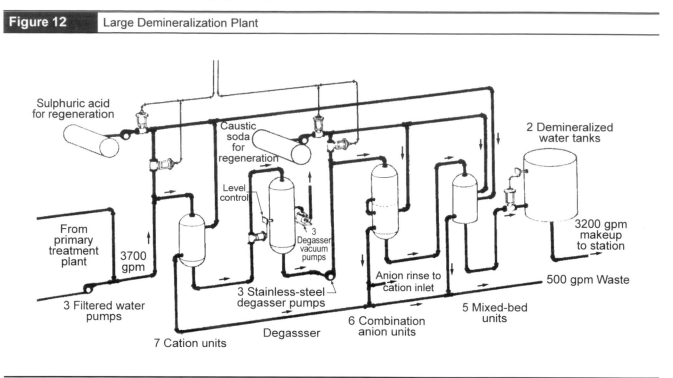

DEGASIFICATION UNITS

Some of the reactions in the cation exchangers produce carbonic acid. Strong anion exchangers will remove carbonic acid downstream of the cation units, but weak anion exchangers will not. If allowed to remain in the water, carbonic acid will break down into carbon dioxide, which causes corrosion. At reduced pressure, carbonic acid will be released as carbon dioxide.

This principle allows for the carbon dioxide removal downstream of a cation exchanger.

Figure 12 shows the locations of degasifiers (decarbonators) in large systems.

Figure 13 shows a simple degasifier, located between two exchangers. The decarbonated water falls into a clearwell and is then pumped to the following exchanger.

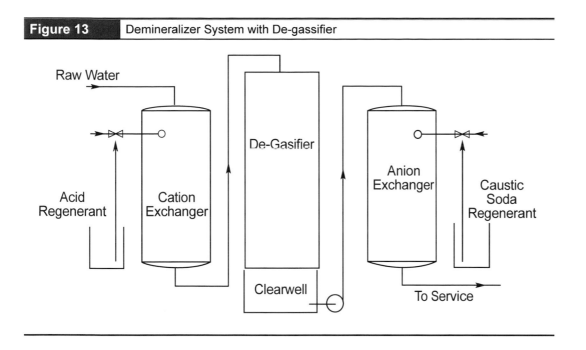

Figure 13   Demineralizer System with De-gassifier

REGENERATION OF DEMINERALIZER EXCHANGERS

Each ion exchanger in a demineralizer system must be regenerated when its resin becomes exhausted. The particular arrangement and the established operating guidelines will determine the specific procedures and parameters for regenerations. The following discussion is generalized to provide a broad understanding of exchanger regeneration. The normal regeneration sequence includes the following major steps.

1. Remove from Service

In some cases, an exchanger is removed from service and regeneration initiated after a predetermined throughput. In this case, the unit is automatically regenerated, even if the resin is not fully exhausted. More often, however, regeneration is initiated after "breakthrough" occurs, as determined by water tests. Breakthrough simply means that the resin is nearing exhaustion and undesirable ions are carrying through the exchanger.

Testing for breakthrough at the exchanger outlet may be done continuously, by automatic test equipment, or manually by the operator. Indications of breakthrough vary with the type of exchanger. For example, weak acid cations will show an increase in alkalinity and pH as the produced acid residuals drop. An alkalinity of 40 ppm or a pH of 5.5 (or similar maximums) may be the targets at which the unit is removed from service. Strong acid cations will show a sharp drop in free mineral acidity and/or a rise in hardness. Strong anion exchangers will show a sharp rise in conductivity and/or silica.

2. Backwash

Water, at a controlled rate and for a specified time, flows backward through the resin bed and discharges to sewer. Its purpose is to loosen and fluff the settled resin and to remove any deposits. This prepares the resin for the regenerant. Backwash flow rate must be kept within reason, to avoid loss of resin from the exchanger.

3. Regeneration

Regenerant solution enters the unit to regenerate the resin. The regenerant must be carefully controlled for concentration, flow rate and total quantity. Dilution water may be mixed with the regenerant flow before it enters the exchanger, to control concentration.

Demineralization units are typically regenerated with the following concentrations:

- Weak acid cations use a solution of less than 0.5% sulphuric acid
- Strong acid cations use a solution of <2% to 8% sulphuric acid
- Weak base anions use a solution of less than 1% caustic soda
- Strong base anions use a solution of about 4% caustic soda

The importance of maintaining the correct concentration and flow rate during regeneration cannot be underestimated. Excessive regenerant can cause damage and fouling of the resin. For example, excessive sulphuric acid can cause a cation resin to be irreversibly fouled with calcium sulphate.

4. Rinsing

Following regeneration, water is passed through the resin bed, usually in two stages. The first stage is a slow rinse in which a small flow gradually pushes all regenerant down through the bed, thus making use of all regenerant. This is followed by a fast rinse, in which a high flow of water displaces all regenerant and undesirable ions from the bed, to the sewer. The fast rinse is continued until tests prove the water is suitable for the exchanger to be returned to service. Testing may include pH, alkalinity, and hardness.

MIXED BED DEMINERALIZERS

Mixed bed demineralizers generally produce the highest quality of treated water. If only a mixed bed unit is used, the equipment cost is low but regeneration chemical costs are high. Mixed bed demineralizers are often used downstream of all other exchangers, as a final treatment or "polisher" of the treated water.

The exchanger bed is a mixture of strong acid cation and strong base anion resins. As the water flows down through the bed, there is an exchange of both cations and anions. When exhausted, the two resins must be regenerated separately.

Figure 14 shows a mixed bed demineralizer.

During normal operation, the anion and cation resins are mixed together, forming a single bed. Figure 14 shows the anion and cation resins reclassified and ready for regeneration. Usually there is a lower sight glass window, which provides a view of the line of separation between the two resins during regeneration. There is a regenerant collector at the interface of the two resins. Anion regenerant enters above the resin and leaves through the collector, while cation regenerant enters below the bed and leaves through the same collector.

| Figure 14 | Mixed Bed Demineralizer |

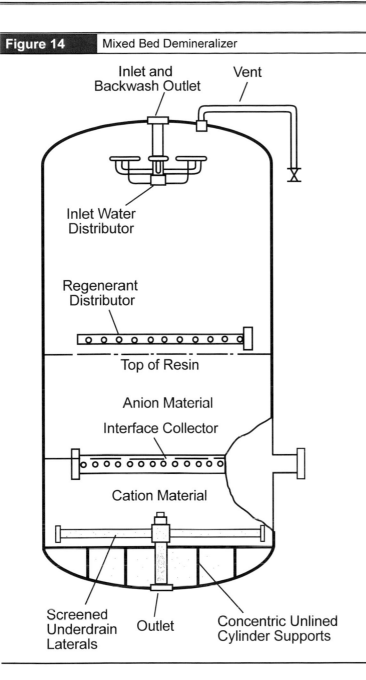

Regeneration of Mixed-Bed Demineralizer

Referring to Figure 15, the regeneration of a mixed-bed demineralizer is somewhat complex. Before regeneration begins, the mixed bed must be backwashed (2). The difference in size of the anion and cation resin beads causes them to separate into two distinct layers during backwash. The operator can confirm this through the sight glass window.

After backwash, the cation resin is regenerated with acid (3), using reverse flow from below the bed. The regenerant rises through the cation resin and exits to drain, through the interface collector. The anion resin is then regenerated with caustic (4), which flows downward through the anion and out the interface collector, to drain. These regenerant draws may be done simultaneously or separately, depending on the particular unit. The resins are rinsed (5) and then the vessel is drained (6). Air is then injected (7) from below the bed to remix the resins. This is followed by a refill (8) and final rinse (9) to remove lingering regenerant and undesirable ions.

Figure 15	Mixed Bed Regeneration

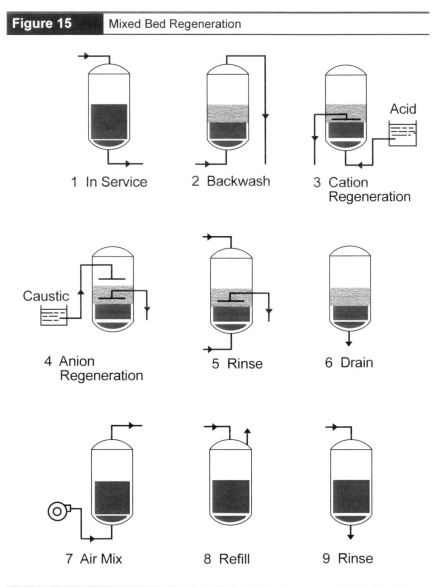

1 In Service 2 Backwash 3 Cation Regeneration

4 Anion Regeneration 5 Rinse 6 Drain

7 Air Mix 8 Refill 9 Rinse

The regeneration time for a mixed bed demineralizer (and therefore the time unavailable for service) is approximately two to three hours. For this reason, some mixed bed systems are designed for external regenerations in which the resins are sluiced from the exchangers and sent to a separate regeneration facility. One advantage of this method is that regenerated, standby resin can replace the spent resin immediately with the exchanger out of service for a relatively short time. Also, external regeneration reduces the chance of contaminating the treated water with acid or caustic soda.

OBJECTIVE 10

Explain the principle and operation of a reverse osmosis system.

REVERSE OSMOSIS

When a semi-permeable membrane separates two solutions that have different concentrations of dissolved solids, the solute (water) from the less concentrated solution will diffuse through the membrane into the more concentrated solution. This process, called **osmosis**, is reversible. If high pressure is applied to the more concentrated solution the water will diffuse through the membrane to the less concentrated solution. This is called **reverse osmosis**.

In a reverse osmosis system, water with a high concentration of dissolved solids is pressurized and forced through a number of membrane modules, connected in parallel. The dissolved solids are left behind and the water on the low pressure side will have a high purity.

Figure 16 shows a simple reverse osmosis module having a tubular membrane wound onto a support spool in a multiple layer helical coil. The raw water is forced under pressure through the helical coil; the water diffuses through the membrane and is collected at the bottom of the module. The dissolved solids and other impurities leave the end of the coil as a concentrate.

Figure 16	Membrane Module

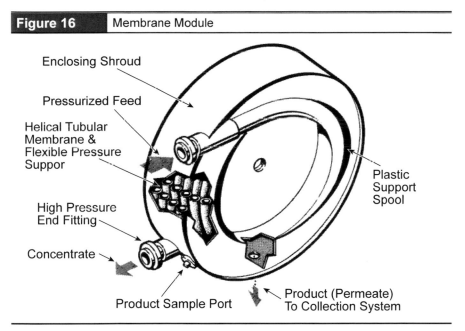

Reverse osmosis can remove 99% of the dissolved salts from water. Over time, suspended solids, scale, and micro organisms may accumulate on the membranes and reduce the water output or increase the salt leakage through the membranes. When this fouling occurs, the membranes may be removed from service and cleaned with available cleaners that are specifically suited to the membrane material and the type of fouling.

Figure 17 shows a typical reverse osmosis system.

The raw water may be pretreated by filtration or settling before it is pumped through the membrane modules (called "permeators" in this case) at high pressure. Usually, pressures greater than 1000 kPa are required to overcome the high osmotic pressures, but the exact pressure depends on the type of the membrane.

Figure 17	Reverse Osmosis System

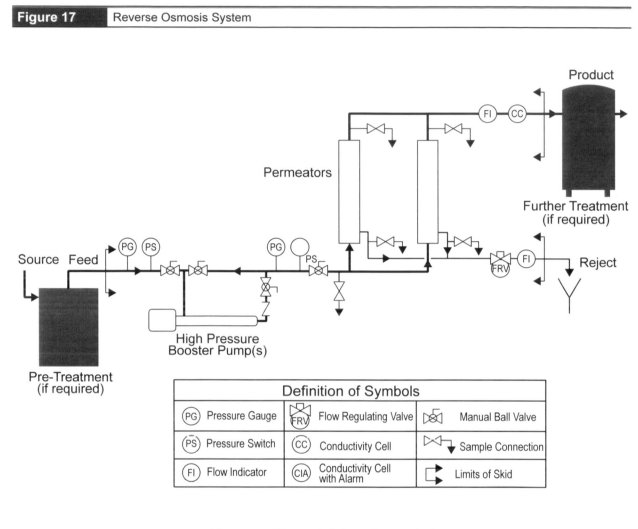

(Courtesy of Permutit Sybron Corporation)

OBJECTIVE 11

Describe the design, principle, and operation controls of a typical deaerator.

SECTIONS OF A DEAERATOR

A deaerator usually contains the following sections:

- A section where the water is heated to saturation temperature
- A section where released gases are scrubbed from the water
- A section for storage of the deaerated water
- A section for condensing any steam that is being carried to the vent along with the released gases

DEAERATOR TYPES

Deaerators are generally classified into three types, according to the methods by which they accomplish the deaeration. These are:

1. Spray type
2. Tray type
3. Bubbler type

Spray Type Deaerators

Figure 18 shows a cutaway view of a spray type deaerator.

In this design the entering water passes through nozzles, which divide it into a fine spray. In the heater compartment, the water is heated by direct contact with steam. It then passes to the scrubber compartment, where it is scrubbed and further heated by entering steam. The heating of the water causes any free oxygen and carbon dioxide to be released from solution.

From the scrubber, the deaerated water flows to the storage section. The steam flows to the heater compartment where it heats the incoming water spray and most of the steam, condenses. The released gases flow to the vent condensing section. Here, most of the steam present is condensed and the gases pass out the vent, to atmosphere.

Figure 18	Spray Type Deaerator

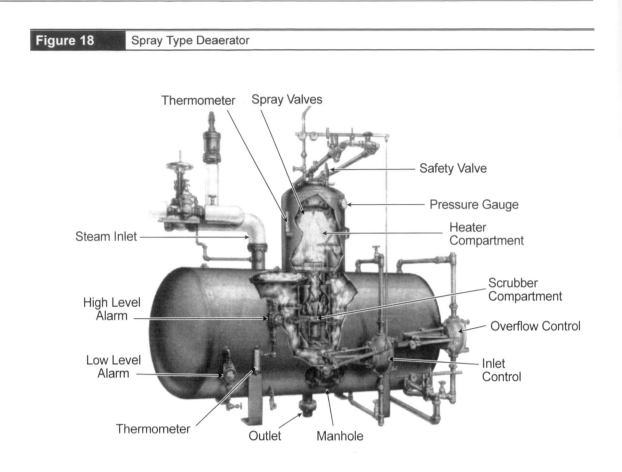

Some manufacturers use sprayers that combine a valve with a nozzle. Figure 19 shows a stainless steel, spring-loaded valve that will open further for greater flow. The shape of the valve disc maintains even distribution of water spray through a wide range of flows.

Figure 19	Spray Valve

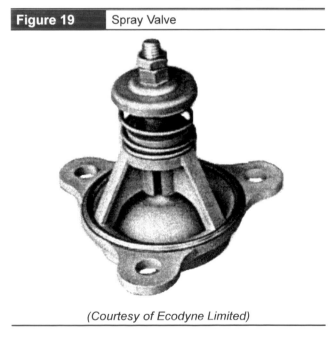

(Courtesy of Ecodyne Limited)

Tray Type Deaerators

In a tray type deaerator, the water flow is broken up by trickling down over a series of trays. The entering steam scrubs the water in the lower trays and heats the water in the upper tray section. The released gases and remaining steam pass to the internal vent condenser, where most of the steam is condensed and the gases are vented to atmosphere.

Some deaerators combine the spray and tray principles, with water first being sprayed into the upper heating section of the deaerator, then trickling over a series of steam-swept trays. Figure 20 shows a deaerator with this combination.

Figure 20	Combination Spray and Tray Deaerator

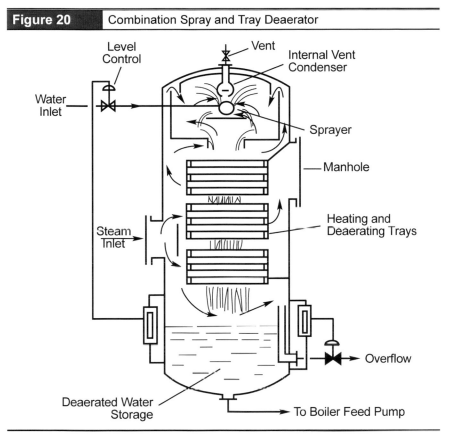

In this combination, the released gases and remaining steam pass through the incoming water spray on their way to the vent opening. This causes most of the steam that is being carried with the gases to condense. This section of the deaerator is called the internal vent condenser. When the vent condenser is mounted outside the deaerator vessel, it is called an external vent condenser.

Bubbling Deaerators

Figure 21 shows a bubbling deaerator, in which steam is forced up through perforated panels as the water flows along the top surface of the panels. The steam bubbling up through the water causes agitation and intimate contact between the steam and water, thus effecting deaeration. There may be several trays in a stack and the steam rises up through each of the trays as the water descends.

| Figure 21 | Bubbling Deaerator |

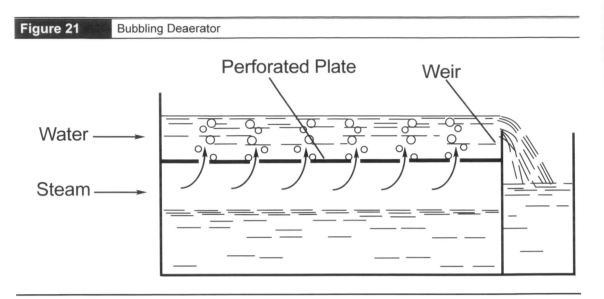

Deaerator Control

Deaerators are designed to operate at a controlled pressure, usually in the range of 35 to 70 kPa. The low pressure, along with the high temperature, is what allows the oxygen to escape from the water. The vent to atmosphere is always open (to remove the oxygen), which tends to reduce the internal pressure. A pressure control valve, reacting to the pressure in the deaerator, controls the steam entering the deaerator. Many deaerators have a second steam valve, which removes steam from the deaerator if there is excess pressure.

Water level in the storage section of a deaerator is controlled by a float-operated level control valve and an overflow valve. During normal operation, a controlled level is maintained by adding water from the treated water storage tank, to ensure a sufficient level for the feedwater pumps, which take suction from the deaerator. In periods of low flow, steam may condense and the level slowly increase, in which case an overflow valve will open to prevent the water from rising above the highest level at which efficient deaeration is possible.

Figure 18 shows some of the normal fittings found on deaerators, such as safety valves, pressure gauges, thermometers, float controls for high and low levels, level alarms, and access openings.

Deaerators are usually elevated several metres above the inlet to the boiler feed pumps. This ensures sufficient head pressure at the pump inlet to prevent cavitation and subsequent damage to the pump housing and impeller.

Ensuring the Effectiveness of Deaeration

To reduce corrosion by oxygen, the concentration of dissolved oxygen in the water should be kept at about 5 to 7 ppb (parts per billion). Using chemical test methods, operators are able to determine the amount of oxygen in the water leaving the deaerator, which indicates the effectiveness of the deaerator operation and may lead to adjustments in operating pressures and steam flows (ie. more steam or less pressure)

An oxygen scavenging chemical is often added to the deaerator reservoir section, using a chemical feed pump. The scavenger mixes with the deaerated water and reacts with traces of oxygen in the water. Chemical tests for a residual of unreacted scavenger helps determine how much protection is available, since a residual of unreacted scavenger should mean that all oxygen has been removed. The aim is to always have a slight residual of scavenger in the water. The residual scavenger carries into the boiler where it continues working. The boiler residual is monitored and scavenger dosage is increased if the residual is too low.

CHAPTER 11 - QUESTIONS

1. Sketch and describe the operation of a clarifier.

2. Make a sketch of a pressure filter. What is the purpose of backwashing this filter and how is a backwash operation carried out?

3. Describe the general operation of a cold lime softener.

4. Describe the general operation of a hot lime softener.

5. Describe, in general terms, ion exchange and name two anions and two cations found in untreated water.

6. a) Explain the general operation of a sodium zeolite softener.

   b) What are the purposes of backwashing, regenerating and rinsing a sodium zeolite softener and how are these processes carried out?

7. State the advantage of a hydrogen zeolite softener over a sodium zeolite softener.

8. Sketch and describe a dealkalization system.

9. With the aid of a simple sketch, describe the following, pertaining to a mixed bed demineralizer.

   a) The main purpose of the unit.

   b) The steps that must be followed to complete a regeneration of the exchanger.

10. Define reverse osmosis.

11. With the aid of a simple sketch, describe the operation of a combination spray and tray type deaerator.

   ANSWERS: All answers are found within the content of the chapter.

CHAPTER 12

Pump Designs & Operation

LEARNING OUTCOME

When you complete this chapter you should be able to:

Describe the designs, principles, components and operating procedures for common industrial pumps.

LEARNING OBJECTIVES

Here is what you should be able to do when you complete each objective:

1. *Explain the principle of operation and describe the components of typical plunger, piston and diaphragm reciprocating pumps.*

2. *Explain the designs and operating principles of the external gear, internal gear, sliding vane, lobe, and screw type rotary pumps.*

3. *Explain the designs and operating principles of volute and diffuser centrifugal pumps, including impeller designs.*

4. *Describe centrifugal pump arrangements, including vertical, horizontal, single and double suction, opposed impellers, multi-staging, split and barrel casings.*

5. *Describe the design and applications of axial and mixed flow pumps.*

6. *Describe the design and components of a multistage centrifugal pump, clearly stating the purpose and general design of: wear rings, shaft sleeves, seals, bearings and lubrication components, vents and drains.*

7. *Explain design features that eliminate thrust in large centrifugal pumps.*

8. *Describe systems used to maintain minimum flow through a centrifugal pump.*

9. *Explain priming, start-up, capacity control and operating cautions for centrifugal pumps.*

OBJECTIVE 1

Explain the principle of operation and describe the components of typical plunger, piston and diaphragm reciprocating pumps.

Introduction

Reciprocating pumps operate on the principle of liquid being drawn into a closed casing or cylinder and then forced toward the outlet of the pump by a reciprocating component within the pump. This component moves in one direction to draw liquid into the pump and then in the opposite direction to push the liquid out. These are referred to as positive displacement pumps, since they displace a definite volume of liquid from the pump with each discharge stroke. The most common reciprocating pump designs use a plunger, a piston or a diaphragm as the reciprocating component

PLUNGER PUMPS

Figure 1 shows the basic design of a plunger type of reciprocating pump.

The operation is as follows. When the plunger starts moving from right to left, the pressure inside the cylinder drops below that in the suction line. The pressure difference overcomes the gravitational force on the suction ball, causing it to rise off its seat. Liquid flows into the cylinder from the suction line. Meanwhile, the higher pressure in the discharge line keeps the discharge ball check firmly on its seat. When the plunger reverses direction and starts moving from left to right, the cylinder pressure rises above the pressure in the discharge line and the suction line. This causes the discharge ball check to open, thus discharging liquid, and the suction ball check to close.

The movement of the plunger in one direction is called the plunger stroke and the distance the plunger moves is the length of stroke. As the sketch shows, liquid is discharged from one end of the cylinder only. Also, it requires two strokes of the plunger to produce one discharge stroke. This is called single-acting and plunger pumps can only be single-acting.

Figure 1	Plunger Pump (Single-Acting)

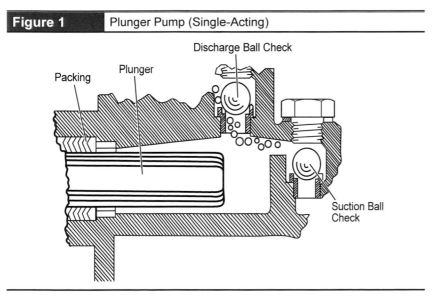

Figure 2 is a cross-sectional view of a power driven plunger pump with a double set of suction and discharge valves, which allows for higher discharge pressures and volumes. It also has an adjustable stroke for volume control. This design is common in chemical feed pumps.

Figure 2	Power Driven Plunger Pump Cross-Section

Figure 3 shows a triplex plunger pump.

This arrangement has three cylinders and three plungers. A single crankshaft drives the three plungers, with their individual cranks set 120 degrees apart. This creates a smoother flow of liquid and a smoother discharge pressure, since each plunger has its own suction and discharge valves and at least one of them is discharging at any given moment. The three cylinders also allow for a higher flow capacity.

Figure 3	Power Driven Triplex Pump

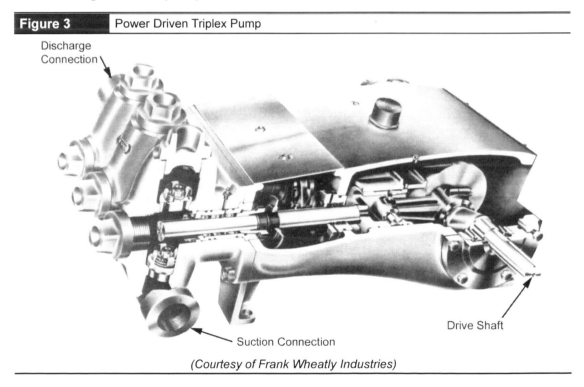

Discharge Connection

Drive Shaft

Suction Connection

(Courtesy of Frank Wheatly Industries)

PISTON PUMPS

A piston pumps consists of a piston inside a closed cylinder. The advantage over plunger pumps is that the piston diameter can be made larger and the cylinder may discharge from both ends, thereby providing much larger capacities. Piston pumps may be single-acting or double-acting.

Figure 4 illustrates the operating principle of a double-acting piston pump. The pump has two discharge valves D A, and D B, and two suction valves, S A and S B.

- In Figure (a), when the piston moves from left to right the pressure on the left side of the piston falls, so liquid is drawn into the left side of the cylinder via suction valve, S A. At the same time the pressure increases on the right side of the piston, forcing liquid out of the right side through discharge valve, D B.

- In Figure (b), when the piston reverses direction and moves from right to left liquid is drawn into the right side of the cylinder via suction valve, S B, and discharged from the left side via discharge valve, DA. Since liquid is discharged from both ends of the cylinder and during each stroke of the piston, this is pump is called "double-acting". The suction and discharge valves are spring loaded and are operated by the pressure differential across them, similar to the ball checks of the plunger pump.

| Figure 4 | Double-Acting Piston Pump |

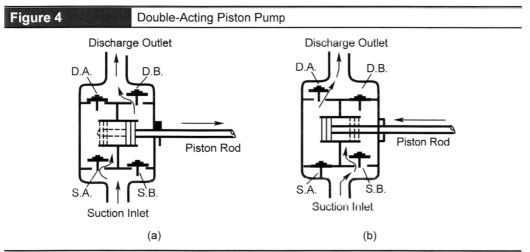

(a)   (b)

A popular arrangement of this design is called the "double-acting duplex pump". In this design, the pump has two double-acting cylinders, driven by the same crankshaft. This doubles the capacity and smooths out the pressure and flow.

One disadvantage of piston and plunger pumps is their susceptibility to leakage along the plunger or the piston rods. The cylinders must have a sealing arrangement where the plunger or piston rod enters the cylinder.

DIAPHRAGM PUMPS

In a diaphragm pump the pumped fluid is completely isolated by a diaphragm from the reciprocating mechanism, thereby eliminating the leakage problems associated with piston and plunger pumps. The diaphragm is a relatively thin, flexible membrane, made of a metallic or non-metallic material, such as plastic, rubber or neoprene, depending on the fluid being pumped. The membrane acts as the liquid displacing component.

Figure 5 shows the cross-section of a mechanically actuated diaphragm pump.

The diaphragm, D, is attached to the piston-like guide, P, by the disc, B. An eccentric, rotating (off-centered) shaft produces a reciprocating motion in the guide, P. The guide is attached tightly to the diaphragm by a bolted disc and as the guide reciprocates, the diaphragm moves up and down.

- When the diaphragm moves upward, it creates greater space, which causes the pressure in the pump to drop. This causes the suction valve (ball), V, to open and the discharge valve, V_1, to close.
- Then, when the diaphragm moves downward, it displaces liquid, causing the pressure to increase. This causes the suction valve to close and the discharge valve to open.

Figure 5	Mechanically Actuated Diaphragm

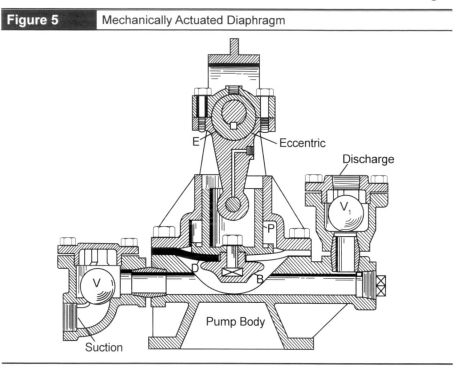

Reciprocating Pump Capacity

Since reciprocating pumps are positive displacement, their capacity is not affected by the discharge pressure. That is, if the pressure increases, the capacity will remain the same.

Pump capacity is the volume of liquid pumped in a given time, usually one minute. For a reciprocating pump, the volume of liquid pumped per stroke is determined by the cross-sectional area of the piston or plunger and the length of the stroke. This will give the volume displaced per stroke. The pump capacity then depends on the number of pumping strokes per minute. Capacity can be changed by changing the number of strokes per minute (ie. change the speed of the pump) or by changing the length of the stroke. Speed control may be used by all reciprocating pumps, while stroke length is only common to plunger pumps.

OBJECTIVE 2

Explain the designs and operating principles of the external gear, internal gear, sliding vane, lobe, and screw type rotary pumps.

ROTARY PUMPS

Rotary pumps consist of a closed casing in which gears, lobes, vanes or screws rotate with a minimum of clearance. These rotating components trap the liquid and carry it around the casing from suction to discharge. The flow of liquid through a rotary pump is continuous and smooth, with minimal pressure fluctuations.

Rotary pumps are capable of handling a wide range of liquid viscosities and are used to pump many different liquids, including fuels, lubricating and hydraulic oils, and liquefied gases, such as propane, butane, ammonia, and Freon. They are positive displacement pumps and, as such, are capable of high pressures and must be protected by a discharge relief valve.

Figure 6 shows the five most common designs of rotary pump. Each one is described below.

Figure 6	Types of Rotary Pumps

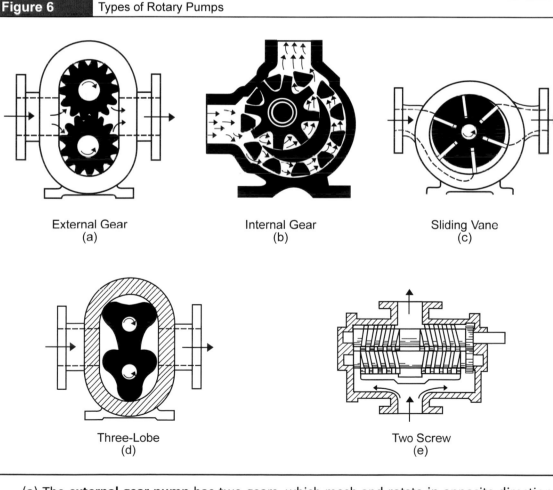

External Gear
(a)

Internal Gear
(b)

Sliding Vane
(c)

Three-Lobe
(d)

Two Screw
(e)

(a) The **external gear pump** has two gears, which mesh and rotate in opposite directions inside the casing. Liquid from the inlet is trapped between the teeth of the gears and the casing wall and is carried around to the discharge side by both gears. The meshing teeth in the centre provide a seal that prevents discharge liquid from flowing back to the inlet side.

(b) The **internal gear pump** has an externally-cut gear, which meshes with a larger, internally-cut gear on one side and is separated from this gear on the other side by a crescent-shaped partition. Liquid from the suction is trapped in the spaces between the teeth of both gears and carried toward the discharge. The partition and the meshing of the gears prevent liquid flowing backwards from the discharge side.

(c) The **sliding-vane pump** has a cylindrical rotor, with vanes that can slide radially in and out of longitudinal slots. The rotor is mounted off-centre in the cylindrical casing with minimal clearance on one side. As the rotor turns, the vanes are forced out against the casing wall by centrifugal force. Inlet liquid is trapped between the vanes and is carried around to the discharge. When pump speed is low the centrifugal force is supplemented by springs installed in the slots between the vanes and the rotor.

(d) The **three-lobe pump** has two rotors, each with three lobes. The rotors are driven by external gears, which synchronize their rotation. The lobes rotate in opposite directions and their shape causes a continuous small clearance between them. Liquid is trapped in pockets between the lobes and the casing and carried to the discharge. Small clearance between the lobes prevents leakage back to the inlet.

(e) The **screw pump** has two long rotors with intermeshing spiral "screws". The protruded lobes of one rotor intermesh with the intruded volutes of the other. As the rotors turn in opposite directions liquid is trapped between the two rotors and is carried axially (along the length of the rotors) towards the discharge.

OBJECTIVE 3

Explain the designs and operating principles of volute and diffuser centrifugal pumps, including impeller designs.

CENTRIFUGAL PUMPS

A centrifugal pump may be defined as a pump that uses centrifugal force to impart energy to a fluid by giving the fluid high velocity and then converting this velocity into pressure. Because there are many different designs of centrifugal pumps, they can be classified into a number of types according to specific characteristics. The main division according to the method of imparting energy to the fluid gives us the following types: volute, diffuser, mixed flow, axial flow and regenerative.

They can also be classified according to the:

- number of stages: single or multi-stage
- suction inlet: single or double suction
- position of shaft: horizontal or vertical
- type of casing: horizontal split or vertical split
- mounting: in-line or base-mounted

Centrifugal pumps can also be identified according to their applications, such as: boiler feed pump, general-purpose pump, vacuum pump, circulating pump, etc. The application will determine the type of pump to be used.

Volute Pump

Basically, the volute centrifugal pump consists of an impeller (consisting of a number of vanes) which rotates in a volute stationary casing, as shown in Figure 7. The term "volute" refers to the gradually increasing cross-sectional area of the spiral casing.

Figure 7	Volute Centrifugal Pump

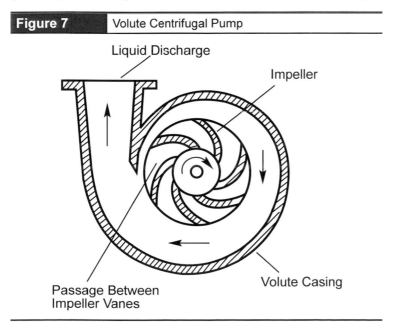

Figure 8 illustrates the fluid velocity within a volute pump casing. The graph shows the relative velocities of the liquid at different points in the pump.

As the impellor turns at high speed, it creates a low pressure at the inlet and liquid is drawn into the centre (called the 'eye') of the impeller. It is picked up by the impeller vanes and accelerated to a high velocity. The liquid now contains kinetic energy and is discharged from the tips of the impeller vanes into the casing by centrifugal force. As the liquid travels through the volute casing to the discharge, its velocity decreases and its kinetic energy is converted into pressure energy.

Since the liquid between the vanes is forced outward, an area of low pressure is constantly created in the eye of the impeller. Therefore there is a continuous flow of liquid into the inlet and the flow of liquid through the pump is constant.

Figure 8	Fluid Velocity within a Volute Pump

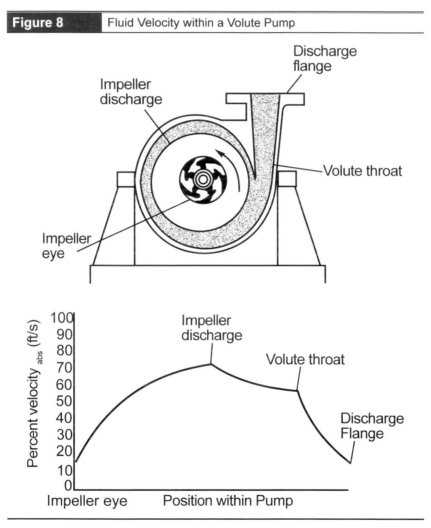

Figure 9 shows the cross-section of a small volute pump.

Figure 9	Single-Stage, Single-Inlet Volute Pump

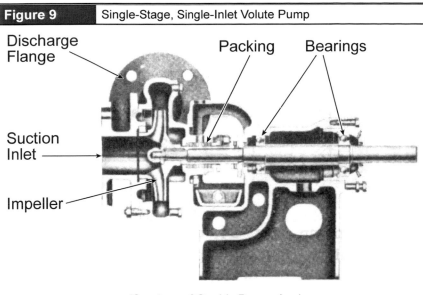

(Courtesy of Goulds Pumps Inc.)

Diffuser Pump

In the diffuser centrifugal pump, the high velocity liquid leaving the impeller passes between the vanes of a stationary diffuser ring. These vanes are shaped in such a way that the channels between them gradually increase in area.

Figure 10 shows two designs of diffuser pump.

- As the liquid passes through the diffuser channels, its velocity energy is converted into pressure energy.
- The liquid is then discharged either into a concentric casing (a) or into a volute casing (b) where further velocity-pressure conversion takes place.

Since the flow of liquid in volute and diffuser pumps is away from the centre, these pumps are often classified as **radial flow** centrifugal pumps.

Figure 10	Diffuser Pumps

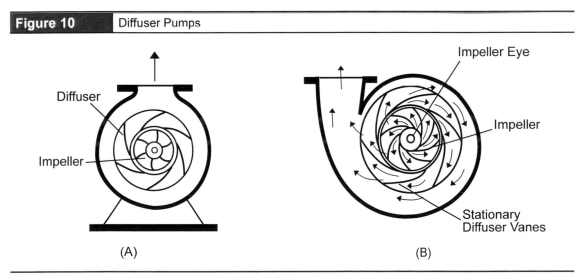

IMPELLER DESIGNS

Centrifugal pumps have three basic impeller designs. As shown in Figure 11, these are: (a) open, (b) semi-closed and (c) closed.

- **Open** impeller: From the impeller hub, the vanes extend radially, without shrouds or cover plates.

- **Semi-open** (or Semi-closed) impeller: Vanes extend radially from the hub, but one side has a cover plate.

- **Closed** impeller: Vanes extend from the hub, and both sides are protected by shrouds or cover plates.

Figure 11	Impeller Designs

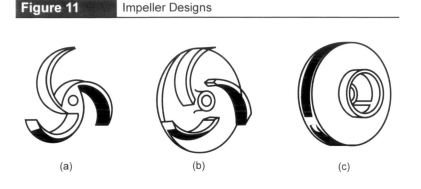

    (a)   (b)   (c)

The open and semi-open impellers are normally used on small centrifugal pumps, where the liquid being pumped contains particles or solids. Such services could be sump pumps, slurry pumps, or even sludge pumps. They allow larger particles, which would become lodged in a fully closed design, to pass through the impeller. Due to internal leakage and recirculation, these impeller designs are often less efficient than closed impeller designs. In larger pumps where the area between the vanes is larger, closed impeller designs are used, since they are more efficient. Multi-stage pumps are typically closed impeller designs.

OBJECTIVE 4

Describe centrifugal pump arrangements, including vertical, horizontal, single and double suction, opposed impellers, multi-staging, split and barrel casings.

VERTICAL PUMPS

Centrifugal pumps may be classified according to the arrangement of their mechanical parts. The most common arrangements are vertical and horizontal pumps. Vertical pumps have a vertical shaft. The pump driver (motor or turbine) is usually mounted above, with the pump below. The pump assembly often is immersed in the fluid being pumped. They can have one or multiple stages.

Figure 12 shows a large vertical propeller pump with the propeller located at the bottom.

Figure 12	Vertical Pump

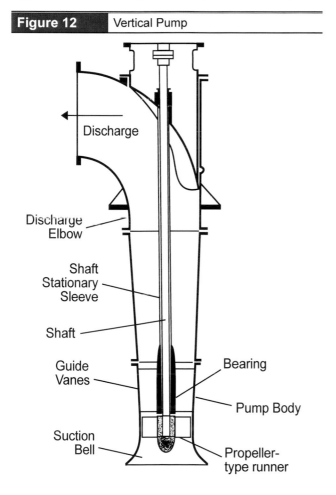

Another type of vertical pump (not shown here) is the **vertical inline** pump. In this arrangement, a centrifugal impeller is mounted at the bottom of a vertical shaft, with the motor above. The pump casing is bolted directly between inlet and discharge flanges. The impeller sits horizontally and the flow of liquid is horizontal, while the shaft is vertical.

HORIZONTAL PUMPS

Horizontal pumps are the most common, with the motor, shaft and pump running horizontal to the mounting surface. Figure 13 shows a typical horizontal pump arrangement.

Figure 13	Horizontal Single-Stage Centrifugal with Ball Bearings

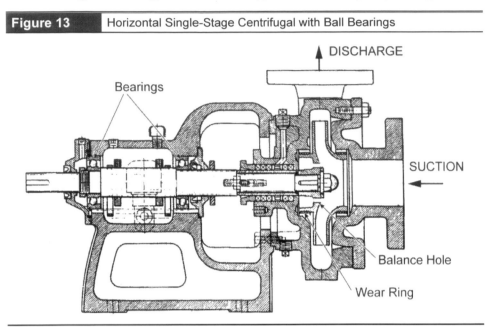

SINGLE & DOUBLE SUCTION

The single suction pump as the name implies has a single suction as in the pump above in Figure 13. Any imbalance of thrust is taken care of by mechanical means, such as a thrust bearing. A double suction pump has two suctions, as in Figure 14. The symmetry of suction and discharge passages balances out most axial forces. A small thrust bearing absorbs the remaining imbalance in thrust.

Figure 14	Double Suction Pump

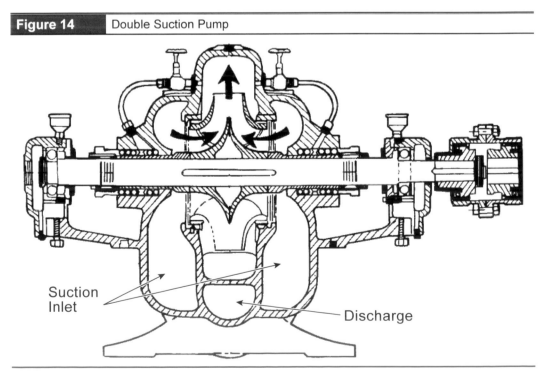

OPPOSED IMPELLERS

Pumps such as the two stage volute pump in Figure 15 can have impellers mounted opposed to each other to balance out thrust forces (see Objective 7 for discussion of thrust).

Figure 15	Two-Stage Volute Pump with Opposed Impellers

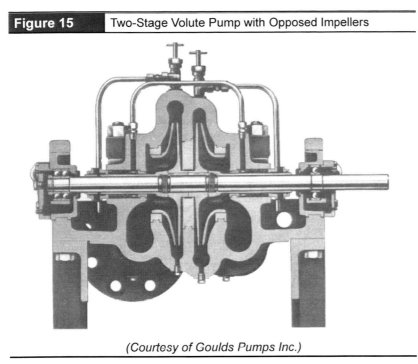

(Courtesy of Goulds Pumps Inc.)

MULTI-STAGE PUMPS

The pressure developed by a centrifugal pump with a single impeller is limited to about 1000 kPa. Many pumps, such as boiler feedwater pumps, are required to deliver much higher discharge pressures. To obtain the higher pressures, centrifugal pumps are designed with two or more impellers operating in series. The discharge of one impeller is connected to the suction of the next impeller. These pumps are classed as multi-stage pumps. The unit in Figure 16 is a five-stage, horizontal volute pump.

Figure 16	Five-Stage Volute Pump

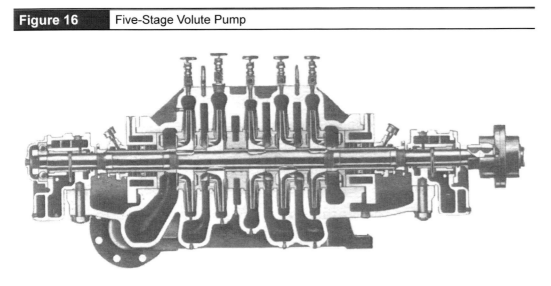

SPLIT CASINGS

Centrifugal pump casings may be split horizontally, vertically or diagonally. A horizontally split casing, also called an axially split casing, is shown in Figure 17. The suction and discharge nozzles are usually in the lower half of the casing. The upper half can be easily lifted for inspection.

Figure 17	Volute Pump with Horizontally Split Casing

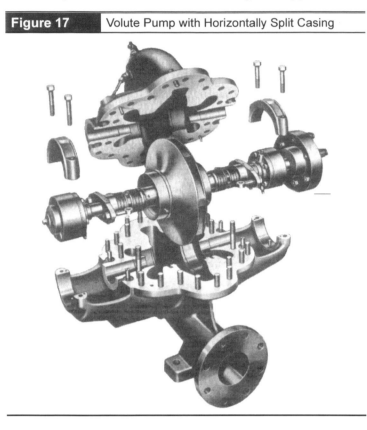

BARREL CASINGS

For multi-stage pumps of the volute or diffuser type with discharge pressures above 10 000 kPa barrel casings are used to avoid the difficulty in maintaining a tight joint between the halves of a horizontally split casing and the sections of radially split casings.

The barrel casing consists of an inner casing fitted inside an outer casing. The space between the two casings is subjected to discharge pressure, which tends to hold the sections of the inner casing together. The inner casing may be made up of two halves, horizontally joined, or a number of sections with circumferential joints. The outer casing, the barrel, has no horizontal joints, but has a removable head at one or both ends.

A cross-sectional view of a barrel type boiler feed pump is shown in Figure 18.

The inner casing is composed of individual ring sections that are joined at their circumference. This inner assembly is fitted into the outer casing through one end, which is then closed by a head.

Figure 18 | High Pressure Nine-Stage Barrel-Type Feed Pump

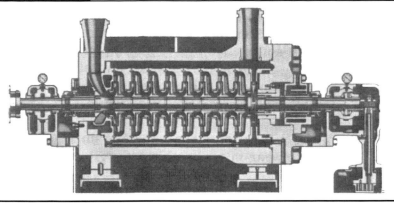

The general arrangement of the two casings is shown in Figure 19. It shows the inner casing contained within the outer barrel casing, which has suction and discharge nozzles welded into place. The inner casing, which contains the rotor and diffusers, is made up of casing rings. The rings are held together by means of tie rods and can be removed from the outer barrel as a unit without disturbing the driver or the piping. Barrel pumps are well suited to multistage, high-pressure applications.

Figure 19 | Barrel Pump Casing Arrangement

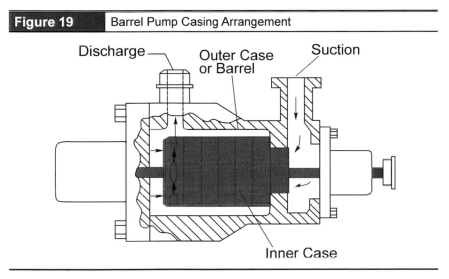

OBJECTIVE 5

Describe the design and applications of axial and mixed flow pumps.

AXIAL FLOW PUMP

The axial flow pump, Figure 20, often called a propeller pump, uses an impeller with vanes similar to a ship's propeller. The pump develops its head by the propelling or lifting action of the vanes on the liquid and the flow of the liquid is through the casing, parallel to the shaft. It is usually of vertical design, although horizontal units are available.

Figure 20	Vertical Axial Flow Pump

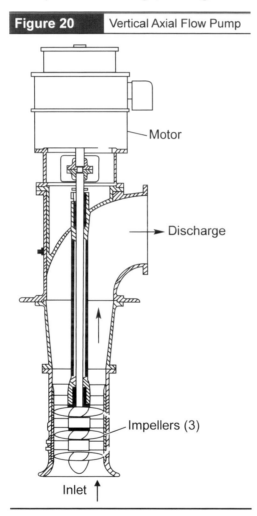

Axial flow pumps have the advantages of compact size and the ability to operate at high speeds. Their disadvantages include low suction lift capacity and a relatively low discharge head capability. They are used mainly for low head, high capacity applications and are available in the single stage design (see Fig. 12) or the multistage design (as shown in Fig. 20).

MIXED FLOW PUMP

The mixed flow pump combines some of the characteristics of the radial flow and axial flow pumps. It develops its discharge head by using both centrifugal force and lift of the vanes on the liquid.

The mixed flow pump shown in Figure 21 has a single inlet impeller with the flow entering the pump in an axial direction and leaving the pump in a direction somewhere between axial and radial. Although the mixed flow pump in Figure 21 is arranged horizontally, this type of pump, like the axial flow type, is frequently arranged for vertical operation. With the vertical arrangement the pump can be placed directly in the suction well and thus be primed at all times.

Like the axial flow pump, the mixed flow type is used mainly on low head, high capacity service and, also like the axial flow pump, it may be fitted with variable pitch impeller vanes.

Figure 21	Mixed Flow Pump

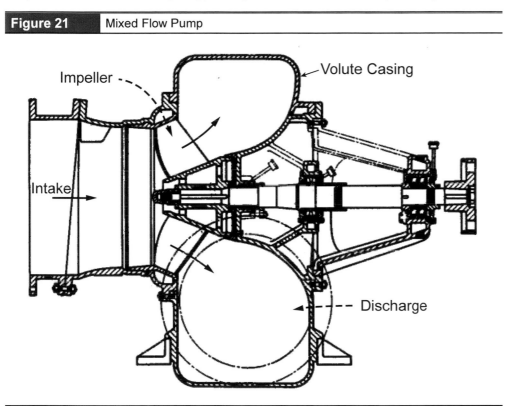

OBJECTIVE 6

Describe the design and components of a multistage centrifugal pump, clearly stating the purpose and general design of: wear rings, shaft sleeves, seals, bearings and lubrication components, vents and drains.

WEAR RINGS

The rotating impeller of the centrifugal pump must be sealed in the stationary casing with a minimum of clearance in order to keep leakage from discharge to suction as small as possible. This seal is provided by the flat joint formed by the rim around the impeller eye and a matching flat circular surface in the casing, as shown in Figure 22(a). However, during operation, the continuous leakage of the liquid through the joint will slowly wear away the surfaces of this joint and pump efficiency will drop off. When the clearance becomes too large, restoration of the original clearance will be necessary, either by building up the worn surfaces or by replacing the casing and impeller. This, however, will be quite costly for all but the smallest of pumps.

The frequency and cost of restoration can be considerably reduced by installing wear rings on the impeller, the casing, or both. The wear rings are renewable and can be replaced at a relatively low cost.

Figure 22	Wear Rings

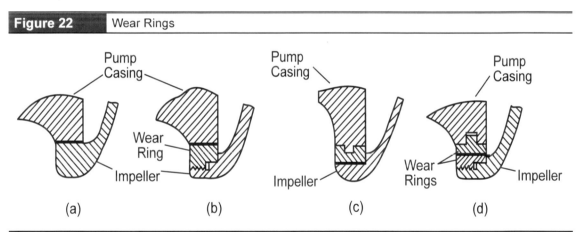

When a wear ring is mounted only on the impeller, as shown in Figure 22(b), it is made of a softer material than that of the casing so that practically all wear is on the ring. Similarly, when a ring is mounted in the casing only (c), its material will be softer than that of the impeller. Most large pumps are equipped with wear rings on the impeller as well as in the casing (d).

Wear rings are often made of bronze or cast iron since these materials tend to wear in a smooth manner. They are installed on the rim of the impeller by either threading or shrinking. Setscrews are used to prevent them from working loose. Casing wear rings consist of either a continuous ring, used in vertically split casings, or two half rings for horizontally split casings. Split rings can be fitted onto a ridge or into a groove of the casing which will prevent any axial movement should the ring work loose.

A cross-sectional view of a centrifugal pump with a double inlet impeller having wear rings on the impeller and in the casing is shown in Figure 23.

Figure 23 | Impeller and Casing Wear Rings

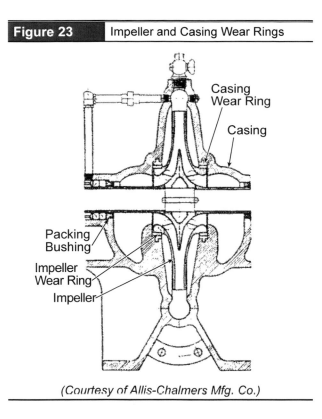

(Courtesy of Allis-Chalmers Mfg. Co.)

PUMP SHAFT SEALING

In order to minimize leakage around the pump shaft, where it passes through the casing, there are two main methods - stuffing boxes and mechanical seals

1. Stuffing Boxes

A stuffing box consists of a cylindrical recess around the shaft that holds rings of packing, which provide a seal between the casing and shaft. The packing is held in place by a gland, which can be adjusted to compress the rings. The bottom or inside end of the stuffing box may be formed by either the pump casing itself or by a bottom bushing. The basic construction of a stuffing box with five rings of packing is shown in Figure 24(a).

Figure 24 | (a) Stuffing Box with Packing | (b) Stuffing Box with Lantern Ring

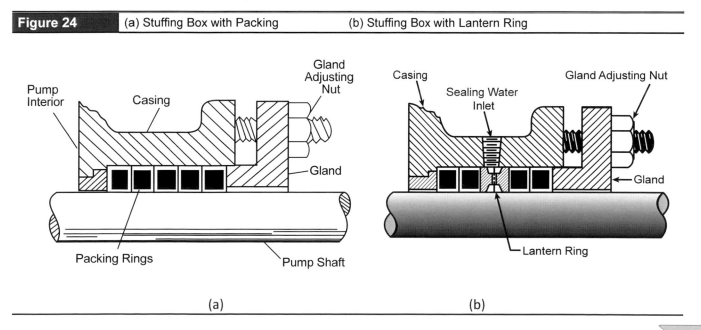

(a)   (b)

Packing rings are made of pliable, yet durable materials, such as nylon, flax or Teflon, or of metals, such as lead, copper or aluminum. They are wound as a foil around an asbestos or plastic core, forming a square cross-section. The packing is usually impregnated with a lubricant, which makes the packing self-lubricating. The packing may be purchased in continuous coils or in pre-cut rings.

Packing should never be compressed so tightly in the stuffing box that leakage is completely stopped. The resulting friction will cause excessive heat, causing the packing to burn and the shaft to be damaged by scoring. Instead, a slight leakage of liquid should be allowed to provide cooling and lubrication between packing and shaft.

When a pump operates with a negative suction pressure, the fully-packed stuffing box will not provide sufficient sealing, since air may be drawn into the casing along the shaft stopping the required leakage of liquid. To provide proper sealing, the stuffing box is then fitted with a lantern ring and a sealing water connection, as shown in Figure 24(b).

The lantern ring (also called seal cage) is a metal ring with channels machined in its inside and outside perimeter, connected by radially drilled holes. It serves to distribute sealing liquid under pressure to the packing, thus preventing air infiltration and providing lubrication. This sealing liquid is usually supplied from the high-pressure section of the pump casing, either through an external connection, as shown in Figure 25, or through a drilled passage in the casing.

Lantern rings are also useful in pumps that must handle liquids containing sand, grit or other abrasive particles, which could damage the shaft and shorten the life of the packing when allowed to enter the stuffing box. Clean sealing liquid, provided by a separate source or by the discharge side of the pump (often via a filter or separator), will then keep the gritty substances out of the stuffing box.

Figure 25	Liquid Pumped to Lantern Rings

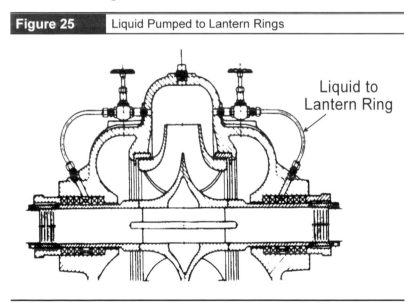

Liquid to Lantern Ring

Shaft Sleeves

Shafts are subjected to corrosion, erosion and wear at the stuffing boxes, which will affect their strength and make effective sealing with packing rings difficult. Shafts of smaller pumps are usually made of corrosion and wear-resistant materials for longer life. Renewable sleeves usually protect large pump shafts, as shown in Figure 26. The sleeve is secured on the shaft by the shaft nut. Rotation of the sleeve is prevented by a key, which joins the shaft and the sleeve.

| Figure 26 | Shaft Sleeve |

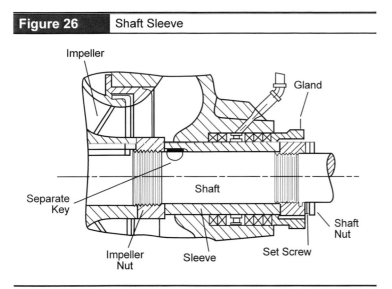

2. Mechanical Seals

Leakage from stuffing boxes is objectionable on pumps handling liquids such as gasoline, acids, and ammonia. Instead, these pumps are equipped with mechanical seals, which reduce leakage to a minute amount. They are also used on pumps where stuffing boxes cannot offer adequate leak protection such as high-pressure pumps.

Basically a mechanical seal consists of two flat rings, each with a polished flat sealing surface. The rings are perpendicular to the pump shaft and the sealing faces slide against each other. One of the rings, called the sealing ring, is made of a carbon based material, such as graphite, and is held in position by a spring. The other ring, called the mating ring, is made of a hard material, such as stellite or ceramic. Mechanical seals may be classified as rotating seals or stationary seals.

Rotating Mechanical Seal

Figure 27 shows a cut-away view of a rotating mechanical seal. Leakage between the sealing ring and shaft is prevented by a Teflon wedge ring; between mating ring and seal housing covered by a flat Teflon ring. The seal housing is provided with a quenching liquid inlet as required on pumps operating with a negative suction pressure. The liquid supplied to the seal prevents air infiltration and provides lubrication and cooling. If the liquid pumped is clear, the quenching liquid can be drawn directly from the pump discharge but if the liquid contains particles of foreign matter, a separator should be installed in the quenching line.

| Figure 27 | Rotating Seal |

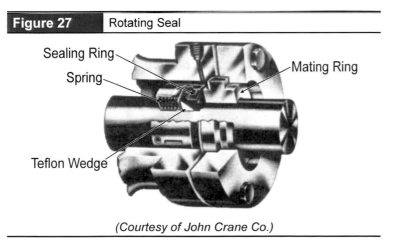

(Courtesy of John Crane Co.)

In the rotating seal sketched in Figure 28, the sealing ring and spring are held in place by a shell, which is fastened to the pump shaft with a setscrew. Therefore, the sealing ring will turn with the shaft. The mating ring, however, is held stationary within the pump casing.

As the pump shaft turns, the rotating sealing ring is forced against the mating ring, thus preventing leakage between the faces. "O" ring type seals prevent leakage between the casing and the mating ring and between the shaft and the sealing ring.

Figure 28	Rotating Seal

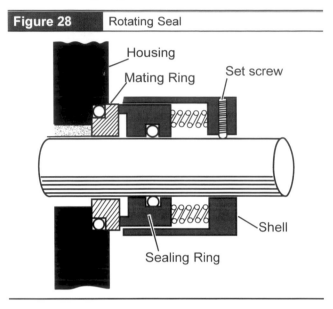

Stationary Mechanical Seal

In the stationary mechanical seal, as sketched in Figure 29, the shell containing the springs and sealing ring is held stationary in the annular space of the pump housing. The mating ring is fastened rigidly to the shaft, usually against a shoulder, so that it rotates with the shaft. The springs force the sealing ring against the mating ring so leakage between the faces is prevented. "O" rings are used to prevent leakage between the sealing ring and the shell and between the mating ring and the shaft.

Figure 29	Stationary Seal

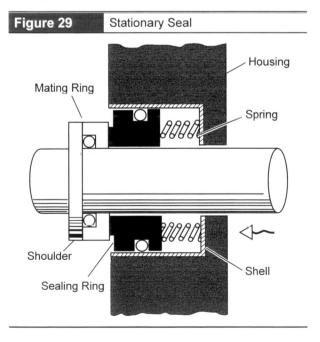

The choice of materials for sealing and mating rings depends on many factors, including the type of liquid pumped, temperature, pump speed and seal design. Materials commonly used are bronze, carbon graphite, ceramics, stellite and tungsten carbide. The friction between the faces of these rings should be kept as small as possible.

When a pump has mechanical seals, the following precautions should be taken before and during operation:

1. Never run the pump unless it is completely filled with liquid.

2. Vent all air out of the seal housings before start up.

3. Make sure an adequate flow of quenching or cooling liquid is flowing to the seals.

It is extremely important that the seals never run in a dry condition since this causes the faces to score and become grooved. Dry seal faces are often indicated by a squealing sound. Absence of this sound should not be interpreted as an indication that sufficient liquid is supplied to the seals. Any of the following may cause a mechanical seal to leak.

1. Seal faces that are scored or grooved.

2. Distortion of the rings due to unevenly tightened bolts of the seal housing gland.

3. "O" ring seals or other gaskets that are cut or nicked during installation.

4. Misalignment of piping resulting in distortion of pump parts.

5. Excessive pump shaft vibration.

PUMP BEARINGS

The functions of the bearings of a centrifugal pump are:

(1) to support the shaft carrying one or more impellers,

(2) to allow the shaft to rotate with a minimum of friction, and

(3) to keep the rotating shaft and impellers in correct position within the stationary parts of the pump.

Pump bearings can be classified into two basic types.

- sleeve and shell bearings, and
- ball and roller bearings.

Sleeve & Shell Bearings

The bearings of small pumps usually consist of bronze bushings or sleeves fitted around the shaft with a small clearance, and held in place by the bearing brackets attached to the casing. On larger pumps the sleeve-type bearing consists of two half-shells made of cast-iron or steel and lined with babbitt, shown in Figure 30. This bearing is usually self-aligning so that it adjusts itself automatically to small changes in shaft position.

Sleeve and shell bearings are usually oil-lubricated. On small pumps drip lubricators supply the oil to the bearings. Medium-sized pumps use the lower part of the bearing housing as an oil reservoir and the oil is supplied to the bearing by endless chains or rings riding on the shaft, as shown in Figure 28. Large pumps are usually equipped with a shaft-driven oil pump, which supplies the bearings with oil under pressure. The system usually has an oil tank as well as oil filters and coolers. A standby pump may also be supplied.

| **Figure 30** | Self-Aligning Shell Bearing |

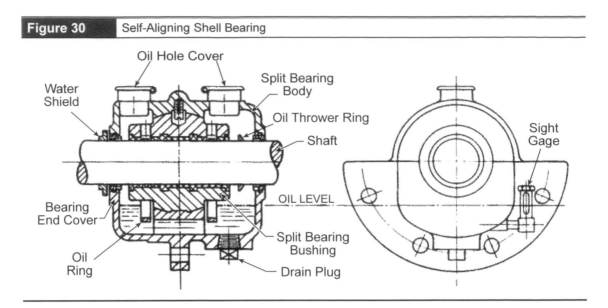

Ball & Roller Bearings

Ball and roller bearings, also called anti-friction bearings, have replaced sleeve bearings in many modern pump designs. Ball bearings of single- or double-row design are mostly used on small and medium sized shafts; roller bearings are widely used on larger shafts. Anti-friction bearings may be lubricated either by oil or grease. Figure 31 shows a single-stage centrifugal pump fitted with oil lubricated, single-row ball bearings.

| **Figure 31** | Single-Stage Centrifugal Pump with Ball Bearings |

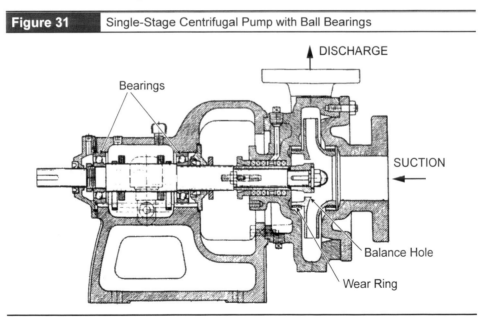

VENTS & DRAINS

All centrifugal pumps are fitted with a drain line to allow the casing to be drained of the operating fluid. The drain line is fitted with an isolation valve as near the pump casing as is practical. A vent line is also connected to the top of the casing, also with an isolation valve. The vent valve can be opened when the drain valve is open to enable the pump casing to completely drain. The drain valve can be closed and the suction valve opened, when filling the pump again. The vent valve is closed when liquid reaches that point. The vent and drain piping is a very necessary part of any pumping system.

OBJECTIVE 7

Explain design features that eliminate thrust in large centrifugal pumps.

AXIAL THRUST

During operation a single-inlet impeller is subjected to hydraulic forces, which create an axial unbalance. This is illustrated in Figure 32, which shows that the area of the eye of the impeller is subjected to suction pressure while the partial shroud on that side and the full shroud on the opposite side are subjected to discharge pressure. The resulting imbalance causes an axial thrust towards the suction that tends to move the impeller out of its proper position in the casing.

Figure 32	Unbalanced Axial Thrust

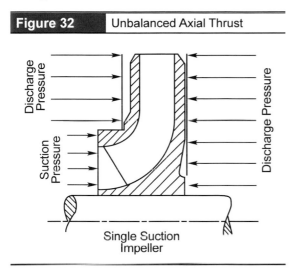

Single Suction Impeller

On low capacity, single-stage pumps, axial movement of the impeller is usually prevented by installation of a thrust bearing on the shaft. On larger capacity, single-stage pumps, however, the axial imbalance is eliminated by one of the following methods.

Single-Inlet Impeller with Backside Wearing Ring & Balancing Holes

As shown in Figure 31, the single-inlet impeller is equipped with a wear ring on its backside with the same diameter as the one on the suction side. By connecting the space inside this ring to the suction side by means of balancing holes, axial balance is achieved.

Double-Inlet Impeller

By using a double-inlet impeller the forces on the impeller are theoretically balanced, as shown in Figure 33. However, in reality the flow to each eye of the impeller is not always equal so there is still some imbalance of thrust and a light thrust bearing is still required.

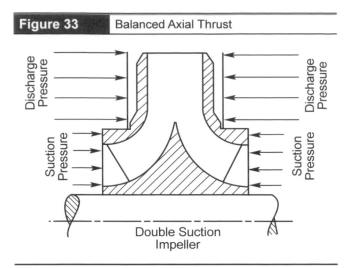

Figure 33 | Balanced Axial Thrust

Double Suction Impeller

Opposing Single-Inlet Impellers

On multi-stage pumps with single-inlet impellers, the axial thrust can be eliminated by the use of opposed impellers. The inlets of one half of the impellers face in one direction, the other half in opposite direction (refer back to Figures 13 and 14). With this arrangement, axial thrust on the first half of the impellers is counter-acted by the opposing axial thrust on the second half.

On multi-stage pumps with single-inlet impellers all facing in one direction, the axial thrust toward the suction end of the pump will theoretically equal the sum of the individual impeller thrusts. This total thrust is partially or fully counter-acted by one of the following hydraulic balancing devices: a balancing drum, balancing disc or combination of drum and disc.

Balancing Drum

A balancing drum, illustrated in Figure 34, is installed on the shaft between the last impeller and the balancing chamber, which is connected to the suction side of the pump. The drum rotates inside the stationary member of the balancing device, the balancing drumhead. The drum and the head are separated by a small clearance allowing some leakage from the high-pressure side of the pump to the low-pressure chamber.

The drum is subjected to two forces: the discharge pressure acting on area B and the suction pressure acting on area C. Since the first force is greater than the second, an axial thrust is produced toward the discharge side of the pump. This thrust counter-acts the axial thrust exerted on the impellers.

Figure 34 | Balancing Drum

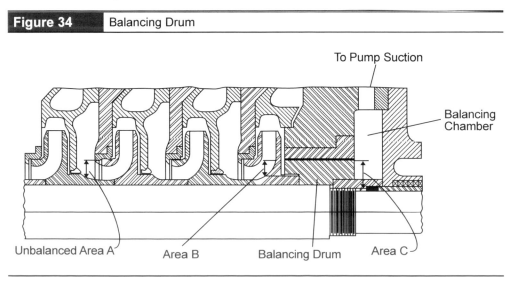

To Pump Suction

Balancing Chamber

Unbalanced Area A   Area B   Balancing Drum   Area C

Balancing Disc

The simple balancing disc consists of a disc mounted on, and rotating with the shaft. It is separated from the balancing disc head attached to the casing by a small axial clearance. The leakage from the high pressure side of the pump flows through this clearance into the low pressure balancing chamber and from there to the suction of the pump via a restricting orifice that normally keeps the pressure in the balancing chamber well above the suction pressure. A simple balancing disc is shown in Figure 35.

Figure 35	Simple Balancing Disc

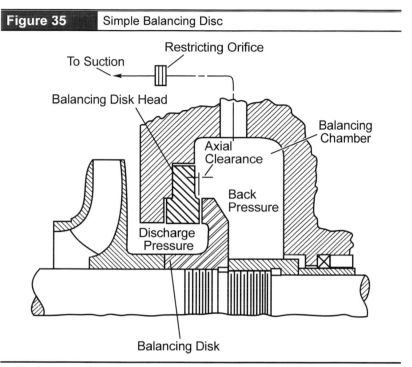

The back of the disc is subjected to the balancing chamber backpressure, while the centre part of the front of the disc is subjected to full discharge pressure and the ring area facing the head, to a pressure gradually dropping from discharge pressure to balancing chamber back pressure. The difference in forces acting on the front and back of the disc produces an axial thrust, which balances the axial thrust on the single-inlet impellers. When the thrusts are balanced, the clearance between disc and head will be a specific amount and the backpressure will be maintained at a specific value.

During operation, if the axial thrust on the impellers increases and exceeds the thrust acting on the disc, the shaft will move slightly over toward the suction side of the pump, causing the clearance between disc and head to be reduced. This reduces the liquid leakage resulting in a drop in backpressure on the disc, which, in turn, causes the thrust on the disc to increase so that it moves away from the head, increasing the clearance again. The increased leakage builds up the backpressure again until equilibrium in thrusts is reached. The opposite will happen when the thrust on the impellers decreases below the thrust on the disc.

While the balancing drum provides only counter-thrust, the balancing disc provides not only counter-thrust but it also restores automatically, the position of shaft and impellers if it changes position due to variations in axial thrust. The use of a simple balancing disc, however, has certain disadvantages and it is therefore seldom used. Most multi-stage pumps are now equipped with a combination of balancing drum, and disc. This combination has all the advantages of both hydraulic devices without their disadvantages.

OBJECTIVE 8

Describe systems used to maintain minimum flow through a centrifugal pump.

MINIMUM FLOW CONTROL VALVE

It is imperative that the flow thorough a multistage pump be kept above a minimum flow rate. The manufacturer of the pump sets the flow rate. Flows below this minimum flow result in overheating of the fluid being pumped and eventually overheating and damage to the pump components. Cavitation may also occur, causing damage to the pump (see Chapter 13, Objective 6 for explanation of "cavitation"). Since it is critical to maintain at least the minimum flow, piping designs incorporate valve arrangements to guarantee the minimum flow will be met.

The standard method is to have a separate recirculation control valve, which allows for liquid to flow back to the pump suction drum. It is called a control valve or control loop system. For a boiler feed pump it means a recirculation line returning to the deaerator.

A typical arrangement is shown in Figure 36.

The flow-sensing orifice on the suction of the pump sends a signal to the FIC (flow controller). The FIC will open the regulation control valve if the flow drops below the FIC set point. The control valve allows liquid to be returned to the deaerator, or recirculated. When the flow is above the set point of the FIC the control valve will be closed.

The total flow will be sent to the boiler.

Figure 36	Pump with Recirculation Control Valve

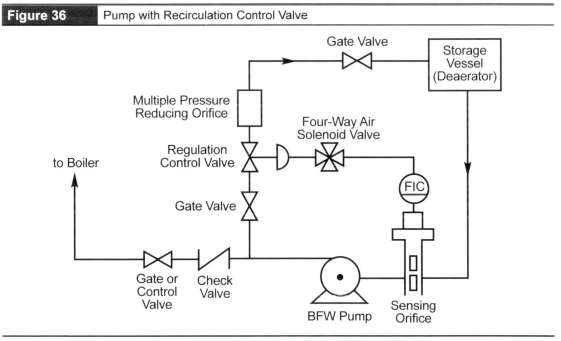

AUTOMATIC RECIRCULATION VALVE SYSTEM

Another way of accomplishing the same thing is shown in Figure 37. It uses an automatic recirculation valve. This is a combination check valve and minimum flow valve in one unit. Below the pump minimum flow, the check valve (disc) is closed and the bypass valve is open. When the check valve opens, the bypass element gradually shuts. Thus the pump's minimum flow is always maintained. The ARC valve is sized specifically to match the flow rate of the pump.

Figure 37	Pump with Automatic Recirculation Valve

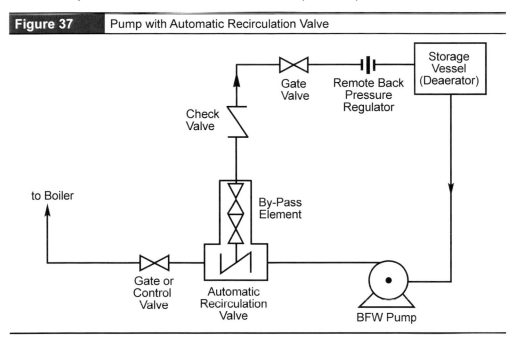

Figure 38 is a cutaway of an automatic recirculation valve. It shows the valve in the recirculation position, with the main flow disc closed and the recirculation valve open.

Figure 38	ARC Valve Cutaway

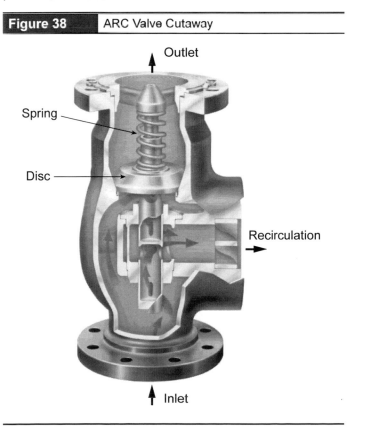

OBJECTIVE 9

Explain priming, start-up, capacity control and operating cautions for centrifugal pumps.

PRIMING OF PUMPS

The term "priming," as used in connection with pumps, simply means the filling of pump casing and suction line with the liquid to be pumped, before the pump is started. Positive displacement pumps, reciprocating and rotary, are self-priming for total suction lifts up to about eight metres at sea level when in perfect condition. But with long suction lines, high lifts, or poor mechanical condition, they must be primed.

Centrifugal pumps are not self-priming. They must be primed before start-up otherwise the impeller will simply churn air and no suction will be produced. Also, when the pump is started without proper priming, the mechanical seals will run dry causing the seal faces to score or, if stuffing boxes are used, shaft and packing rings may wear. Some of the methods used to prime a centrifugal pump are shown in Figure 39.

Figure 39	Pump Priming Methods

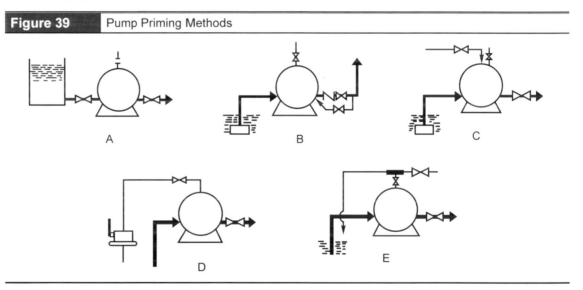

During priming of a centrifugal pump, the discharge valve is closed. When the pump is below the source of supply, as in Figure 39(A), the pump has positive suction head. It is primed by opening the air vent valves on the pump casing, then slowly opening the suction valve. The incoming liquid forces the air out of the casing. When the liquid flows through the vents, they can be closed. The pump is then primed and ready to be started.

When the pump is located above the source of supply, (pump has suction lift), various methods of priming can be used. The suction line should be equipped with a foot valve, a flap-type valve attached to the lowest part of the suction line. The foot valve acts as a check valve. The foot valve allows the liquid to enter the line but prevents liquid from draining out of the line.

Figure 39(B) shows how the pump can be primed by filling suction line and casing with liquid supplied through a bypass around the discharge valve. Vents are kept open until the liquid escapes. In C, the suction line and casing are filled by liquid supplied through an auxiliary line. In D, a separate priming pump is used to draw the air from the casing, creating a vacuum, which draws the liquid in through the foot valve. The same result can be achieved by the use of an ejector as shown in E.

PUMP CAPACITY CONTROL

Reciprocating and rotary pumps are classified as positive displacement pumps, which means that, at a constant speed, they move a specific amount of liquid regardless of pump head. Varying their speed usually regulates the capacity or flow rate through these pumps. The capacity of centrifugal pumps, however, changes when the pump head changes. Hence, this pump is not a positive displacement pump. When the head is increased, the capacity of the pump decreases and when the head is lowered, the capacity increases. When the head is increased so much that it exceeds the design head of the pump, the output drops to zero.

Varying the speed can regulate the capacity of a centrifugal pump but this requires a pump driver capable of varying its speed (steam turbine, internal combustion engine, variable speed electric motor (VFD), etc. Most centrifugal pumps are driven by a constant speed electric motor.

When driven by a constant speed electric motor, the capacity of volute and diffuser pumps (the radial flow type) can be regulated by adjusting the discharge valve. Throttling the discharge valve increases the flow resistance, thus enlarging the friction head, and reducing the flow. The discharge pressure of the pump will increase moderately, but not enough to endanger the pump as with positive displacement pumps. Even with the discharge valve completely closed, the pressure increase will be well within safe limits.

When the flow is throttled, the power requirement of the radial flow centrifugal pump is also reduced, even with the resulting pressure increase. Advantage is taken of this fact by starting large, electrical motor-driven centrifugal pumps with closed or nearly closed discharge valve. Since the no-flow power requirement is relatively small, excessive power surging during start-up can be avoided.

The power requirement of axial and mixed flow centrifugal pumps, when operated at low capacity, is actually higher than at full capacity. These pumps should always be started with the discharge valve wide open.

OPERATING CAUTIONS

- Never run a centrifugal pump continuously with the discharge valve completely closed. The mechanical power applied to the impeller is dispelled as friction to the water trapped and churned about in the casing. This friction causes overheating of the water to the point where it turns into steam, which may result in damage to the pump. This is known as cavitation due to friction.

- Always operate a centrifugal pump with its suction valve wide open. Never use the suction valve for flow control. Throttling or closing of the suction valve starves the impeller of its supply of water. The casing becomes partially empty resulting in excessive vibrations, which may ruin the bearings. The lack of liquid may also damage mechanical seals and stuffing boxes. If the water temperature is high enough, this reduction in pressure can cause cavitation to occur.

CHAPTER 12 - QUESTIONS

1. Explain how a diaphragm pump differs from a piston pump.

2. Sketch a sliding vane pump and describe its principle of operation.

3. Name four ways in which centrifugal pumps may be classified.

4. What is the purpose of a diffuser in a centrifugal pump?

5. Sketch and describe a centrifugal pump with opposed impellers. What is the advantage of this arrangement?

6. Using a simple sketch, describe a stationary mechanical seal.

7. What are three ways of balancing thrust in a centrifugal pump?

8. Using a simple sketch, describe a pumping system with an automatic recirculation valve.

9. What types of pumps require priming? Which types of pumps are self-priming?

10. How is the flow from a centrifugal pump controlled or regulated? Is this different than a positive displacement pump? Explain.

ANSWERS: All answers are found within the content of the chapter.

Pump Head Calculations

LEARNING OUTCOME

When you complete this chapter you should be able to:

Define terms associated with pumping and perform pump head calculations.

LEARNING OBJECTIVES

Here is what you should be able to do when you complete each objective:

1. Explain the relationship between the height of a liquid, the density of the liquid and the pressure exerted at the bottom of the liquid. Perform simple calculations involving this relationship.

2. Define equivalent head and calculate equivalent heads for water and other liquids.

3. Define static suction head, static suction lift, static discharge head, total static head, pressure head, and calculate each of these for a given pump arrangement.

4. Define and calculate friction head and velocity head.

5. Define dynamic suction head, dynamic suction lift, dynamic discharge head, total dynamic head, and calculate each of these for a given pump arrangement.

6. Explain vapour pressure, cavitation, and net positive suction head. Calculate the required suction pressure for a water pump, given the manufacturers required NPSH.

OBJECTIVE 1

Explain the relationship between the height of a liquid, the density of the liquid and the pressure exerted at the bottom of the liquid. Perform simple calculations involving this relationship.

PRESSURE DUE TO LIQUID HEIGHT

When a liquid exists at a certain level in a container, the liquid creates a downward force, due to its mass, on the bottom of the container. Because this force is distributed evenly over the base, a pressure results and is given by:

$$\text{Pressure} = \frac{\text{Force}}{\text{Area}}$$

The amount of force at the base, and hence the amount of pressure, is dependent on the height of the liquid level above the base. If the height increases, then the pressure also increases.

In Figure 1, a square tank is filled to a level, 'h' metres, with liquid. The area of the tank is 'A' square metres and a pressure gauge is connected to measure the pressure, 'P', in kilopascals (kPa), at the base of the tank.

Figure 1	Liquid Head and Pressure in a Tank

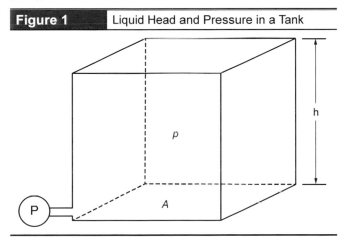

Using the formula, Pressure (P) = Force (F)/Area (A), we can determine the pressure at the base of the tank, in relation to the height of liquid, as follows:

Force (due to gravity acting on the liquid) equals the mass times the acceleration due to gravity:

$$\text{Force} = \text{mass} \times \text{acceleration}$$

or 	$$F = m\,g$$

Note that force (in Newtons) is equal to mass (in kg) times acceleration (in m/s^2).

by substitution, then:

$$\text{Pressure} = \frac{mg}{A}$$

The mass of the liquid can be found from its known density, where the density is the mass per unit volume, or

$$\text{Density } (\rho) = \frac{\text{mass (m)}}{\text{volume (V)}}$$

therefore

$$\text{mass (m)} = \text{volume (V)} \times \text{density } (\rho)$$

Substituting this for mass in the pressure formula gives:

$$\text{Pressure (P)} = \frac{V\rho g}{A}$$

but   Volume = area × height, or V = Ah

so $$P = \frac{Ah\rho g}{A}$$

which simplifies to $$P = h\rho g$$

The pressure at the bottom of the liquid is therefore equal to the height of the liquid, times the density of the liquid, times acceleration due to gravity.

The units of measurement for these factors are as follows:

Pressure(P) N/m^2 or Pa

Height (h)   m

Density (ρ) kg/m^3

Gravity (g)   9.81 m/s^2

Example 1

An open, cylindrical tank contains a liquid to a height of 7.5 m. If the density of the liquid is 4.5 x 10^3 kg/m^3, what is the pressure exerted by the liquid at the bottom of the tank?

Solution

$$P = h\rho g$$
$$= 7.5 \text{ m} \times 4.5 \times 10^3 \text{ kg/m}^3 \times 9.81 \text{ m/s}^2$$
$$= 331\ 100 \text{ N/m}^2$$
$$= 331\ 100 \text{ Pa}$$
$$= \textbf{331.1 kPa (Ans.)}$$

Example 2

A pressure gauge is located in the side of a tank at 2 m up from the bottom, which is the minimum tank level to ensure suction to the pumps. If the gauge reads 260 kPa and the level in the tank is 8 m, what is the density of the liquid in the tank?

Solution

$$P = h\rho g$$
or $$\rho = \frac{P}{hg}$$
$$= \frac{260 \times 10^3 \text{ N/m}^2}{(8-2)\text{m} \times 9.81 \text{ m/s}^2}$$
$$= \textbf{4.417} \times \textbf{10}^3 \textbf{ kg/m}^3 \textbf{ (Ans.)}$$

Self Test Problems

1. A process solution has a density of 3.4×10^3 kg/m^3 and is held in a rubber-lined tank that is 9 metres high. If the tank is exactly 2/3 full, what reading, in kPa, would the operator see on a level-indicating pressure gauge, located at the base of the tank?

(Ans. 200 kPa)

OBJECTIVE 2

Define 'equivalent head' and calculate equivalent heads for water and other liquids.

EQUIVALENT HEAD

In the previous discussion we used the word 'height' to refer to the level of the liquid. In practice, however, particularly when dealing with pumps, it is common to refer to this liquid height as the **head** of the liquid.

In Figure 1, the pressure, P, at the bottom of the tank is a result of the height, or head, of the liquid surface above the location of the pressure gauge. While the pressure gauge will normally indicate a pressure, in kPa, it would be possible, and quite correct, to convert this pressure to an **equivalent head** measurement. The equivalent head is the height of liquid that produced the indicated pressure. In a simple system this can be found by rearranging the formula, P = h ρ g, as follows:

$$\text{Head (h)} = \frac{\text{pressure}}{\text{density x gravity}}$$

or

$$h = \frac{P}{\rho g}$$

Yes, this is the same equation we established in Objective 1, but here we are simply changing the terminology to indicate head pressure.

Equivalent Head for Water

The density of water at 4°C is 1000 kg/m³. Therefore, a column of water 1 metre high, at this temperature, would exert a pressure of:

$$P = h \rho g$$
$$= 1 \text{ m} \times 1000 \text{ kg/m}^3 \times 9.81 \text{ m/s}^2$$
$$= 9810 \text{ Pa} = 9.81 \text{ kPa}$$

It follows that, since 9.81 kPa is equal to 1 m of head, then

$$1 \text{ kPa} = 1/9.81 \text{ m} = 0.102 \text{ m of head}$$

That is, the equivalent head of 1 kPa pressure, for water at 4°C, is 0.102 metres.

Note: When considering water at any temperature other than 4°C, it is necessary to realize that the density of the water will not be exactly 1000 kg/m³. The correct density may be found using the value of specific volume, v_f, listed in Table II of the Steam Tables, and the formula:

$$\rho = \frac{1.0}{v_f} \text{ gm/cm}^3 \text{ or } \frac{1000}{v_f} \text{ kg/m}^3$$

For example, if the water temperature is 80°C, the density will be:

$$\rho = \frac{1000}{1.0291} \text{ kg/m}^3 = 971.7 \text{ kg/m}^3$$

Example 3

What height of water is necessary to exert a pressure of 1 kPa at a temperature of 150°C? (Use Steam Tables to find v_f)

Solution

$$P = h\rho g$$

or $\quad h = \dfrac{P}{\rho g}$

we know $\quad P = $ 1 kPa or 1000 Pa = 1000 N/m²

$\quad g = $ 9.81 m/s²

and $\quad \rho = \dfrac{1.0}{v_f \text{ at } 150°C}$

$\quad = \dfrac{1.0}{1.0905 \text{ cm}^3/\text{g}}$

$\quad = $ 0.917 g/cm³ or 917 kg/m³

therefore $\quad h = \dfrac{1000 \text{ N/m}^2}{917 \text{ kg/m}^3 \times 9.81 \text{ m/s}^2}$

$\quad = $ **0.1112 m (Ans.)**

Example 4

The pressure at the discharge of a water pump is 150 kPa and the temperature of the water is 80°C. Find the equivalent head in metres.

Solution

$\quad h = \dfrac{P}{\rho g}$

$\quad P = $ 150 kPa or 150 000 Pa

$\quad g = $ 9.81 N/kg

$\quad \rho = \dfrac{1.0}{1.0291 \times 10^{-3} \text{ m}^3/\text{kg}}$

$\quad = $ 971.72 kg/m³

therefore $\quad h = \dfrac{150\,000}{971.72 \times 9.81}$

$\quad = $ **15.74 m (Ans.)**

Equivalent Head for Liquids Other than Water

If the liquid is anything other than water, then the liquid's relative density must be known in order to determine heads and pressures. Remember that the relative density of a substance is the density of the substance divided by the density of water, or:

$$\text{Relative density} = \frac{\text{density (kg/m}^3)}{1000 \text{ kg/m}^3}$$

therefore

$$\text{Density (} \rho \text{)} = \text{Relative density} \times 1000 \text{ kg/m}^3$$

Example 5

If a column of mercury has an equivalent head of 50 cm, calculate the pressure produced at the bottom of the column. Relative density of mercury is 13.6.

Solution

$$P = h \rho g$$

$$\text{where} \quad h = 0.5 \text{ m}$$

$$g = 9.81 \text{ m/s}^2$$

$$\rho = 13.6 \times 1000 \text{ kg/m}^3$$

$$\text{therefore} \quad P = 0.5 \text{ m} \times 13\ 600 \text{ kg/m}^3 \times 9.81 \text{ m/s}^2$$

$$= \textbf{66 708 Pa or 66.7 kPa (Ans.)}$$

Note: It is interesting to realize that the pressures exerted by equal heights of different liquids differ by a factor of their densities. The greater the relative density of the liquid, then the greater will be the pressure exerted by the column. For example, if the column of mercury in Example 5 were replaced with water, the pressure would be:

$$P = h \rho g = 0.5 \times 1000 \times 9.81 = 4905 \text{ Pa or } 4.905 \text{ kPa}$$

Notice that the pressure due to the mercury is equal to 13.6 times the pressure due to the equal height of water.

Example 6

Two open tanks are filled to the same level, but with different liquids. In tank A the liquid has a relative density of 4.32 and the pressure at the base of the tank is 58 kPa. What is the pressure at the base of tank B if the liquid in it has a relative density of 1.45?

Solution

$$\text{Pressure at tank B} = \frac{\text{relative density of B}}{\text{relative density of A}} \times \text{pressure at tank A}$$

$$P = \frac{1.45}{4.32} \times 58 \text{ kPa}$$

$$= \textbf{19.47 kPa (Ans.)}$$

Self Test Problems

2. Water in a treated water storage tank is at 90°C. If the pressure at the bottom of the tank is 42 kPa, what is the water level in the tank?

   (Given that v_f at 90°C = 1.036)

   (Ans. 4.45 m)

3. A raw water supply pump is sitting idle with its discharge valve open. The equivalent discharge head is known to be 35 metres and the water is at 70°C. What pressure, in kPa, should be indicating on the pump discharge gauge?

   (Given v_f at 70°C = 1.0228)

   (Ans. 336 kPa)

4. A chemical in a storage tank has a relative density of 7.60. What is the equivalent head at the outlet of the tank where a pressure gauge reads 250 kPa?

   (Ans 3.35 m)

5. Two tanks sit side by side, with equal levels in the two tanks. However, pressure gauges (assumed accurate) at the bottom of the tanks read differently. The gauge on tank A reads 120 kPa, while the gauge on tank B reads 210 kPa. Compare the densities of the liquids in the two tanks.

   (Ans. Density of tank B = 1.7 times the density of tank A)

OBJECTIVE 3

Define static suction head, static suction lift, static discharge head, total static head, and pressure head, and calculate each of these for a given pump arrangement.

INTRODUCTION TO PUMP HEAD

In general, a pump is designed to move a liquid through a certain maximum head. That is, the size, speed and design of the pump are chosen so it is capable of pumping the liquid through an equivalent height of the liquid. This total height (or head) of liquid becomes a measure of the pump's ability to move the liquid.

For example, if two pumps in a system are taking a liquid from the same suction source, but one pump is delivering the liquid to a height of 50 feet and the other to a height of only 30 feet, then the pump discharging to 50 feet must be designed for a greater head.

There are many factors that determine the equivalent head through which a pump must deliver a liquid and for which the pump must be designed. These factors include liquid levels, vessel pressures, pipe friction, and liquid velocity.

STATIC HEAD

The word "static" implies zero motion. In a pumping system, the pump is required to move a liquid from a source location, on the suction side of the pump, to a destination location, on the discharge side of the pump. In most cases, both the source and the destination contain a level of liquid in some reservoir, or vessel. The levels of the liquid in the suction and discharge sides of the pump create respective head pressures that are equivalent to the height of the liquid above the pump. Since these heads exist, even if the pump is not in operation, they are referred to as static heads.

Figure 2 shows the two most common arrangements of a pump in relation to the suction and discharge reservoirs. In both cases we will assume that the reservoirs are open-top tanks, exposed only to atmospheric pressure.

Explanations of static head terms follow the figure.

| Figure 2 | Pump Static Head Arrangements |

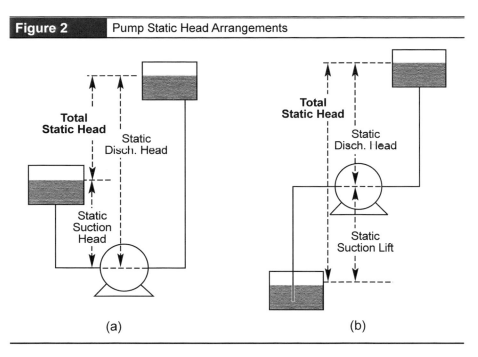

(a)   (b)

Static Suction Head

In Figure 2(a), the pump is located below the suction source and the height of the liquid creates a positive head on the suction side of the pump. This head is termed the **static suction head**. It is defined as the vertical distance, in metres, from the center line of the pump UP to the surface of the liquid in the suction source above the pump. Static suction head assists the pump by forcing water down into the suction.

Static Suction Lift

In Figure 2(b), the pump is located above the suction source. In this case, the pump is required to "lift" the liquid from the source to the pump inlet before it can deliver the water into the discharge. The equivalent head required to lift the liquid is called the **static suction lift**. It is defined as the distance, in metres, from the centre line of the pump DOWN to the surface of the suction liquid below the pump.

Static Discharge Head

In both (a) and (b) of Figure 2, the pump is discharging to a tank that is located above the pump. The pump is required to overcome the head created by the height of the liquid, in order to pump liquid up to the tank. This head is called the **static discharge head**. It is defined as the distance, in metres, from the center line of the pump UP to the surface of the liquid in the discharge tank, located above the pump, or to the height of free discharge. 'Free discharge' refers to the open end of a pump discharge line.

Figure 3 demonstrates this with a pump discharging into the side of a tank at a point that is above the liquid level in the tank. Here the static discharge head is the height, above the pump, at which the line enters the tank, since this is the maximum height to which the liquid must be pumped.

Figure 3	Static Discharge Head above Liquid Level

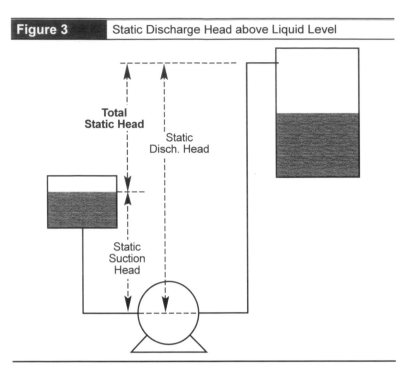

Total Static Head

The total head effect of liquid levels on a pump is referred to as the total static head. By definition, the total static head is the distance, in metres, from the surface of the suction source to the surface of the discharge tank (or to the point of free discharge). Referring back to Figure 2, one can see that:

for a pump with suction lift:

Total Static Head = static discharge head + static suction lift

and for a pump with suction head:

Total Static Head = static discharge head - static suction head

Example 7

A pump sits in a sump and takes suction from an open tank, located 2 metres above it and having a water level of 3.5 metres. The pump discharges into the bottom of an open tank that is 8 metres above the pump. When the pump is shut down and its suction valve (located at the pump) is closed, the discharge pressure gauge indicates 130 kPa. Assuming the water is at 4°C, what is the level in the discharge tank and what is the total static head for the pump?

Solution

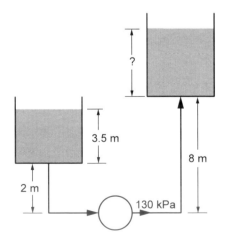

For water at 4°C,   1 kPa = 0.102 m of head

therefore   130 kPa = 130 × 0.102 = 13.26 m

and   the tank level = 13.26 m - 8 m

$$= \textbf{5.26 m (Ans.)}$$

Total static head = static discharge head - static suction head

$$= 13.26 \text{ m} - (2 + 3.5) \text{ m}$$

$$= 13.26 - 5.5 \text{ m}$$

$$= \textbf{7.76 m (Ans.)}$$

Example 8

A rotary pump draws oil from a waste collection sump and delivers it into a storage tank. The level in the sump is 2 m below the base of the storage tank and the level in the tank is 4.5 m. If the pump sits 1 m above the tank base and discharges into the side of the tank at a height of 3 m, what is the total static head on the pump?

Solution

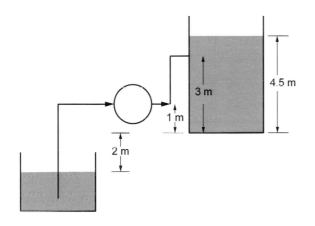

Static suction lift = 2 m + 1 m = 3 m

Static discharge head = 4.5 m - 1 m = 3.5 m

Total static head = 3 m + 3.5 m = **6.5 m (Ans.)**

PRESSURE HEAD

So far we have considered suction and discharge reservoirs that are open to atmosphere. However, in many process situations a pump is required to take suction from one pressure vessel and transfer it to another. The pump must move a liquid against the internal pressure of the vessel into which it is discharging. This pressure creates an equivalent head on the discharge side of the pump. Also, if the suction source is pressurized, then this suction pressure creates an equivalent suction head on the pump.

Pressure head is defined as the equivalent head, in metres of liquid, exerted on a pump by the internal pressure of a closed vessel into which the pump discharges or from which it takes suction.

Figure 4 shows a similar arrangement to Figure 2, except that the suction and discharge vessels are pressurized.

Figure 4	Pressure Heads on a Pump

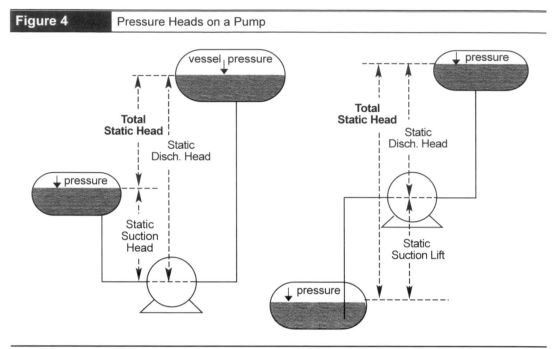

Notice in Figure 4 that the static suction and discharge heads still exist, due to the levels of the liquids in the vessels. However, the total head on each side of the pump is increased by the addition of the internal pressure. In the case of suction lift in Figure 4(b), the pressure in the suction vessel aids in the lift of the liquid. If the pressure head in the suction vessel is greater than the static suction lift, there will be a positive suction head on the pump.

Example 9

A feedwater pump supplies water to a boiler, which is operating at 700 kPa. If the water enters the boiler at a height of 8 m above the pump and 30 cm below the boiler water level, what is the discharge head of the pump? Ignore the effects of water temperature.

Solution

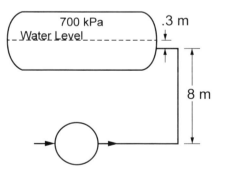

$$1 \text{ kPa} = 0.102 \text{ m head}$$

therefore   Pressure head $= 700 \times 0.102 = 71.4$ m

static discharge head $= 8$ m $+ 0.30$ m $= 8.30$ m

and   Total discharge head $= 71.4$ m $+ 8.30$ m $= \textbf{79.7 m (Ans.)}$

Example 10

Calculate the pressure differential across the pump in a pressurized water system if the liquid level in the suction vessel is 3 m below the pump and the vessel has a gas blanket of 45 kPa, the discharge pressure head is 150 m and the discharge level is 18.5 m above the pump.

Solution

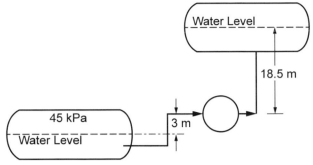

Suction pressure head = 45 × 0.102 m = 4.59 m

Total suction head = 4.59 - 3 m = 1.59 m

so: Suction pressure = 1.59/0.102 = 15.59 kPa

Total discharge head = 150 m + 18.5 m = 168.5 m

Discharge pressure = 168.5 × 9.81

= 1653 kPa

Pressure differential = 1653 - 15.59

= **1637.41 kPa (Ans.)**

Self Test Problems

6. A pump is sitting at rest with its discharge valve open and the pressure gauge showing 210 kPa. The total static head of the pump in this situation is 11 m. If the pump takes suction from a transfer tank located 4 m above it, what is the current level in the transfer tank? The liquid is water at 42°C.

   (Ans. 6.59 m)

7. A pump sits in a pit at the bottom of a chemical sump, which has a level of 2.6 m. At rest, the pump discharge indicates a pressure of 300 kPa. The pump delivers to a storage tank located above it. If the relative density of the chemical is 1.73, find (a) the static discharge head of the pump, and (b) the total static head

   (Ans. (a) 17.68 m, (b) 15.08 m)

8. A deaerator has a pressure of 100 kPa and supplies feedwater to a boiler, which operates at 1200 kPa. If the standby feedwater pump is located 7 m below the water level in the deaerator and 6 m below the water level in the boiler, what is the total head on the pump, ignoring water temperature?

   (Ans. 111.1 m)

OBJECTIVE 4

Define and calculate friction head and velocity head.

FRICTION HEAD

When a liquid flows through a system it encounters resistance to flow due to physical contact with the surfaces of pipes, valves and fittings. This resistance is commonly referred to as friction. The frictional resistance causes a pressure drop in the liquid, in the direction of flow.

The pump must overcome the pressure drop and, therefore, it creates an equivalent head on the pump. This friction head can be defined as the equivalent head, in metres of the liquid being pumped, due to the resistance to flow caused by pipes, valves and fittings.

In general, the friction head will increase if the length of the piping (ie. the distance pumped) is increased, the diameter of the piping is reduced, flow velocity is increased, or more fittings or valves are added to the system.

For design purposes, there are tables available that specify the friction losses for liquids in terms of the piping material and diameters. The loss is given in terms of head, or metres of liquid, per 25 metres of pipe length. For example, the following excerpt is from a table for water in a steel, schedule 40 system.

Table 1	Friction Losses in Steel, Schedule 40 Pipe (Excerpt)	
Diameter (mm)	**Flow (L/s)**	**Friction Loss (m water/25 m of pipe)**
50.8	25	36.5
101.6	25	1.22
101.6	75	12.6
152.4	75	1.54
203.2	75	0.39

Similarly, tables are available that indicate the resistance to flow for various pipe fittings. In this case the flow resistance is given in terms of the length of pipe of the same diameter that would offer the same resistance as the fitting. One can then use the piping table to convert the fitting resistance to head (in m. of the liquid).

Table 2	Friction Losses in Steel Pipe Fittings (Excerpt)			
Diameter (mm)	**Standard Elbow**	**Tee**	**Open Globe Valve**	**Open Gate Valve**
50.8	1.68	3.35	17.4	0.37
101.6	3.35	6.7	33.5	0.7
152.4	4.88	10.1	48.8	1.07
203.2	6.4	13.1	67.0	1.37

By adding up all the fittings and the length of pipe in a system and knowing the pipe diameter and flow rate, one can estimate the friction loss (or friction head).

Example 11

Schedule 40, steel pipe, 50.8 mm diameter, is used to construct a piping system. The length of piping is 60 m and there are 4 standard elbows, 1 tee and 1 globe valve. If the flow is 25 L/s, what is the friction head of the system?

Solution

$$\text{Equivalent resistance in elbows} = 4 \times 1.68 = 6.72 \text{ m of pipe}$$

$$\text{Equivalent resistance in tee} = 1 \times 3.35 = 3.35 \text{ m of pipe}$$

$$\text{Equivalent resistance of valve} = 1 \times 17.4 = 17.4 \text{ m of pipe}$$

$$\text{Metres of piping} = 60$$

$$\text{Total equivalent metres of pipe} = 60 + 6.72 + 3.35 + 17.4$$

$$= 87.47 \text{ m}$$

From Table 1, at 25 L/s, $\quad$ Friction head $= 36.5$ m per 25 m of pipe

therefore $\quad$ Friction head $= (87.47/25) \times 36.5$

$$= \textbf{127.7 m (Ans.)}$$

VELOCITY HEAD

A pump must impart motion to a liquid in order to transfer the liquid from one location to another. When a substance is in motion it contains energy, more specifically kinetic energy. Therefore, a pump must create this kinetic energy in a liquid. Remember that the kinetic energy of a mass is given by the formula:

$$KE = \frac{1}{2}mv^2$$

where $\quad m = $ mass, in kg

$\quad v = $ velocity, in m/s

Also, if a substance is at a height it contains potential energy, which is given by the formula:

$$PE = mgh$$

where $\quad m = $ mass, in kg

$\quad g = $ gravity or 9.81 m/s^2

$\quad h = $ height, in m

In a pumping system, the kinetic energy of the liquid must equal the potential energy at the height of the liquid. That is:

$$KE = PE$$

or $\quad \frac{1}{2}mv^2 = mgh$

and, solved for height $\quad h = \frac{v^2}{2g}$

This formula defines the equivalent head, in metres, that a liquid exerts as a result of its velocity in a piping system. It is called the velocity head of a pump. In other words, the velocity head is the pressure (in m of liquid) that is required to give a liquid its motion through a system at a given velocity.

Normally a pump has two velocity heads, one on the suction side and one on the discharge side. This is because the suction piping is usually larger in diameter, so that for a given flow the velocity is lower in the suction line than in the discharge line. The suction velocity head is required to move the liquid into the suction of the pump. The velocity head required on the discharge side is then only equal to the head required to increase the velocity to that of the discharge line.

Example 12

If a centrifugal pump is required to move 20 000 kg of water per hour at a velocity of 12 m/s through a 4 cm diameter line, what velocity head must be considered in the system design?

Solution

$$h = \frac{v^2}{2g}$$

$$= \frac{144}{2 \times 9.81}$$

$$= \ \textbf{7.34 m (Ans.)}$$

Example 13

What is the velocity in the discharge of a centrifugal pump if the velocity head is 12 m?

Solution

$$h = \frac{v^2}{2g}$$

therefore $\quad v^2 = 2 g h$

$$v = \sqrt{2 g h}$$

$$= \sqrt{2 \times 9.81 \times 12}$$

$$= \sqrt{235.44 \ m^2/s^2}$$

$$= \ \textbf{15.34 m/s (Ans.)}$$

Self Test Problems

9. A 152.4 mm diameter piping system is 50 m long and contains 3 elbows, 2 gate valves, one globe valve, and 2 tees. If flow in the system is 75 L/s, calculate the friction head.

   (Ans. 8.37 m)

10. A pump has a discharge velocity head of 12 m and a suction velocity head of 7.5 m. How does the suction velocity compare to the discharge velocity?

   (Ans. discharge velocity is 1.26 times the suction velocity)

OBJECTIVE 5

Define dynamic suction head, dynamic suction lift, dynamic discharge head, total dynamic head, and calculate each of these for a given pump arrangement.

13-19

DYNAMIC HEAD

"Dynamic" generally refers to a system in motion. All the pump terms discussed so far collectively play a role in the dynamics of a pump, when the pump is not in service. The following terms are specifically used to define a dynamic pumping system.

Dynamic Suction Head

When a pump is located below the suction source, the dynamic suction head is the numerical result, in metres, of all the equivalent heads acting on the suction side of the pump. Therefore:

Dynamic suction head = static suction head

PLUS suction pressure head

PLUS suction velocity head

MINUS suction friction head

Notice that the static suction head, the pressure head, and the velocity head contribute to the dynamic suction head, while the suction friction head reduces the dynamic suction head.

Dynamic Suction Lift

When a pump is located above the suction source, the dynamic suction lift is the numerical result, in metres, of all the equivalent heads and lifts acting on the suction side of a pump.

Dynamic suction lift = static suction lift

PLUS suction friction head

MINUS suction velocity head

MINUS suction pressure head

Notice that the suction pressure head and velocity head act to reduce the dynamic suction lift.

Dynamic Discharge Head

The dynamic discharge head is the numerical sum, in metres, of all the equivalent heads acting on the discharge side of the pump.

Dynamic discharge head = static discharge head

PLUS discharge pressure head

PLUS discharge friction head

PLUS discharge velocity heads

Total Dynamic Head

The total head on an operating pump (also called the total dynamic head) can be calculated as follows.

- For a pump with suction head:

Total head = dynamic discharge head - dynamic suction head

- For a pump with suction lift:

Total head = dynamic discharge head + dynamic suction lift

Example 14

A vacuum evaporator has an absolute pressure of 25 kPa. The evaporator level is 10 m above the center line of the pump. The pump discharges into a storage tank, located 20 m above the pump. This tank has a level of 6 m and a pressure blanket of 100 kPa (gauge). Liquid velocities are 3 m/s in the suction piping and 4 m/s in the discharge line. Friction loss in the suction line is 0.5 m and in the discharge line, 1.8 m. Calculate the pump's total dynamic head.

Solution

Total head = dynamic discharge head - dynamic suction head

First, find dynamic suction head:

Dynamic suction head = static suction head - suction friction head + suction velocity head + pressure head

Static suction head = 10 m

Suction friction head = 0.5 m

$$\text{Suction velocity head} = \frac{v^2}{2g}$$

$$= \frac{(3 \text{ m/s})^2}{2 \times 9.81 \text{ m/s}^2}$$

$$= \frac{9 \text{ m}^2/\text{s}^2}{19.62 \text{ m/s}^2}$$

$$= \ \mathbf{0.459 \ m}$$

Pressure head on the suction side of the pump is less than atmospheric:

(25 - 101.3) kPa = -76.3 kPa

and   1 kPa = 0.102 m

suction pressure head = -76.3 x 0.102 m = **-7.783 m**

so Dynamic suction head = 10 m - 0.5 m + 0.459 m + (- 7.783 m) = **2.176 m**

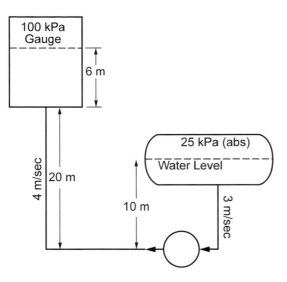

Then, find dynamic discharge head:

Dynamic discharge head = static head + friction head + discharge velocity head
+ pressure head

Discharge static head = 20 m + 6 m = 26 m

Discharge friction head = 1.8 m

Discharge velocity head $= \dfrac{v^2}{2g}$

$$= \frac{(4 \text{ m/s})^2}{2 \times 9.81 \text{ m/s}^2}$$

$$= \frac{16 \text{ m}^2/\text{s}^2}{19.62 \text{ m/s}^2}$$

= 0.815 m

Discharge pressure head = 100 kPa

= 100 × 0.102 m

= 10.2 m

Dynamic discharge head = 26 m + 1.8 m + 0.815 m + 10.2 m = **38.815 m**

therefore   Total head = dynamic discharge head - dynamic suction head

= 38.815 m - 2.176 m

= **36.64 m (Ans.)**

Self Test Problems

11. What is the dynamic suction head for a pump that has static suction head = 8 m, suction pressure head = 12 m, suction friction head = 2 m, and suction velocity head = 3 m?

(Ans. 21 m)

12. A water pump is located 4 m above its source, which is an open tank. The pump discharges to a level 15 m above the pump. Given the following data, calculate the total dynamic head of the pump:

   - suction friction head = 1.5 m
   - suction velocity head = 0.3 m
   - discharge pressure head = 16 m
   - discharge friction head = 3.7 m
   - discharge velocity head = 0.7 m

(Ans. 40.6 m)

13. A chemical pump discharges into the side of a process vessel at a point 15 m above the pump. The operating level in the vessel is 12 m above the pump and operating pressure in the vessel is 220 kPa. The discharge velocity of the pump is 4.2 m/s, friction losses are negligible, and the relative density of the chemical is 1.40. If the total dynamic head is 27.0 m, what is the dynamic suction head of the pump?

(Ans. 4.92 m)

OBJECTIVE 6

Explain vapour pressure, cavitation, and net positive suction head. Calculate the required suction pressure for a water pump, given the manufacturers required NPSH.

VAPOUR PRESSURE

All liquids form vapours at their free surface, creating a pressure that is known as vapour pressure. This pressure increases in value as the temperature of the liquid increases.

In a closed system completely filled with liquid, no vapours will form as long as the liquid is subjected to a pressure that is greater than the vapour pressure of the liquid, at the existing temperature. However, should the pressure exerted on the liquid be allowed to drop below the vapour pressure, some of the liquid will flash into vapour.

This is an important factor to consider in a pumping system where the pressure on the suction side of the pump could drop below the vapour pressure of the liquid. This drop may be caused by insufficient head, high suction lift, excessive friction head, or high liquid temperature. If the liquid flashes, the formed vapour can partially or completely stop liquid flow into the pump. The pump is then said to be vapour-bound or vapour-locked.

CAVITATION

When the pressure, at any point inside a centrifugal pump, drops below the vapour pressure of the liquid, vapour bubbles will form, creating cavities in the liquid flow. These bubbles are carried along with the flow until they reach a region of higher pressure where they collapse, producing a shock wave. This phenomenon is called cavitation.

When the bubbles are carried onto the surface of the impeller and collapse there, the impact of the liquid suddenly filling the void and hitting the metal will damage the surface by gouging out small pieces. When this action is repeated in rapid succession, it produces noisy operation and vibration. Prolonged operation under these conditions may result in mechanical damage to the pump impeller and/or casing.

Cavitation should not be confused with the possible inclusion of air bubbles in the liquid flow. Although air bubbles are not desirable in liquid flow, they do not have the same destructive characteristics as do vapour voids. Air bubbles become smaller when they are compressed, but vapour bubbles totally collapse, producing the shock wave referred to earlier.

NET POSITIVE SUCTION HEAD

To prevent cavitation and vapour-binding and to ensure maximum flow through a pump, it is necessary to provide sufficient head on the pump suction so that the suction pressure will always be greater than the vapour pressure of the liquid.

This available pressure, in excess of the vapour pressure, at the pump suction is expressed in metres of liquid head and is called the net positive suction head (NPSH).

- **Available NPSH** is the head at the pump suction under operating conditions in the system.

- **Required NPSH** is the head necessary at the pump suction for the pump to perform properly. Pump manufacturers will specify the required NPSH for their pumps, as determined by testing the pump under varying conditions of speed, load, and so on.

When considering the suitability of a pump to perform the duties required in a system, the 'Available NPSH' must be calculated and checked to ensure that this is at least equal to (and preferably greater than) the required NPSH specified by the manufacturer.

Example 15

A manufacturer specifies a required NPSH of 5 m for a certain pump. To satisfy this requirement, what must the minimum pressure be at the suction of the pump if the liquid being moved is water at 120°C?

Solution

From Steam Tables, at 120°C:

$$\text{Vapour Pressure} = 198.53 \text{ kPa}$$

$$v_f = 1.0603 \text{ cm}^3/\text{g}$$

$$\rho = \frac{1000}{v_f} \text{ kg/m}^3 = \frac{1000}{1.0603} = 943 \text{ kg/m}^3$$

$$\text{Pressure due to 5 m of NPSH} = P$$

$$= h\,\rho\,g$$

$$= 5 \text{ m} \times 943 \text{ kg/m}^3 \times 9.81 \text{ N/kg}$$

$$= 46\ 254 \text{ Pa}$$

$$= 46.254 \text{ kPa}$$

therefore $\quad$ Pressure required $= 198.53 + 46.254$

$$= \textbf{244.78 kPa (Ans.)}$$

Self Test Problems

14. A boiler feedwater pump is to supply water from a boiler at 110°C. According to the manufacturer, this pump must have a minimum suction pressure of 210 kPa to ensure the required NPSH is maintained. What value of NPSH has been specified by the manufacturer?

(Ans. 7.15 m)

15. A liquid with a vapour pressure of 110 kPa and density of 840 kg/m³ is moved by a pump that has an NPSH of 6 m. How much pressure must exist at the pump suction?

(Ans. 159.44 kPa)

CHAPTER 13 - QUESTIONS

1. a) Explain how liquid flow is created and maintained into the suction of an operating pump.

   b) Suggest at least three ways in which the flow into a pump suction can be assisted.

2. a) Why do equal columns of different liquids exert different pressures at their bases?

   b) Calculate the pressure exerted by a 15 m column of a liquid with a relative density of 3.7.

3. Ignoring friction and velocity heads, which of the following pumps must operate against the greatest total head and how much greater is this head than the other pump?

   Pump A

   liquid = water at 4°C; pump is 2 m above suction surface; suction tank is open to atmosphere; discharge vessel has a 180 kPa gas blanket and level is 5 m above the pump

   Pump B

   liquid has relative density of 2.6; suction is from a vessel with 250 kPa pressure and liquid level is 3 m above pump; discharge tank is open and located 18 m above the tank with a level of 4.5 m

4. a) Explain how cavitation can occur in a pump and describe its potential effects.

   b) Define net positive suction head and explain how it prevents cavitation.

   c) If a liquid at operating conditions has a vapour pressure of 320 kPa and a density of 1078 kg/m³, what must the minimum operating pressure be at the suction of the pump if the manufacturer requires an available NPSH of 6 m?

   ANSWERS: *Calculation answers and answers not directly found in the content of the chapter are provided on the next page.*

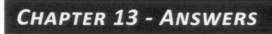

CHAPTER 13 - ANSWERS

2. b) 544 kPa

3. Pump A has 15.67 m more total head than Pump B.

4. c) 383.5 kPa

Welding Procedures & Inspection

LEARNING OUTCOME

When you complete this chapter you should be able to:

Explain the processes and applications of different welding techniques and describe the testing of welds and procedures.

LEARNING OBJECTIVES

Here is what you should be able to do when you complete each objective:

1. *Describe the equipment, procedure and applications of shielded metal arc welding (SMAW). Explain the classification of arc welding electrodes.*

2. *Describe the equipment, procedure and applications of submerged arc welding (SAW).*

3. *Describe the equipment, procedure and applications of gas tungsten arc welding (GTAW).*

4. *Describe the equipment, procedure and applications of gas metal arc welding (GMAW).*

5. *Explain weld preparation and terminology of a butt weld; explain preheating and post-weld heat treatment.*

6. *Describe common defects in welds, including undercut, lack of penetration, porosity, slag inclusion, and cracking; explain how each occurs and its effect on the integrity of the weld.*

7. *Explain the equipment and procedures for dye penetrant, magnetic particle, radiographic, and ultrasonic inspection of a weld; explain the potential weld defects revealed by each test.*

8. *Explain the requirements and process for Weld Procedure and Welder Performance qualification, per the ASME Code, Section IX.*

OBJECTIVE 1

Describe the equipment, procedure and applications of shielded metal arc welding (SMAW). Explain the classification of arc welding electrodes.

SHIELDED METAL ARC WELDING (SMAW)

Fusion welding involves melting metals and allowing them to fuse together. Of all fusion welding methods, shielded metal arc welding (SMAW) is the most common. It is the principal method for joining structural type steels.

Figure 1(a) shows the SMAW process. A coated, consumable electrode consisting of a coated core wire, is capable of carrying electrical current. The electrode and work piece (metals being welded) are connected to an external electrical source and when the electrode is brought close to the work piece, an electrical arc is created, which melts the work piece, the core wire, and the coating on the electrode. The temperature produced by the arc ranges from 3000°C to 8300°C, resulting in a molten pool of metal forming on the weld site at the arc location. The coating, made of organic material (minerals and clays), provides a gaseous shield over the arc to protect it from the atmosphere. It also creates a slag, which covers the molten puddle, protecting it while it cools.

Figure 1	Shielded Metal Arc Welding (SMAW)

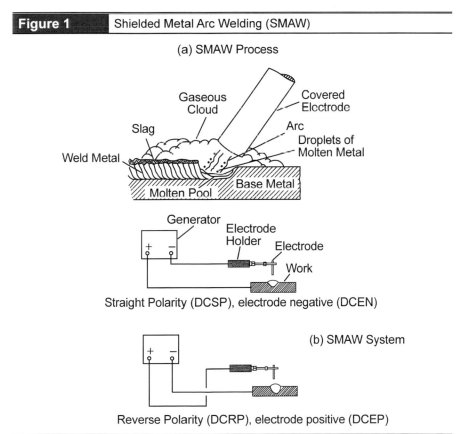

(a) SMAW Process

(b) SMAW System

Straight Polarity (DCSP), electrode negative (DCEN)

Reverse Polarity (DCRP), electrode positive (DCEP)

The major advantage of SMAW is its low cost and ease of handling in all welding positions. Its major disadvantage is that the open arc creates intense radiation. Welders must wear helmets, fitted with dark lenses to protect their eyes from the ultraviolet and infrared light. It also produces toxic fumes, so adequate ventilation is required. SMAW is a manual process (that is, the progress of the arc is controlled by hand) and requires considerable skill in all applications.

SMAW equipment consists of a constant direct current generating source (ie. a welding machine) with current adjustment controls, welding cables that connect to the work piece and the electrode, an electrode holder, and the electrodes.

Figure 1(b) shows two possible connection methods.

- In direct current straight polarity (DCSP), current flows first to the electrode, then arcs to the work piece before returning to the welding machine to complete the circuit.
- In DC reverse polarity (DCRP), the current flows first to the work piece, then to the electrode.

In straight polarity, about 2/3 of the arc energy is concentrated at the electrode, which means less heat at the work piece, requiring faster welding speed. The weld tends to be wider, but shallower. In reverse polarity, the work piece contains about 2/3 of the energy of the arc, which allows for slower welding speed. The penetration is usually deeper and the weld is narrower.

SMAW Electrodes

The Canadian Standards Association (CSA) and the American Welding Society (AWS) have specific classifications for covered electrodes. The major groupings of electrodes are those specified as low carbon steel electrodes, low alloy steel electrodes and corrosion resisting (stainless steel) electrodes. Other significant groupings for SMAW electrodes include:

- Nickel and nickel alloy electrodes
- Aluminum and aluminum alloy electrodes
- Copper and copper alloy electrodes
- Electrodes for cast iron

These specifications are referenced in welding standards and codes. For example, ASME Boiler and Pressure Vessel Code, Section IX, selects the AWS electrodes suitable for welding vessels and prefixes the AWS. Specifications with the letters "SA" designate the electrode's suitability for vessel fabrication. Another example is CSA Z 184, Gas Pipelines that references the CSA W 48 series of electrodes, recommended for pipeline construction. Table 1 shows some typical specifications.

Table 1	CSA/ASW Shielded Metal Arc Welding Electrode	
AWS/CSA CONSUMABLES CHART		
CSA Specification	**AWS Specification**	**Specifications Title**
W48.1-M1980	A5.1	Carbon steel covered arc welding electrodes
	A5.3	Aluminum & aluminum alloy arc welding electrodes
W48.2-M1980	A5.4	Corrosion-resisting chromium & chromium-nickel steel covered welding electrodes
W48.3-M1982	A5.5	Low-alloy steel covered arc welding electrodes
	A5.6	Copper & copper alloy covered electrodes
	A5.15	Welding rods & covered electrodes for welding cast iron
W48.5-M1982	A5.21	Composite surfacing welding rods & electrodes

Each specification contains a number of electrode classifications. For example, classifications for SMAW low carbon steel electrodes use a letter-number system, which describes the electrode in terms of its tensile strength in the as-welded condition, whether it is suitable for flat, horizontal, vertical or overhead welding positions, the type of coating, current and polarity. Coatings provide information as to the arc and depth of penetration characteristics of the electrode.

The following is an example of the AWS Classification system for low carbon steel electrodes, using E7018 electrode as the example.

E	Electrode
70	The first two or three digits denote tensile strength in thousands of pounds per square inch in the as-welded condition, 70,000 psi.
1	The second to last digit denotes welding position.
	1 - All position
	2 - Flat and horizontal position
	3 - Flat only
8	The last digit denotes type of coating, current and polarity. (See Table 2).

The following is an example (using E48018) of the CSA classification system for low carbon steel electrodes:

E	Electrode
480	First three digits denote tensile strength in megapascals in the as-welded condition
1	The second to last digit denotes welding position.
	0 - All position
	1 - All position except vertical down
	2 - Flat and horizontal position
	3 - Flat only
	4 - Vertical down only
8	The last digit denotes the type of coating, current and polarity. (See Table 3)

Table 2		AWS and CSA Classification of Low Carbon Steel Electrodes		
CLASSIFICATION		**Type of Coating**	**Welding Positions**	**Current** [1]
W48.1 A5.1	**W48.1-M**			
----	E41000	Cellulose, sodium	F, VU, VD, O, H	DC
----	E48000	Cellulose, sodium	F, VU, VD, O, H	DC
E6010	E41010	Cellulose, sodium	F, VU, O, H	DC
E7010 [2]	E48010	Cellulose, sodium	F, VU, O, H	DC
E6011	E41011	Cellulose, potassium	F, VU, O, H	AC or DC
E7011 [2]	E48011	Cellulose, potassium	F, VU, O, H	AC or DC
E6012	E41012	Titania, sodium	F, VU, O, H	AC or DC
E7012 [2]	E48012	Titania, sodium	F, VU, O, H	AC or DC
E6013	E41013	Titania, potassium	F, VU, O, H	AC or DC
E7013 [2]	E48013	Titania, potassium	F, VU, O, H	AC or DC
E7014	E48014	Titania, iron powder	F, VU, O, H	AC or DC
E7015	E48015	Basic, sodium	F, VU, O, H	DC
E7016	E48016	Basic, potassium	F, VU, O, H	AC or DC
E7018	E48018	Basic, iron powder	F, VU, O, H	AC or DC
E6022 [3]	E41022	Titania, iron powder	F, H-F	AC or DC
----	E48022	Titania, iron powder	F, H-F	AC or DC
E7024	E48024	Titania, high iron powder	F, H-F	AC or DC
E6027	E41027	Iron oxide, high iron powder	F, H-F	AC or DC
E7027	E48027	Iron oxide, high iron powder	F, H-F	AC or DC
E7028	E48028	Basic, high iron powder	F, H-F	AC or DC
E7048	E48048	Basic, iron powder	F, VD	AC or DC

Table 3	Last Digit Designation for CSA/AWS Low Carbon Steel Electrode Classifications		
AWS A5.1, A5.5	**FOURTH DIGIT INDICATES CURRENT & POLARITY**		
Classification	**Current, Polarity**	**Degree of Penetration**	**Coating Type**
EXXX0*	dcep	Deep	Cellulose, sodium
EXXX1	ac, dcep	Deep	Cellullose, potassium
EXXX2	ac, dcen	Medium	Rutile, sodium
EXXX3	ac, dcep, dcen	Light	Rutile, potassium
EXXX4	ac, dcep, dcen	Light	Rutile iron powder
EXXX5	dcep	Medium	Low-hydrogen sodium
EXXX6	ac, dcep	Medium	Low-hydrogen potassium
EXXX7	ac, dcep, dcen	Medium	Iron powder, iron oxide
EXXX8	ac, dcep	Medium	Low-hydrogen, iron powder

*Except E6020, which runs on dcen, dcep, or ac; medium penetration; iron oxide-sodium coating.

OBJECTIVE 2

Describe the equipment, procedure and applications of submerged arc welding.

SUBMERGED ARC WELDING (SAW)

The submerged arc welding process (SAW) is a high deposition, high quality welding process widely used to join thick sections in the flat, horizontal position. High deposition rates and minimal weld defects make this an extremely popular and economical process widely used in the structural steel and pressure vessel industry. Submerged arc welding is usually limited to common varieties of ferrous metals and some corrosion resisting metals.

Figure 2 shows the SAW process, which joins metal by the heat of an electric arc between a continuous wire filler metal and the work piece. In this case, a blanket of granular, fusible flux, which completely submerges the arc and provide protection for the weld. The welding arc also melts the flux, forming a molten slag, which absorbs oxides and excludes the atmosphere from the molten weld pool.

Figure 2	Submerged ARC Welding

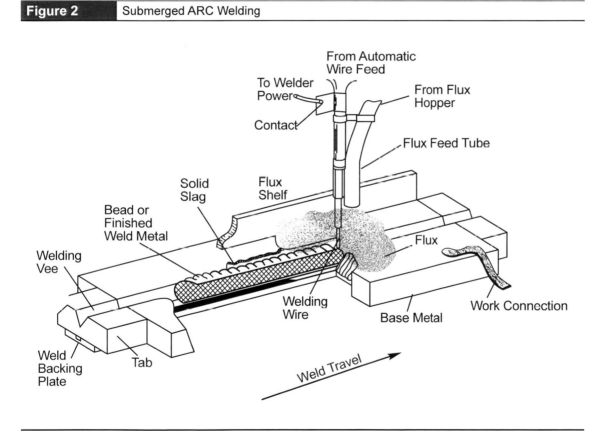

Submerged arc welding may be a semi-automatic or a fully automatic process. In the semi-automatic process, the welding gun is handheld, so the movement of the arc and the flux are done totally by hand. In the automatic process, all welding parameters are preset and the arc and flux are initiated and moved along the weld joint by a tracked carriage. The only operator input is to adjust the welding current and voltage as the weld progresses, if necessary. An alternative method is to keep the weld head stationary and move the work piece. In this case, the work is mounted on a positioner and moved under the stationary arc.

Figure 3 shows an automatic SAW arrangement.

The equipment consists of a high amperage power source and a welding head, which contains the wire feeder, flux hopper and remote voltage and amperage controls. The head is usually moved along a track by a motor driven side-beam carriage. Once the voltage, amperage and speed of travel are set, a single start button simultaneously sets the welding carriage and side-beam carriage in motion. The flux hopper feeds flux to the arc by gravity. The flux is either attracted to the arc by magnets or is force fed by compressed air. The flux may be guided to the arc through the same nozzle as the electrode wire or it may be fed through a separate tube ahead of the electrode wire. The electrode wire is fed continuously to the arc, using constant or variable speed wire feed motors.

Figure 3	Automatic Submerged ARC Welding Setup

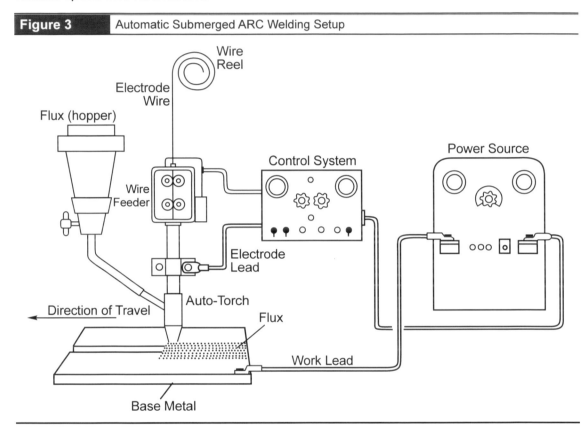

The SAW process has some distinct advantages over other processes. Fluxes provide excellent protection of the arc from the atmosphere and can be designed to reduce chemical reactions in the molten weld puddle, thus eliminating the formation of oxides and nitrides in the weld deposit. This reduces weld defects. Current densities (the ratio of amperes to the cross-sectional area of the filler metal) are very high, which results in a high deposition rate (a large volume of weld metal is deposited, per unit of time). Metal powders may be mixed with the flux or added separately, in addition to the flux, to further improve the deposition rate. The process can be adapted to multiple arc applications (ie. more than one electrode), which further increases deposition rate.

The biggest disadvantage of the SAW process is that it is limited to the flat and horizontal positions, since the flux is kept in place by gravity. Another disadvantage is the high heat input to the base metal, which may cause some alloys to lose impact strength. This can be offset by selecting wire-flux combinations that reduce the effects of oxygen in the weld deposit, or by post-weld heat treatment. Another problem is the tendency of the flux to absorb moisture and transfer it to the weld deposit, resulting in hydrogen cracking after the weld has cooled. Heating the flux in a dryer, prior to its use, helps control this problem.

The SAW process demands some specific operator training welding skill. The most important aspects this training are awareness of the correct flux-wire combinations for the different base materials and how the fluxes react in the heat of the arc.

OBJECTIVE 3

Describe the equipment, procedure and applications of GTAW.

14-9

GAS TUNGSTEN ARC WELDING (GTAW)

The gas tungsten arc welding process (GTAW) is shown in Figure 4.

It joins metal by the heat of an electric arc between a nonconsumable tungsten electrode and the work piece, with or without the addition of a filler metal. The arc melts the base metal and forms a molten puddle. An inert gas usually shields the arc and the molten weld puddle, preventing access to the air.

Figure 4	Gas Tungsten ARC Welding (GTAW)

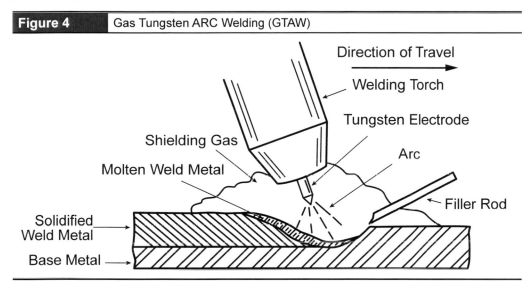

GTAW can join most metals, but is particularly suited to welding difficult-to-weld metals, where high quality welds, free of defects, are required.

Most GTAW applications involve manually feeding filler rods to the arc. A semi-automatic variation involves continuously feeding a preheated filler wire. Fully automatic GTAW systems use power sources that produce pulsing arcs, plus computerized servomotors, which allow torches to be mounted on carriages and moved on orbital tracks. This produces the precision welds necessary for attaching tubes to tubesheets and for welding thin walled pipe.

Figure 5 shows the equipment used in a GTAW system.

Figure 5	Gas Tungsten ARC Welding (GTAW)

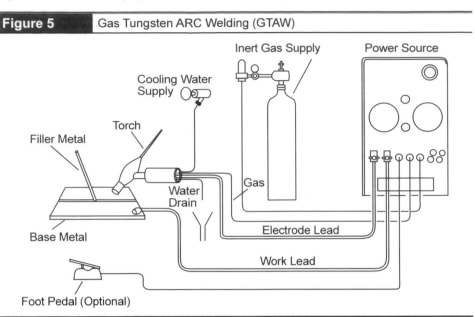

Gas tungsten arc welding has some advantages over other processes.

- It is well suited to welding difficult nonferrous and highly alloyed steels. Stainless steels, copper, aluminum, magnesium and some refractory type metals, such as titanium, are readily joined by GTAW.
- It is particularly suited to welding dissimilar metals. When correctly applied, it is the preferred process for welding thin materials in all positions.
- The process is extremely clean, since there is no spatter and no flux is required.
- Fume rate is low.
- It is a relatively low cost process, requiring conventional power sources and gas coverage equipment.

The GTAW process has some disadvantages.

- The process demands highly skilled operators.
- Contaminants on the base metal or filler metal can introduce porosity into the weld pool, so utmost cleanliness is required in the preparation and handling of the base filler metals.
- Loss of coverage gas can result in overheating of the tungsten, causing particles of tungsten to enter the weld pool.
- Touching the tungsten electrode to the deposited weld, plus the use of covering gas, makes it necessary to devise back purging of the exposed root face, which adds cost by increasing set up time.
- Gas tungsten arc welding is a low production process. It cannot match the deposition rates of semi-automatic welding processes, such as gas metal arc welding (GMAW), flux-cored arc welding (FCAW) and submerged arc welding (SAW).

GAS METAL ARC WELDING (GMAW)

Gas Metal-Arc Welding (GMAW) is an arc-welding process that fuses metals by heating them with an electric arc between a continuous, consumable, metal filler electrode and the base metal. Shielding gas, such as carbon dioxide, is supplied from an external without the application of pressure.

Figure 6 shows the GMAW process.

Figure 6	Gas Metal ARC Welding (GMAW)

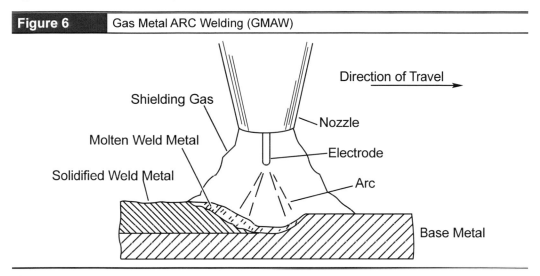

The process utilizes a constant voltage power source and direct current. GMAW is always performed with DC reverse polarity, so the arc current flows from the base metal to the electrode. The continuous filler metal is pushed or pulled to the arc by a constant-speed motor, through a gun and cable assembly. The gun trigger activates the motor, which drives the wire to the arc at a speed that is set by the operator. The speed of the wire determines the current; the faster the speed, the higher the current. The arc and molten weld metal are protected from the atmosphere by a constant flow of inert or reactive gas, through a nozzle at the end of the welding gun.

The level of current and the type of coverage gas can be varied to satisfy various metal thicknesses. Through the use of pulsing arcs, the process can be used on very thin sections. With higher currents the process can be used to weld thick sections. At lower currents GMAW can be adapted to all welding positions. At higher currents, it is best suited to flat and horizontal welding.

The GMAW process is capable of achieving high deposition rates and quality welds. For these reasons it is quickly surpassing shielded metal arc (aka "stick") welding. It is the only arc welding process capable of welding all commercial ferrous and non-ferrous alloys. The process is widely used in the construction of pressure vessels and process piping. It is well suited for the root passes when welding pipe.

In production applications, the techniques of operating the GMAW process are readily learned. Out of position welding, requires more skill and training.

GMAW is the process most often chosen for robotic arc welding.

GMAW is available in both semi-automatic and fully automatic modes. In semi-automatic mode, the operator presets the voltage, current, wire speed and coverage gas flow rate, but manipulates the welding gun manually. In the fully automatic mode, all parameters are preset and the process set in motion, without further input by the operator.

Figure 7 shows a GMAW setup.

Figure 7 GMAW Setup

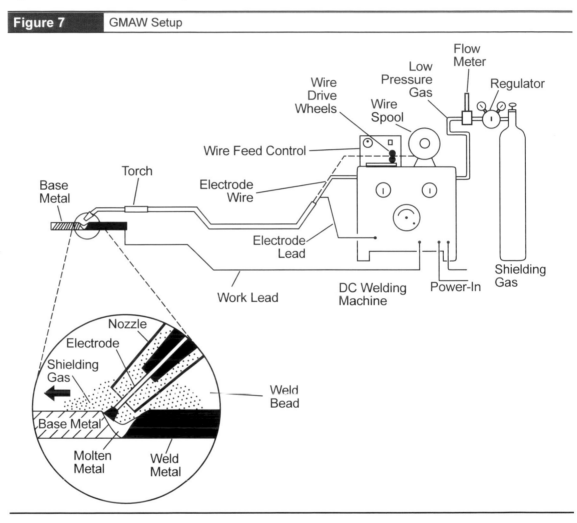

OBJECTIVE 5

Explain weld preparation and terminology of a butt weld; explain preheating and post-weld heat treatment.

WELD PREPARATION

On pipe larger than 51 mm the ends are usually butt welded together or butt welded to valves or fittings. Butt welding requires that the pipe ends first be beveled, which forms a groove for depositing of the weld metal. The beveling is done by machining, grinding or flame cutting.

The process used, the material thickness, and the joint type determine the geometry of the edge of the parent metals. Pipe edge preparation, as shown in Figures 8(a) and 8(b), establishes the included angle of the groove and bevel, the size of the root face, the root radius, and the size of root opening. Improperly designed or prepared joint geometry may prevent proper access to the joint by the welding arc, resulting in structural defects in the weld.

Figure 8	Standard Edge Preparation for Pipe

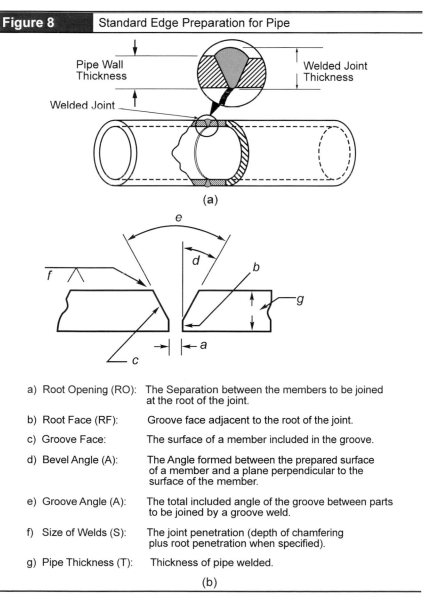

(a)

(b)

a) Root Opening (RO):   The Separation between the members to be joined at the root of the joint.

b) Root Face (RF):   Groove face adjacent to the root of the joint.

c) Groove Face: The surface of a member included in the groove.

d) Bevel Angle (A):   The Angle formed between the prepared surface of a member and a plane perpendicular to the surface of the member.

e) Groove Angle (A):   The total included angle of the groove between parts to be joined by a groove weld.

f) Size of Welds (S):   The joint penetration (depth of chamfering plus root penetration when specified).

g) Pipe Thickness (T):   Thickness of pipe welded.

Backing (or backup) rings are frequently used to prevent the weld metal from protruding past the inner wall of a pipe. The ring fits snuggly inside the pipe, covering the gap at the bottom of the weld groove.

Figure 9	Butt Weld with Backing Ring

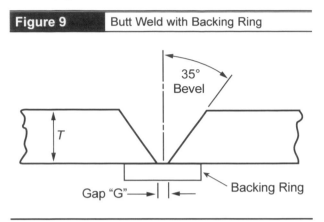

HEAT TREATMENT OF WELDS

During the process of welding, stresses are set up in both the weld metal and in the base metal adjacent to the weld. These stresses are due to temperature differences in the weld zone. The temperature of the fused metal may be around 1480°C, or more, while only a few millimeters away the metal is just above room temperature. The resulting stresses, due mainly uneven expansion and internal metallurgy effects, may be minimized by preheating the base metals before welding and/or by postweld heating of the base metals and weld.

Preheating

Preheating is done before the first welding pass. In some cases, where metal thickness is great and several weld passes are required, preheating is repeated between passes. In any case, the acceptable preheat temperature range will be specified in the weld procedure. The temperature depends largely upon the material and thickness of the parts.

Postweld Heat Treatment (Stress-Relieving)

Postweld heat treatment, often called stress relieving, consists of uniformly heating the welded parts to a temperature sufficient to relieve most of the stresses created by the welding process. The parts are then cooled at a constant rate.

In the field, the heating of welded pipe joints may be accomplished by electrical induction, electrical resistance or gas burners. Shop assembled parts (including whole drums, etc.) may be stress-relieved by placing the entire part inside a controlled furnace.

When using induction heating coils to perform postweld heating of a pipe joint, the general procedure is as follows:

- Thermocouples are welded to the joint, at several points.
- The joint is then wrapped with thick asbestos cloths.
- Hollow copper induction coils are then wrapped around the joint. During the induction heating process, cooling water is pumped through the hollow coils by a small pump.
- The joint is finally wrapped with additional layers of asbestos.
- The induction coil transformer is then put into operation. The output from the transformer is controlled automatically, to raise the temperature slowly and evenly. It is held for the required time, and the temperature is then lowered, slowly and evenly. In addition, the temperature at the joint is recorded on a time-temperature chart.

Table 4 gives recommended preheat and postweld temperatures, as specified in the Process Piping code, ASME B31.3. The "Notes" following the table give the required heating rates and the holding times. **Please note: The values and notes quoted here are for general understanding only, since many may have been revised in more recent editions of this code.**

Table 4	Preheat/Postweld Temperatures		
P - Number	**Material Group**	**Minimum or Preheating Range Temperature (°C)**	**Range of Post Heat Treatment Temperature (°C)**
P - 1	Carbon Steel	15.5	593 - 649
P - 2	Wrought Iron	15.5	Not Required
P - 3	Alloy steels - Cr ¾% max Total Alloy 2% max	149 - 316	690 - 732
P - 4	Alloy steels - Cr ¾% to 2% Total Alloy 2 ¾% max	204 - 371	704 - 760
P - 5	Alloy Steels - Total Alloy 10% max	204 - 371	704 - 774
P - 6	High-Alloy Steels Martensitic	204 - 371	760 - 816
P - 7	High-Alloy Steel Ferritic	15.5	Not Required
P - 8	High-Alloy Steels Austenitic	15.5	Not Required
P - 9	Nickel Alloy Steels	149 - 260	593 - 649
P - 10	Other Alloy Steels		As required for special composition

Notes: (Table 4)

1. a) Heating rate for furnace, gas electric resistance, and other surface heating methods:

   For thickness over 50 mm, heating rate shall be 316°C per hour divided by half the thickness, in millimetres. For thickness of 50 mm and under, the maximum heating rate shall be 316°C per hour.

   b) Heating rate for induction heating:

   For thickness less than 38.1 mm at 60 Hz and 400 Hz, the maximum heating rate shall be 316°C per hour.

   For thickness 38.1 mm and over, maximum heating rate, at 60 Hz, shall be 260°C per hour, and at 400 Hz, shall be 204°C per hour.

2. Holding Time at Temperature

   For a thickness over 50 mm, the minimum holding time at temperature shall be 2 hours. For a thickness 50 mm and under, holding time at temperature shall be 1 hour per 25 mm thickness, but not less than 1 hour.

OBJECTIVE 6

Describe common defects in welds, including undercut, lack of penetration, porosity, slag inclusion, and cracking; explain how each occurs and its effect on the integrity of the weld.

UNDERCUT

Undercut, as shown in Figure 10, is excessive melting away of the parent metal in the vicinity of the weld, which, in effect, reduces the thickness of the welded joint. An external undercut results from gouging out the base metal along the edge of the top or "external" surface of the weld. When the thickness of the material is designed for the operating pressure, undercutting compromises the integrity of the weld. Undercutting may be caused by wandering of the welding rod, advancing too slowly and/or excessive current setting.

Figure 10	Undercut

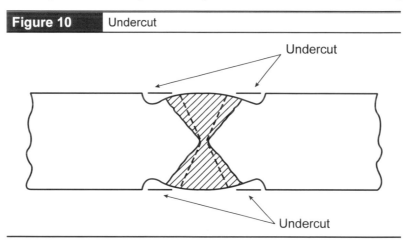

LACK OF PENETRATION (LACK OF FUSION)

Lack of penetration (also called lack of fusion) is shown in Figure 11. This is a group of weld discontinuities in which the weld metal and base metal have not fused completely. It also occurs when subsequent weld passes do not fuse completely with each other or when the weld has not fully penetrated the root. The latter is called insufficient root penetration.

Lack of fusion may result when the pieces being welded are not properly aligned (particularly at the root) or due to unacceptable transition from a thicker to a thinner material. Other causes include advancing the welding electrode too quickly, holding the electrode too far from the joint or at the wrong angle, or using too little current (insufficient heat). These welds are weak and must be ground out and reapplied.

Figure 11	Lack of Fusion

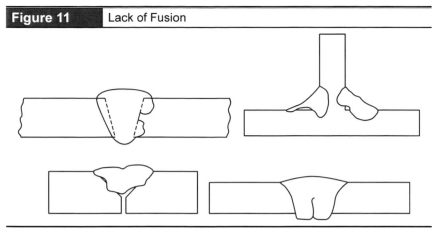

Overlap

Figure 12 shows overlap, which is another type of lack of fusion. It is characterized by excess deposit of weld metal, which is not fused to the base metal. While the weld itself may be strong, the excess is wasteful, creates possible flow restrictions and, in some locations, an opportunity for overheating and fatigue failure. One cause is applying too much filler to the weld, particularly to the top pass.

Figure 12	Overlap

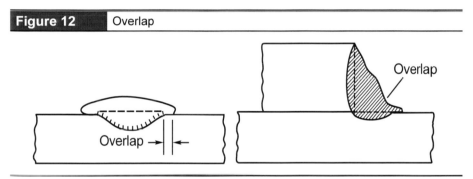

Underfill

Figure 13 shows examples of underfill, which is insufficient weld deposit, resulting in a reduction in the thickness of the groove. This produces a very weak weld, which must be ground out and redone. Underfill can result from advancing the electrode too quickly, unevenly, or using insufficient heat.

Figure 13	Underfill

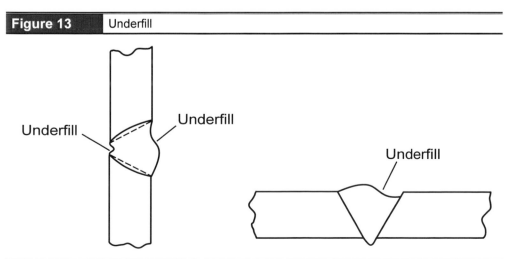

POROSITY

Porosity is spherical or tube like defects, cavities, or voids caused by gases trapped inside the weld or gases that have evolved to the surface. Surface porosity, shown in Figure 14, appears as tiny cavities on the surface. Internal porosity, as shown in Figure 15, forms linear, cluster, spherical, or wormlike voids.

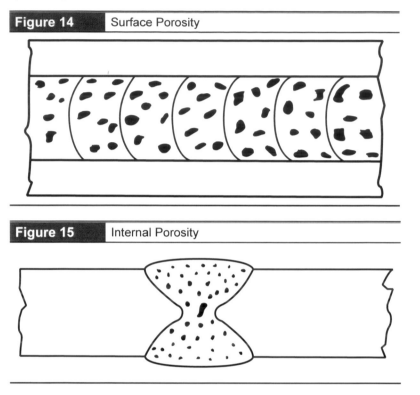

| Figure 14 | Surface Porosity |

| Figure 15 | Internal Porosity |

SLAG INCLUSIONS

Slag inclusions, shown in Figure 16, are solid non-metallic inclusions trapped below the surface of the weld metal or, more often, between deposited weld metal and the base metal. Internal solid inclusions can occur randomly, continuously, or intermittently. Advancing the electrode too quickly may cause quick cooling of the weld, which allows less time for the slag to rise to the surface. Slag weakens the weld.

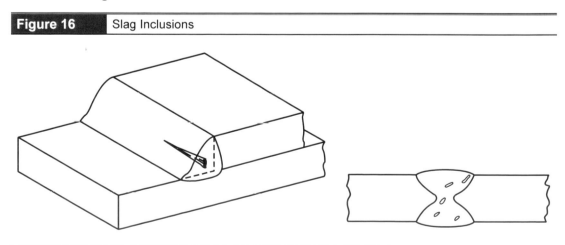

| Figure 16 | Slag Inclusions |

CRACKS

Cracks are the most serous structural defects in welds. By definition, a crack is a fracture-type discontinuity, characterized by a sharp tip and high ratio of length to width (ie. opening). Cracks occur when localized stresses exceed the ultimate strength of the metal.

There are several categories of cracks. They can be identified as surface or subsurface cracks, weld and heat affected zone cracks, or hot and cold cracks. Surface cracks are visible, while subsurface cracks can only be detected and measured by special inspection techniques. Surface cracks may only be the visible portion of a much larger and extensive subsurface crack. Weld cracks occur in the fusion zone where there is a mixture of filler and base metal or melted base metal. The heat affected zone refers to the area adjacent to the weld zone where the metal has been affected by heat, but has not been melted. Hot cracks are caused by shrinkage stresses while cold cracks result from slow evolution of gasses, usually hydrogen, or stresses that occur after the cooling of highly restrained joints.

- **Hydrogen cracking** deserves special mention since it is a prime cause of cracking in the welding of steels. It is called hydrogen cracking because hydrogen is always present. However, the hydrogen alone does not cause cold cracking; other conditions must be present. For hydrogen cracking to occur after the weld has cooled down, these three conditions must exist:

1. Hydrogen must be present in the weld

2. There must be stress where the crack initiates

3. The metal temperature must be less than 100°C

Preventing hydrogen cracking involves procedures that control these factors. Steps are taken to keep base metals and electrodes free of moisture, since moisture releases hydrogen when heated. Electrodes are designed with coatings that produce carbon dioxide in the arc, thereby reducing the amount of hydrogen in the weld deposit. To ensure the electrodes function as designed, they are kept in baking ovens to remove any moisture content. To avoid stress, the piping or material containing the weld joint should be designed to avoid high tensile or compressive forces. Preheating the base metal to well above 100°C (to reduce the cooling rate of the weld) provides sufficient time for any hydrogen gas to evolve from the weld.

Weld cracks are usually either parallel to the axis of the weld (ie. longitudinal) or transverse to the axis of the weld. Several types of cracks are shown in Figures 17 and 18.

Figure 17	Cold Cracks in Butt Welds

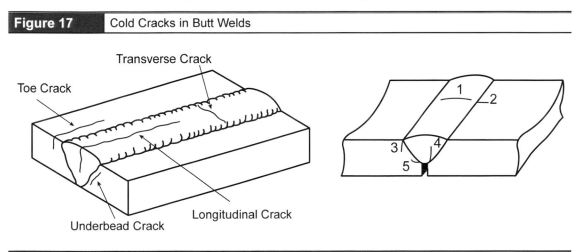

Figure 18 | Cold Cracks in Fillet Welds

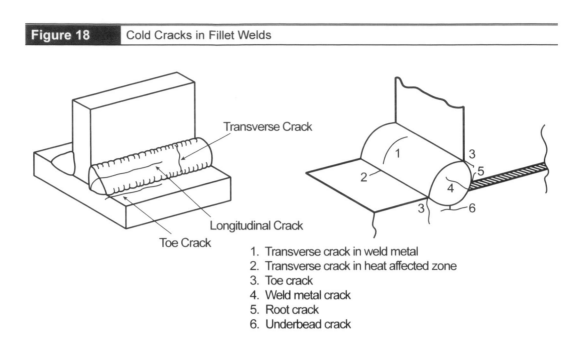

1. Transverse crack in weld metal
2. Transverse crack in heat affected zone
3. Toe crack
4. Weld metal crack
5. Root crack
6. Underbead crack

Figure 19 demonstrates additional crack types and terminology.

- Cracks in the throat of the weld usually extend to the root.
- Root cracks generally run longitudinally to the axis of the weld.
- Crater cracks occur at completion of the weld when the arc is pulled away too quickly. A shallow crater remains and the rapid quench effect results in hairline cracks radiating from the arc termination point.
- Toe cracks occur where the face of the weld terminates at the surface of the parent metal. At this point, thermal stresses are very high and cracking often occurs in a direction normal to the parent.

Figure 19 | Surface Cracks

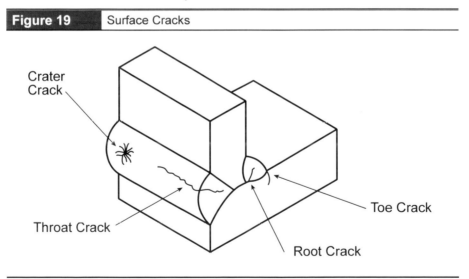

Figures 20 and 21 show further types of cracks.

Underbead cracking may occur in either the weld or the heat affected zone. Lamellar tears are cracks that occur due to high restraint (tension) and subsequent high residual stress. They appear at the interface of the weld and the base metal or completely in the base metal.

Figure 20	Underbead Cracking

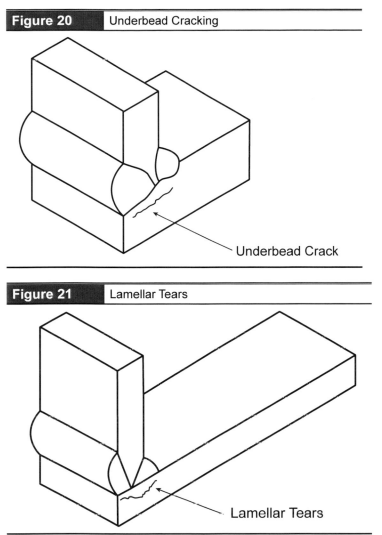

Underbead Crack

Figure 21	Lamellar Tears

Lamellar Tears

Another term for flaws in the weld deposit or heat affected zone is "structural discontinuities". The potential for failure is directly related to the shape and location in the weld. Planar type defects, such as cracks and lack of fusion, are sharp and pointed in shape and create high potential for failure. Pores and non-metallic inclusions are usually rounded and pose less of a potential for failure.

OBJECTIVE 7

Explain the equipment and procedures for liquid penetrant, magnetic particle, radiographic, and ultrasonic inspection of a weld; explain the potential weld defects revealed by each test.

INTRODUCTION

Nondestructive examination (NDE) is the testing of materials without destroying the integrity of the material or reducing its ability to perform its primary function.

In the pressure equipment industry, NDE is used to test for three types of defects:

1. Inherent defects, which are defects that are created during the initial production of the material.

2. Processing defects, which are defects created in the metal during the construction of the pressure equipment.

3. Service defects, which are defects created in the equipment during service.

A variety of NDE techniques are used to test the properties of materials. The most common techniques are:

- Liquid Penetrate Testing (PT)
- Magnetic Particle Testing (MT)
- Radiographic Testing (RT)
- Ultrasonic Testing (UT)

This chapter briefly discusses each method. The standards and requirements for examination of pressure components are found in Section V, Article 6, ASME Boiler and Pressure Vessel Code.

LIQUID PENETRANT TESTING

Liquid penetrant testing (PT), also called dye penetrant testing, is an NDE technique that detects flaws that are open to the surface. The examined surface cannot be rough or porous, since these conditions interfere with the PT inspection.

One principle that applies to PT is capillary action. To understand capillary action, think about what takes place when a drinking straw is placed in a liquid. The liquid level in the straw is actually higher than the level in the glass. This phenomenon is called capillary action, with the straw acting as a capillary tube. Cohesive forces between the liquid and the straw are greater than the cohesive forces within the liquid itself, so the liquid tends to rise slightly in the straw. The height to which the liquid rises in the straw is directly proportional to the surface tension and the contact angle; whereas it is inversely proportional to the density of the liquid and the radius of the straw.

Another principle that affects PT is the ability of the liquid penetrant to wet the surface of the examined material. Wetting occurs when the liquid spreads over the surface of the metal, providing it with a uniform liquid coating. The liquid must be capable of migrating and the ability to migrate depends upon surface tension and contact angle.

The liquid must be able to penetrate the material, but also must be retained in any flaws and then be drawn out of the flaw. The same principle that allowed the liquid to penetrate the flaw also allows the liquid to emerge from the flaw. When excess penetrant is cleaned from the surface, the entrapped penetrant can be coaxed out of the flaw.

Liquid penetrant testing can be used to examine pressure components that are welded, cast, rolled or forged. Keeping in mind that in liquid penetrant testing the discontinuity must be open to the surface, typical discontinuities that can be detected are:

- Stress Cracks
- Porosity
- Shrinkage
- Cracks
- Blow Holes
- Undercut
- Seams
- Center Cracks
- Overlap
- Laps
- Laminations
- Lack of Fusion
- Hot Tears
- Bursts
- Lack of Penetration

Liquid Penetrant Procedure

There are six essential steps in a liquid penetrant test:

1. Pre-cleaning: The surface is cleaned with solvents, degreasers, etc. to remove any contaminants that might interfere with the penetrant or prevent the penetrant from entering the defects.

2. Penetrant (Dye) application: The penetrant is sprayed or brushed onto the surface and time is allowed for the penetrant to enter all the defects. On vertical and overhead surfaces there must be time for the capillary action to occur. There are two types of penetrant, visible and fluorescent. With visible penetrants the defects can be seen using normal incandescent light. Fluorescent penetrants require ultraviolet light to see the defects.

3. Excess penetrant removal: All excess penetrant is removed from the surface using a solvent or water, depending on the type of penetrant used. This cleaning leaves penetrant in the defects only.

4. Developer application: A developer is a chemical that draws the penetrant out of the defects and reacts with the penetrant to produce an outline of the defect. The developer is sprayed onto the surface, forming a consistent, even coating.

5. Inspection/interpretation: After the developer works for a few minutes, the entire surface is carefully inspected, using the appropriate light source for the type of penetrant (see step 2 above). Defects should be clearly visible and should be marked to identify they require repair.

6. Post-cleaning: The final step is to thoroughly clean the penetrant and developer from the surface, being careful not to remove defect markings. These markings may be done with paint sticks, circled with chalk, etc.

Figure 22(a) shows liquid penetrant entering a defect by capillary action.

In Figure 22(b), the discontinuity is revealed when the developer draws out the penetrant.

Figure 22	Schematic of Liquid Penetrant Inspection

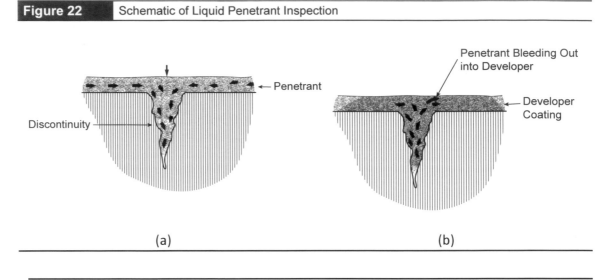

(a)   (b)

MAGNETIC PARTICLE TESTING

Magnetic particle testing (MT) is an NDE technique that detects surface or slightly subsurface defects. It can only be applied on ferromagnetic materials. It is carried out in accordance with the requirements of Section V, Article 7 of the ASME Code.

The principle behind MT is that the magnetic flux in a material is distorted by any defects. The nature of the distortion is determined by the orientation of the defect to the magnetic field (flux lines). Distortion is greatest when the defect is perpendicular to the magnetic field. When distortion of the magnetic field is large enough, a pair of magnetic poles, which act as small magnets, are created at the defect. If magnetic particles are applied to the surface they become attracted to the poles and gather at the defect, thus indicating the location of the surface or sub-surface defect.

Magnetic particles may be wet or dry, both of which are available in various colors (silver-grey, black, red, yellow and green) or as fluorescent particles. The availability of various colors helps to ensure maximum contrast between the surface and the defect. Fluorescent particles are extremely visible when viewed under ultraviolet light and have a high contrast with the surface being examined.

Magnetic particle testing can be used on ferromagnetic pressure components that are welded, cast, rolled or forged. Typical defects detected are lack of penetration and cracks (whether caused by quenching, grinding, fatigue, stress corrosion, or welding).

Figure 23 shows the arrangement for magnetic particle examination.

Figure 23	Schematic of Magnetic Particle Inspection

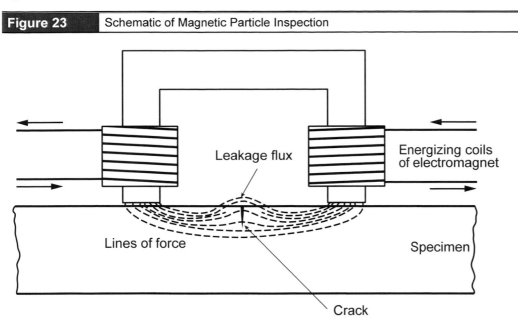

Leakage flux

Energizing coils
of electromagnet

Lines of force

Specimen

Crack

Magnetic Particle Procedure

There are six main steps in a magnetic particle test:

1. Pre-cleaning the surface: Remove any oil, grease, scale, etc. that might interfere with the process. In some cases grinding of the surface may be required to ensure good electrical contact.

2. Magnetizing the component: A longitudinal magnetic field is established by placing an electromagnetic yoke (or equivalent) in contact with the test material and energizing the coil of the electromagnet. This creates a magnetic field (ie. lines of force) through the test material. The yoke is then moved around the entire surface, testing section by section.

3. Applying the magnetic particles: Two methods, dry or wet, may be used. In the dry method, dry iron oxide particles are spread on the surface. In the wet method, the magnetic iron oxide particles are held in a carrier liquid, such as kerosene, and the liquid is sprayed or painted onto the surface. The particles are usually colored or coated with fluorescent dye.

4. Interpretation: The particles will attract to and accumulate at any defects. Observing dry particles under normal light or wet particles under ultraviolet light will reveal the defects.

5. Post-demagnetization of the component: After the defects have been found and marked throughout the entire surface, the surface is demagnetized by applying an AC current, which scatters the magnetic fields. A special demagnetizing tool is used for this. The demagnetization is necessary to prevent damage to moving parts, arc deflection during welding, interference with machining and interference with coating or painting

6. Post-cleaning: In preparation for repairs, all particles and liquid are cleaned from the surface.

RADIOGRAPHIC TESTING

Radiographic testing (RT) is an NDE method that identifies defects that are internal to the weld or the base metal.

The principle behind RT is that different amounts of penetrating radiation will be absorbed in the good material than in the defective material. Unabsorbed radiation passes through the test material and exposes a film on the opposite side. The different exposures on the film indicate the varying amounts of radiation passing through the material, thus indicating the defects and giving a permanent record of the test.

The penetrating radiation can be x-rays or gamma rays, which differ only in the way they are produced. X-rays are produced when high-speed electrons strike a metal target, causing a transfer of energy. An x-ray tube, located in an x-ray machine, produces the high-speed electrons. Gamma rays are emitted from the decay of radioisotopes, such as Cobalt 60 and Iridium 192.

Table 5 shows the maximum penetration of steel for x-rays and gamma rays.

Table 5	Radiation Penetration
Source	**Max. Thickness (mm)**
X-ray	76.2
Cobalt-60	177.8 - 203.2
Iridium-19	276.2

Radiography can be used on all materials. It is best suited for detecting three-dimensional, internal flaws. It is also useful for locating foreign objects inside pressure components, such as an object stuck in a pipe or liquid trapped between the double walls of an expansion joints. Material thickness can be measured, which can help to determine corrosion rates. The most popular use is for non-destructive examination of welds.

Typical weld discontinuities that can be detected are:

- Porosity
- Incomplete Penetration
- Incomplete Fusion
- Thickness Variations
- Corrosion
- Pitting
- Slag Inclusions

Radiography will only detect cracks if they are parallel to the radiation beam. Also, for flaws to be detected they must be at least as large as 2% of the penetration thickness.

Radiographic Procedure

here are four main steps in a radiographic test.:

- Source selection: Determine which radiation source should be used, based on the thickness of the material.
- Set up: About 60% of the test time is spent on set-up. The tested material should be cleaned and ground smooth is irregularities are excessive. Access to the far side of the material is necessary, so the receiving film can be placed in a holder at the appropriate location. The radiation source must be setup and aligned correctly. Safety procedures must be initiated to protect personnel in the vicinity.
- Exposure of test component to the radiation source: The radiation source is energized and held for a specified period of time.

- Film development: The film is retrieved and developed. The picture is left in a negative form, since this provides more clear indication of the different exposures.

Of all NDE methods, RT requires constant attention to safety. Large doses of x-rays or gamma rays will kill human cells, while massive doses may cause severe disability or death. Safety does not only concern the RT technician, but any individual in the vicinity of the test. If an NDE contractor is being employed, their safety program and procedures should be carefully reviewed.

ULTRASONIC TESTING

Ultrasonic testing (UT) uses high frequency sound waves to detect surface and sub-surface flaws. "Ultrasonic" means sound waves of a frequency higher than is detectable by the human ear. There are three principles used to detect flaws:

1. Reflection: Sound reflects differently from flaws, boundaries or interfaces.

2. Time: Sound travels at different velocities through different materials and through defects.

3. Attenuation: Sound is absorbed and scattered differently by different materials.

In the pressure equipment industry, ultrasonics is primarily used to determine part thicknesses, with less than 1% error, and to detect internal flaws and crack sizes. This makes UT suitable for corrosion measurements and for corrosion surveys. Ultrasonic testing is useful during manufacture or shutdown, but can also be done on equipment that is in service. It is useful on components that are cast, forged, rolled or welded. Lined pressure vessels can also be tested.

Typical discontinuities that can be detected by ultrasonics are:

- Laminations
- Voids
- Cracks
- Inclusions
- Bursts

- Flakes
- Lack of Bonding
- Lack of Fusion
- Seams

- Forging Laps
- Rolling Laps
- Incomplete Penetration
- Corrosion

Ultrasonic examination of welds in piping is carried out in accordance with the requirements of Section V, Article 5, of the ASME Code.

Ultrasonic Procedure

Figure 24 shows a typical ultrasonic test arrangement.

High frequency sound waves (ranging up to 50 MHz) are generated by a transducer, which is moved over the tested surface. It is usually separated from the surface by a thin film of fluid. The transducer is connected to a diagnostic machine, which indicates the received signal on a graph. The transducer may act as the transmitter and the receiver, in which case the principle used is reflection. The sound waves penetrate the material and reflect back to the transducer from any defect surface or from the back surface of the material. The intensity of the reflection and the time to return are indicated on the screen. A high intensity indicates a defect and also gives an indication of the depth of the defect.

Alternatively, the transducer may act as the transmitter only, with a separate receiver located on the far side of the material. This method uses attenuation. The sound waves pass through the material and the amount of sound received by the receiver indicates the presence, or not, of defects. A reduction in received sound waves indicates a defect.

Figure 24	Schematic of Ultrasonic Inspection

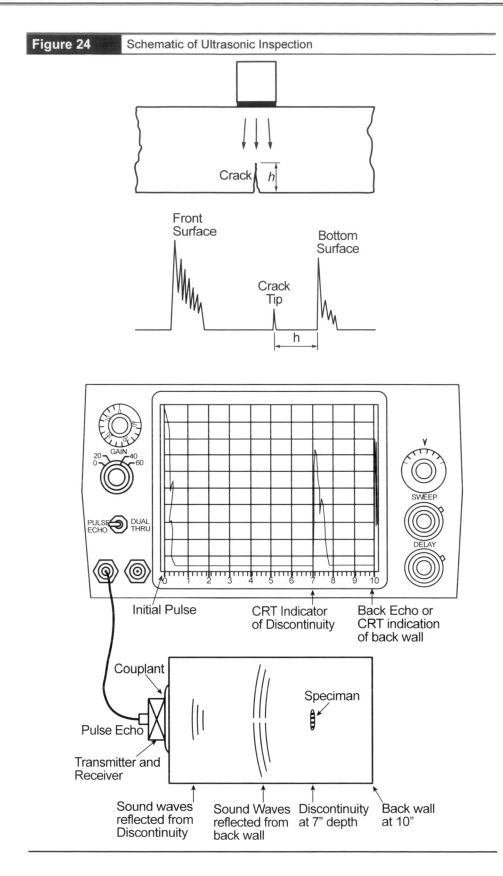

Figure 25 is another illustration (similar to those in Objective 2) of typical weld defects that are detectable by nondestructive inspection methods.

Figure 25	Weld Defects

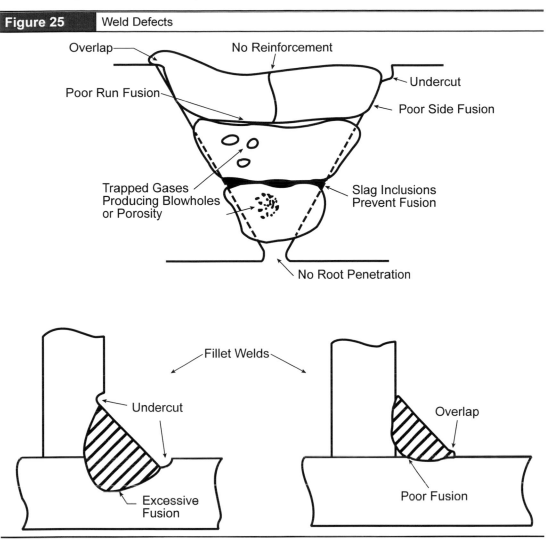

OBJECTIVE 8

Explain the requirements and process for Weld Procedure and Welder Performance qualification, per the ASME Code, Section IX.

INTRODUCTION

One example of jurisdictional authority over welding in Canada is the Province of Alberta "Safety Codes Act". Part of this Act is the "Pressure Equipment Safety Regulation AR49/2006, which contains the following excerpt from Section 27(1):

- A person who uses welding or brazing to construct or manufacture any pressure equipment: (a) must comply with the requirements of the ASME Boiler and Pressure Vessel Code, Section IX, Welding and Brazing Qualifications, and ..."

ASME Section IX is divided into two parts:

1. QW – Requirements for Welding

2. QB – Requirements for Brazing

This chapter introduces the student to ASME Section IX Part QW, Requirements for Welding. It is recommended that the student have available ASME Section IX, for reference.

There are two reasons for establishing Section IX:

- Procedure qualification
- Performance qualification

PROCEDURE QUALIFICATION

Procedure qualification determines if the material to be welded has the required properties for the intended application. Tests evaluate the metallurgical and mechanical properties of the material, but not the skill of the individual performing the weld.

Before a manufacturer can build ASME Code boilers and other pressure vessels, he must show that this method of welding or procedure complies with the Code. In other words, the welding procedure must be qualified under Code provisions.

To qualify a welding procedure, the manufacturer must supply a detailed written description of the procedure, listing such information as:

- Type of welding process
- Type and thickness of material to be welded
- Welding electrode specifications
- Method of material preparation
- Type of heat treatment to be used

In addition, the manufacturer must supply test plates that have been welded according to this procedure. These test plates are then subjected to tension and bend tests, in order to prove their soundness.

Figure 26 shows a welded test plate, with sections or coupons marked, according to the type of test to be used. The shaded area is the actual weld. The test piece is divided into eight sections and the description of what each section will be used for is indicated.

Figure 26	Welded Test Plate

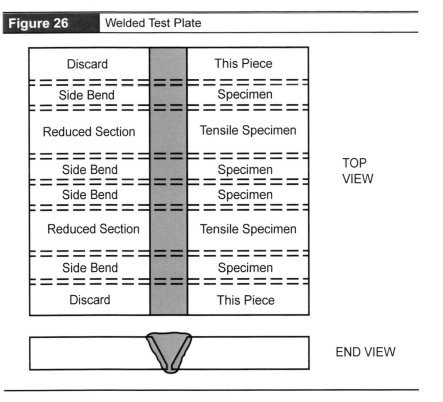

PERFORMANCE QUALIFICATION

A pressure welder must hold a Pressure Welder's Certificate of Competency. Qualifying for a Pressure Welder's Certificate of Competency requires a welder to hold a First Class Certificate of Proficiency or a journeyman welder's red seal certificate of competency from a jurisdiction, outside Alberta.

To receive the Grade B Pressure Welder's Certificate of Competency, a welder must first pass a performance qualification test conducted by an ABSA Inspector. A welder failing to pass this performance qualification test cannot be retested for a period of one month, unless permitted to do so by an inspector. The certificate expires two years after the testing date. A welder must apply to an accredited organization for retesting, before the expiry of the card.

In addition to the two-year rule of expiration, the welder's performance qualification can expire for the following reasons:

- The welder has not welded with the process for six months, or more
- When specific reasons exist to question the welders' ability

Each corporation, engaged in pressure welding, is responsible for the welding done by its personnel. Welders are not permitted to perform any welding process on a boiler, pressure vessel, pressure piping system, or pressure fitting unless they have proven qualifications to properly perform that specific welding process.

Performance qualification testing of welders must be in accordance with:

- Safety Codes Act "Pressure Welders Regulations"
- ASME Section IX–"Welding and Brazing Qualifications"

The following components must be completed, when conducting performance qualifications:

1. Testing
2. Documentation

Testing

The welder must present a Pressure Welder's Certificate of Competency, as proof of eligibility to take the performance qualification test. Welding on any boiler and pressure vessel equipment in the province of Alberta requires writing and qualifying the Welding Procedure Specifications (WPS). ASME Section IX, Article III, Welding Performance Qualification, sets the standards for the performance qualification of the welder and welding operator.

The welder completes this test in accordance with a welding procedure specification, which is registered to the accredited organization, by ABSA. Successful completion of the test verifies to the manufacturer, contractor, or owner of the pressure equipment that the welder has the ability to produce sound welds.

Documentation

An Inspector administers the performance qualification test. Upon successful completion of a test, the candidate is issued a performance qualification card by the presiding examiner.

CHAPTER 14 - QUESTIONS

1. Define the following:
   a) Porosity
   b) Post heating
   c) Pre-heating
   d) Procedure qualification
   e) Slag inclusion
   f) Under cut
   g) Backing ring
   h) Base metal

2. Explain the following welding processes
   a) Gas Metal Arc Welding
   b) Gas Tungsten Arc Welding
   c) Shielded Metal Arc Welding
   d) Submerged Arc Welding

3. Explain the procedure to prepare the ends of pipe for butt-welding.

4. Explain the advantages and disadvantages of Gas Tungsten Arc Welding.

5. a) Explain the purpose of weld heat treatment.
   b) Describe a method of heat-treating a pipe joint weld.

6. Briefly describe three different methods for testing the quality of a weld.

7. Define the following terms:
   a) Welding Procedure Qualification
   b) Welding Performance Clarification

ANSWERS: All answers are found within the content of the chapter.

Pressure Vessels

LEARNING OUTCOME

When you complete this chapter you should be able to:

Explain pressure vessel design, stresses, and operating considerations.

LEARNING OBJECTIVES

Here is what you should be able to do when you complete each objective:

1. Define "pressure vessel" and explain, in general terms, how pressure vessels are regulated in design, construction and repair (including purpose of Section VIII, ASME).

2. Explain the stamping/nameplate requirements for pressure vessels and identify terms and specifications on a typical nameplate.

3. Describe the weld locations on a typical pressure vessel and identify head designs, including ellipsoidal, torispherical, hemispherical, conical, and toriconical.

4. Describe acceptable nozzle attachment methods, including reinforcements; describe inspection openings.

5. Explain the loads that contribute to stresses in pressure vessels, including pressure, thermal, attachments, static, wind, seismic, and cyclic loads.

6. Explain the components and fittings of a typical pressure vessel.

7. Explain operating and maintenance considerations for the safe operation of pressure vessels, including the appropriate use of hydrostatic and pneumatic testing.

OBJECTIVE 1

Define "pressure vessel" and explain, in general terms, how pressure vessels are regulated in design, construction and repair (including purpose of Section VIII, ASME).

PRESSURE VESSELS - DEFINED

The definition of a pressure vessel is derived from the ASME Code Section VIII, Division 1.

Pressure vessels are leak proof containers that have an internal or external operating pressure. An unfired pressure vessel is a container having a design pressure between 103 kPa and 20 685 kPa and does not contain an integral source of heat, for example, a burner. Pressure vessels are usually spherical or cylindrical in shape and may be oriented vertically or horizontally.

Vessels of the vertical design are fractionating towers, treating towers and vertical separators. Horizontal vessels may be separators, accumulators or pressure vessels generating steam.

APPLICABLE CODES & STANDARDS

The jurisdiction mandates by law the codes and standards that must be complied with during the construction of the equipment. In Canada, most of the United States and some other countries, the ASME Boiler and Pressure Vessel Code is the required construction standard.

In Canada, compliance with the CSA B-51 Boiler, Pressure Vessel, and Pressure Piping Code is also required. This code addresses requirements that are unique to Canada, such as the design registration system, and imposes more stringent requirements in a few specific cases. The CSA B-51 standard takes precedence over the ASME Code, if a conflict exists.

A pressure vessel manufacturer may have a quality control program audited and approved by ASME. The manufacturer is then permitted to apply the ASME Code symbol stamp to the vessel nameplate, signifying that the vessel has been designed and constructed, according to the ASME Codes.

Some Canadian jurisdictions permit manufacturers to construct pressure vessels without applying the ASME Code symbol stamp. In these cases, the manufacturer must have quality control program audited and approved by the jurisdiction. The code of the jurisdiction is still required. Many manufacturers start out in business being approved by the jurisdiction only. If they wish to serve only a local market, they may remain under this system. However, since most businesses grow, ASME certification may become necessary to expand and compete in the national and international market.'

ASME Code Section VIII Division 1

ASME Section VIII, Division 1 sets forth minimum requirements for ensuring safe design and construction. It does not focus on system functions, degrading conditions or perceived integrity of a pressure vessel.

It applies to a broad spectrum of industries and provides uniform rules developed through consensus. It typically covers requirements for general application and design for structural integrity. This approach has reduced industrial accidents related to overpressure, faulty design, and construction.

DESIGN RESPONSIBILITIES

The manufacturer is responsible for performing the design calculations and making them available to the inspectors for the jurisdiction and owner.

In Canada, CSA B51 mandates design review by the jurisdiction prior to the start of construction. This review is usually carried out by a design group, rather than by the jurisdiction inspector who visits the manufacturing facility. However, to meet ASME Code requirements, the jurisdiction inspector who does the inspection must review the design calculations. Due to the competence of the design group, this review usually takes more of an audit role in Canada.

In accordance with provincial regulations, the owner is generally responsible for ensuring that equipment has been inspected by a jurisdiction inspector before it is placed into service, and regularly inspected thereafter by the jurisdiction or the owner/user inspector. Although there is no specific requirement for the owner to perform design calculations for pressure vessels, ASME Section VIII, Division 1, Paragraph U-2 states that "the user or his designated agent shall establish the design requirements for pressure vessels, taking into consideration such factors associated with normal operation and other such conditions as startup and shutdown."

CONSTRUCTION RESPONSIBILITIES

The construction of pressure equipment is inspected or monitored by at least two parties with different interests and responsibilities.

The representative of the jurisdiction inspects the pressure vessel to ensure that code requirements are met. The client may have an inspector present to ensure that the requirements of the contract are fulfilled. The manufacturer's quality control group has specific responsibilities to ensure that the equipment meets the requirements of the applicable code or standard as well as the customer's specifications.

The duties of the jurisdiction and the manufacturer are mandated by code. The role of the owner's inspector is to represent the interests of the end user of the equipment. Reputable manufacturing facilities do not deliberately intend to ignore customer's specifications, however, mistakes can occur. While these may not be code violations, they can cost the client time and money while the problem is resolved. For this reason, some clients are prepared to invest in the services of an independent inspector to avoid costly delays.

At various stages during construction, the inspectors check fit up; weld sizes, shell out-of-roundness, nozzle sizes, and fitting ratings. The QC (Quality Control) inspector is responsible for verifying all details of construction.

The jurisdiction inspector verifies code compliance. In the case of nozzles, the size and rating are important. Location is only critical if the nozzles are placed close together and ligament efficiency is a factor. Jurisdiction inspectors generally do not concern themselves with the precise location of the nozzle on the vessel and the orientation of the flanges. These items are important to the owner, especially if the vessel is to be installed in an existing location. Therefore, it is important for the owner's inspector to verify these items.

Generally, a hold point is placed for internal inspection. This means that the final head on the vessel cannot be installed until all inspectors have completed a visual inspection of the interior of the vessel. This inspection will include a check for fit up, out-of-roundness, weld sizes, physical damage, and installation of internal non-pressure parts. If the vessel has a manway, the internal inspection may be done after all the welding is complete.

REPAIR RESPONSIBILITIES

An external inspection may be done as the construction progresses. However, a final inspection must be completed. If the inspection locates an incomplete weld or external undercut, repairs can easily be made before the hydrostatic test or heat treatment. Repairs afterward, may require repeating the hydrostatic test or heat treatment, thereby, increasing the manufacturing cost and delaying delivery of the equipment.

OBJECTIVE 2

Explain the stamping/nameplate requirements for pressure vessels and identify terms and specifications on a typical nameplate.

STAMPING OF VESSEL

Once the construction of the pressure vessel has been completed, the manufacturer attaches a nameplate to the vessel and completes and certifies the vessel data report. The jurisdiction inspector then signs the report. There is no provision for the owner's inspector to sign the data report. In some Canadian provinces, the jurisdiction inspector will also stamp the vessel or vessel nameplate with a number, which serves as the provincial identification number.

The manufacturer who fabricates the vessel may only use the ASME Code symbol if:

- A valid Certificate of Authorization has been issued by ASME
- The inspector has accepted the vessel

The official ASME Code "U" symbol, as shown in Figure 1, must be applied to pressure vessels that have been inspected "in accordance with the requirements in UG-90 through UG-97" (from ASME Section VIII, Division 1). This stamp verifies that a pressure vessel has been inspected and tested according to the requirements of Section VIII.

Figure 1	ASME Code 'U' Symbol

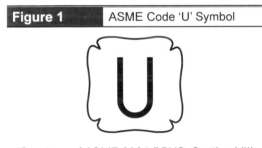

(Courtesy of ASME 2001 BPVC, Section VIII. Div. 1 by permission of The American Society of Mechanical Engineers. All rights reserved.)

The "UM" symbol, as shown in Figure 2, is applied to pressure vessels constructed "in accordance with the provisions in U-1(j) (from ASME Section VIII, Division 1). In effect, this stamp indicates a pressure vessel that is exempt from inspection by Inspectors for the reasons and conditions mentioned in U-1(j). For example, these are very small pressure vessels that are exempt from full radiographic inspection. The term "miniature" pressure vessels is sometimes used.

Figure 2	ASME Code 'UM' Symbol

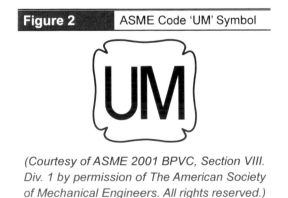

(Courtesy of ASME 2001 BPVC, Section VIII. Div. 1 by permission of The American Society of Mechanical Engineers. All rights reserved.)

NAMEPLATE

ASME Code Section VIII, Division 1, UG-116 states the following information shall be marked on the nameplate.

1. The official Code symbol, as shown in Figure UG-116 (a, b).

2. The name of the Manufacturer of the pressure vessel, preceded by the words "certified by".

3. The maximum allowable working pressure (MAWP) or Design Pressure, _____ psi, at _____ °F.

4. The maximum allowable external working pressure _____ at design temperature _____.

5. The minimum design metal temperature _____ at maximum allowable working pressure _____.

6. Manufacturer's serial number.

7. year built

The Code symbol, and the manufacturer's serial number, shall be stamped on the nameplate, but the other required data may be stamped, etched, cast, or impressed.

The nameplate must be permanently applied to the vessel. It is usually attached by either welding, brazing, soldering, or by mechanical fasteners of suitable metal construction. As stated in ASME Code Section VIII, Division 1, UG-119, the nameplate should be located on the vessels in a conspicuous place, preferably near a manhole or handhole opening.

A typical nameplate is illustrated in Figure 3.

Figure 3	ASME Code Section VIII, Division 1 Nameplate

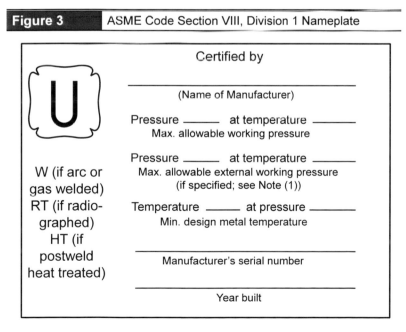

(Courtesy of ASME 2007, Section VIII. Div. 1 by permission of The American Society of Mechanical Engineers. All rights reserved.)

OBJECTIVE 3

Describe the weld locations on a typical pressure vessel and identify head designs, including ellipsoidal, torispherical, hemispherical, conical, and toriconical.

WELD LOCATIONS

The design, fabrication and assembly of all pressure vessels follow procedures identified in ASME Code Section VIII, Division 1 and ASME Code Section IX. Pressure welders, following a qualified welding procedure that has been accepted by the jurisdiction, must do the welding.

ASME Code Section VIII, Division 1 describe the type of welded joints involved in pressure vessel construction. These joints must meet the requirements of Code Part UW.

Figure 4 defines the locations of welded joints, using the following A, B, C, D descriptions.

A. Longitudinal joints within the main shell, nozzles, flat head.

   Circumferential joints connecting hemispherical heads to the main shell.

   Any welded joint in a sphere.

B. Circumferential welded joints within the main shell, nozzles, torispherical, ellipsoidal heads and angle joints not greater than 30°.

C. Welded flanged joints; Van Stone laps, tube sheets, flat heads to main shell.

D. Welded nozzle joints to main shell; spheres, flat-sided vessels.

Figure 4	Pressure Vessel Guide to Welded Joints

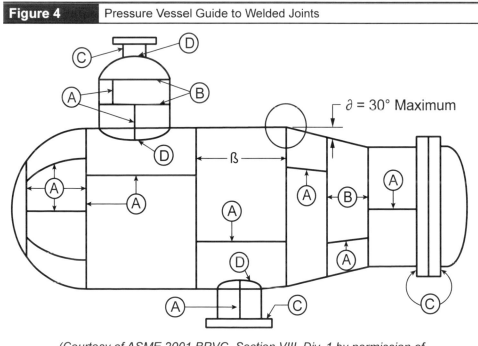

(Courtesy of ASME 2001 BPVC, Section VIII. Div. 1 by permission of The American Society of Mechanical Engineers. All rights reserved.)

HEAD DESIGNS

Figure 5 shows the five types of formed heads. The designs are briefly described as follows.

(a) Ellipsoidal   The long axis (D) is twice the length of the minor axis (2h).

(b) Torispherical   Often referred to as flanged or dished heads. The most common and commercially available design has the minimum knuckle radius (r) equal to 6% of the inside crown radius (L).

(c) Hemispherical   Are half of a perfect sphere (D = 2 x L) and calculated with the same equation used for spherical pressure vessels.

(d) Conical   Are used when the apex angle (2 x alpha) does not exceed 60°.

(e) Toriconical   Are conical heads with transition knuckles, radius "r", which are used when the apex angle (2 x alpha) exceeds 60°.

Figure 5	Principal Dimensions of Typical Heads

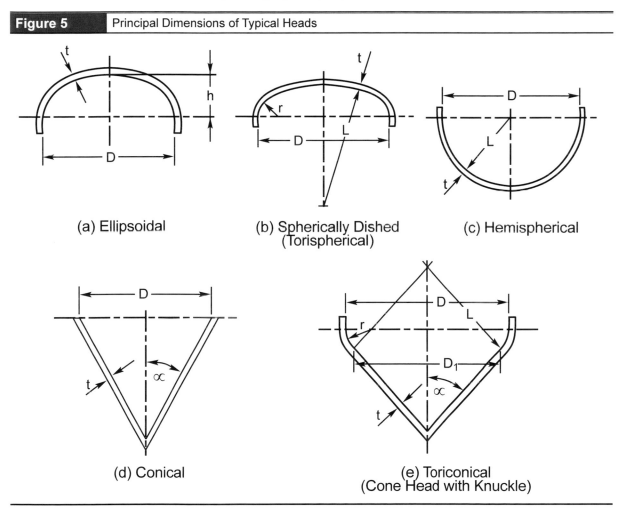

(a) Ellipsoidal   (b) Spherically Dished (Torispherical)   (c) Hemispherical

(d) Conical   (e) Toriconical (Cone Head with Knuckle)

OBJECTIVE 4

Describe acceptable nozzle attachment methods, including reinforcements; describe inspection openings.

NOZZLE ATTACHMENT METHODS

ASME Section VIII, Division 1, UW-15 "Welded Connections" and UW-16 "Minimum Requirements for Attachment Welds at Opening", provide rules for the fabrication of reinforced openings by welding.

Figure 6 shows details of some acceptable methods of welding nozzles to shells, drums and headers.

Figure 6	Types of Welded Nozzles

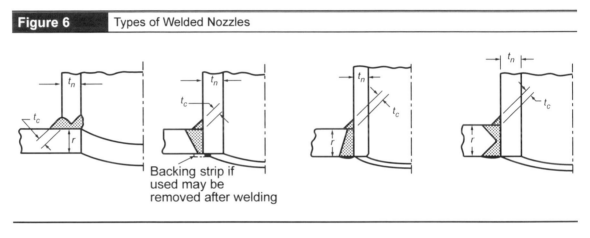

Backing strip if used may be removed after welding

NOZZLE REINFORCEMENT

Stress loads, caused by the piping and equipment attached to the pressure vessel, are transferred to the vessel by the nozzles. These loadings are in addition to the stresses caused by the internal operating pressure of the vessel. As a result, the combined loads may cause a failure at the nozzle if not accounted for in the design.

To allow the nozzle to support the applied loads, reinforcement may be required. This reinforcement can be provided by:

- Reinforcing pads on the shell
- Extra material thickness in the shell or nozzle
- An increase in weld metal
- Heavier shell plate in the section around the opening

Reinforcing is in addition to the shell thickness required for pressure, wind, earthquake or weight loads. The reinforcement material must have an allowable stress value that is equal to or greater than that of the vessel material. Lower strength material may only be used if the area of reinforcement is increased proportionately. If reinforcement material has a higher allowable stress value than the vessel material, the reinforcement will be considered to have equal strength as vessel material.

The ASME Code uses area replacement as the basis for reinforcement calculations. In any plane normal to the surface of the pressure vessel, an opening in the vessel surface will remove an area of material, as shown in Figure 7. Area replacement means that adequate reinforcement of the vessel requires an equal amount of excess material to be attached near the opening as was removed to create the opening.

For circular openings in cylindrical shells, the greatest loading occurs in a plane containing the axis of the shell. Therefore, this plane is generally used for calculation purposes.

Figure 7	Area of Opening

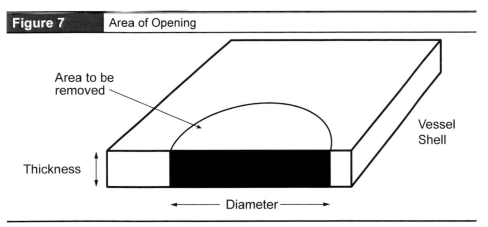

It is standard practice to reinforce an opening with the same cross-sectional area that was removed.

Figure 8 shows typical areas of material that can be considered as reinforcement. It is a simplified sketch, based on ASME, Section VIII, Fig. UG-37.1. Refer to UG-37.1 for more detailed descriptions of the various areas mentioned below.

Figure 8	Cross-Sectional Areas used to Calculate Shell Reinforcement

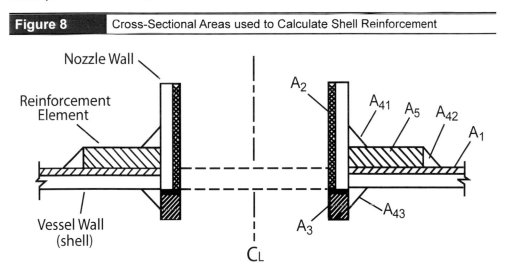

A = Total required cross-sectional area of reinforcement.

A_1 = Area in the excess thickness of the vessel wall that is available for reinforcement.

A_2 = Area in the excess thickness of the nozzle wall that is available for reinforcement.

A_3 = Area available for reinforcement when the nozzle projects inside the vessel wall.

A_{41} / A_{42} / A_{43} = Cross-sectional area of various welds available for reinforcement.

A_5 = Cross-sectional area of material added as reinforcement (reinforcement element)

$$A \leq A_1 + A_2 + A_3 + A_{41} + A_{42} + A_{43} + A_5$$

The area requirement, for reinforcement, must be satisfied for all planes through the center of the opening and normal to the vessel surface. The circumferential stress in a cylinder is twice the longitudinal stress. At the nozzle opening, the plane containing the axis of the shell is the plane of the greatest loading due to pressure.

When considering the need for reinforcement, more is not always better. Adding more material than required creates a hard spot on the vessel. This can result in large local stresses due to shell restraint. Reinforcing material should be located immediately adjacent to the opening. Care must be taken to minimize stress concentrations at the nozzle/shell/reinforcement joints. Thus, all connections between nozzle, reinforcement and the shell should be rounded to prevent high local stresses. Nozzles will be a significant factor in establishing the fatigue life of a vessel under cyclic loading conditions.

At a circular opening in a vessel, local stresses are highest at the edge of the circular hole and decrease rapidly with distance from the edge of the hole. For greatest reinforcing effect, it is recommended that 66% of the reinforcing material be located surrounding the opening, within a distance of half the radius of the hole.

ACCESS & INSPECTION OPENINGS

ASME Section VIII, Division 1 discusses the general requirements for openings and reinforcements. Access must be provided to all parts of a pressure vessel in order to carry out inspection, cleaning and repair operation. Manholes are provided to allow entry into vessels, and access to smaller parts such as headers, is gained by the use of handholes.

According to UG-46(g), manholes can either be elliptical, obround, or circular, in shape. The ASME Code specifies that the size of an elliptical obround manhole must not be less than 300 mm x 400 mm. Circular manholes must not be less than 400 mm, inside diameter. When a manhole opening is made in a vessel or shell; the shell becomes weaker due to the amount of metal removed. Therefore; reinforcement is provided either by forming a flange around the opening or by welding a frame to the shell around the opening.

Handholes must not be less than 50 mm x 75 mm and the Code recommends using larger sizes of handholes, wherever possible.

Manhole and handhole cover plates are usually made of steel. The parts of the manhole and handhole covers, which come in contact with the opening flange or frame, are machined to provide a smooth surface. A suitable gasket can be used between the cover and the flange or frame. The covers, which fit on the inside of the vessel, are held in place by means of bolts and yoke pieces.

Other vessel enclosures can employ blind flanges as closures. Due to the weight of the blind flange, a davit or hinge is used to hold up the flange, while the manway is open.

OBJECTIVE 5

Explain the loads that contribute to stresses in pressure vessels, including pressure, thermal, attachments, static, wind, seismic, and cyclic loads.

PRESSURE VESSEL DESIGN CRITERIA

Pressure vessels can be subjected to various loads as a result of their operating conditions and surroundings. These loads or forces are the causes of internal stresses to the material making up the pressure vessel. The principal types of loads are:

- Internal pressure
- Thermal
- Attached piping and/or equipment
- Static
- Wind
- Seismic
- Cyclic

Internal Pressure Loads

"Operating pressure" is the normal operating pressure required by the process for which the vessel is being designed. Pressure vessels are designed to withstand the most severe combination of pressures and temperatures, under normal operating conditions.

"**Design Pressure**" is a higher pressure than the operating pressure and is used to determine the minimum required thickness for the pressure vessel. "Design Thickness" is the minimum required thickness plus the corrosion allowance. "Normal Thickness" is the design thickness that is commercially available in the material chosen to build the vessel.

"**Maximum allowable working pressure**" (MAWP) is determined by the weakest element in the pressure vessel and its corresponding loading. To establish this maximum allowable working pressure,, the vessel is assumed to be:

- Corroded
- Under adverse temperature conditions
- In operating position
- Under wind loading (if applicable)
- Under normal operating conditions for determining static head

The term, maximum allowable working pressure, new and cold, may be used. "New" is when there is not any corrosion and "cold", means operating at room temperature. Therefore, corrosion and operating temperatures are not considered.

Thermal Loads

The design temperature for a vessel is the expected normal operating temperature, with some factor of safety included. Design temperatures apply to both a maximum and minimum expected temperature. ASME Section VIII, Division 1 UG-20 "Design Temperature" defines design temperature as not less than the mean metal temperature expected under normal operating conditions. This design temperature is calculated by standard heat transfer formulas or by actual temperature measurement of equipment in service, under equivalent operating conditions.

Thermal stresses are defined as stresses resulting from restraints that prevent the natural expansion or contraction of the pressure vessel with changes in temperature. Thermal stresses do not generally cause a failure by rupture in ductile metals upon the initial applications of the stress. Rather, thermal stresses cause fatigue failures by repetitive cycling.

Carbon steel decreases in strength with rising temperatures and become more brittle, at low temperatures. At elevated temperatures, carbon steel will deform without any increase in stress. This phenomenon is known as "creep". Carbon steel has a temperature range below which it becomes susceptible to brittle fracture with little absorption of energy. This very small, low temperature range is often referred to as transition temperature, referring to the abrupt transition from ductile to brittle behaviour.

Attachment Loads

Loads, caused by piping and equipment attached to the pressure vessel are transferred to the vessel, by nozzles. These loadings are in addition to the stresses caused by the internal operating pressure of the pressure vessel. As a result, such attachments, due to the combined loads, can cause a failure if not accounted for in the design process.

Static/Dead Loads

A pressure vessel may be subjected to three different states of dead load during its service life and all these conditions must be considered.

1. Erection dead load is the weight of the stripped vessel as hoisted, at the plant site. This may or may not include internals of the vessel.

2. Operating dead load is the weight of the vessel, in operation. This includes all structures, equipment and piping supported by the vessel, internals, external cladding (insulation, fire proofing, etc.) and all the process fluids.

3. Hydrostatic testing dead load is the weight of the vessel (may or may not include internals) and the hydrostatic test fluid's weight.

The dead load of a vessel results in compressive stress when the resultant force coincides with the axis of the vessel. Therefore, the above three conditions have the most effect on the design of tall towers.

Wind Loads

Pressure vessels located outdoors have additional stresses imposed by wind. ASME Section VIII, Division 1, UG-22 "Loadings" states wind loading must be considered when designing a pressure vessel that will be used outdoors. When designing for wind loads, the designer must consider the following:

- Geographical location
- Maximum regionally measured wind velocity
- Vessel shape factors
- Wind gust factors
- Height of the vessel and the possibility of varying wind velocities, at various heights
- Additional items attached to the vessel contributing to the total area the wind can act on, such as insulation, ladders, platforms, piping, lifting devices and other attached equipment

Vessels, with wind loading, can be treated as a cantilever beam to determine bending stresses. Vessels, that are tall and narrow, pose a special problem as these vessels can experience wind-induced vibrations, which result in severe oscillations and excessive deflections.

Seismic Loads

ASME Section VIII, Division 1, UG-22 "Loadings" states that where required, loads created as a result of seismic reactions, will be considered when designing a pressure vessel. Seismic loads are transient and, when they occur, can result in the production of vibratory forces. A designer will consider the following points, when designing a pressure vessel for seismic loading.

- The probability of an earthquake
- The earthquake acceleration. This is assuming the earthquake accelerates in the horizontal direction only and the forces are transmitted directly to the vessel.
- The intensity and duration of the seismic action
- The minimum horizontal shear force, applied to the base of the vessel
- The vessel will be rigid or flexible, in response to lateral loads
- The shape, size and height of the pressure vessel

Maps, with the given probability of an earthquake occurring, are researched. Vessels, located in seismic risk zones, will have to withstand a minimum horizontal shear force applied at the base of the vessel, in any direction. Tall vessels will be subjected to bending, as the loading condition is very similar to a cantilever beam when the loading is increased uniformly, to the free end. For shorter vessels, the main concern is base shear. Seismic forces act at the center of gravity of the pressure vessel structure.

The method used to support the pressure vessel is important in seismic design considerations. Vessels can be supported by legs (braced or unbraced), rings, lugs, skirts or saddles. Leg supports are not advised where high vibration, shock or cyclic conditions, are present. Vessels, supported by lugs and rings, are attached to super structures. The effects of seismic forces will be handled by these super structures. Skirts are the most frequently used method of support for vertical vessels and they must be anchored to withstand the overturning moment caused by seismic loading. Saddle supports are used for horizontal vessels.

Cyclic Loads

ASME Section VIII, Division 1 UG-22, states that cyclic loadings caused by thermal or pressure variations, mechanical loadings or equipment mounted to the vessel must be considered in the design of pressure vessels. A pressure vessel may be in a service such that the process results in cycles of temperature, pressure or both on a routine basis. Other situations may see mechanical vibrations transmitted to the vessels by attachments.

Fatigue is the tendency for a metal to break under conditions of repeated cycles of stress at values below the ultimate tensile strength. Cyclic loads can cause repetitive stressing and unloading or repetitive stress reversal, which can result in fatigue and subsequent failure of pressure vessel components. Fatigue of pressure vessel components is a common cause of failure. Fatigue failure is a function of:

1. The endurance limit or fatigue limit of the material. Below the fatigue limit, failure does not occur, irrespective of the number of cycles.

2. The environment or service the pressure vessel is in. Corrosion can establish sites for notches or reduce material thickness thus increasing the magnitude of the stress. Corrosion can assist in fatigue failures by promoting crack growth.

3. The total number of cycles combined with the level of stress, not time under load. In other words, fatigue damage can occur in a very short time or it may take years to accumulate enough loading cycles to fail the material, by fatigue.

4. Material surface conditions. Discontinuities, grooves or notches produce stress concentrations. These points of stress concentration act as sites for crack initiation. Fatigue cracks usually originate at some surface discontinuity.

5. Local stress concentrations, occurring in pressure vessels, make it difficult to design against fatigue. Stress concentrations can be the result of nozzle attachments, structural attachments, welds, and so on.

Cyclic loadings accumulate to result in fatigue failure. Each event occurs over a number of cycles, often with random, fluctuating loads that vary widely in amplitude. When a cyclic loading is damaging a pressure vessel, the pressure vessel material will experience a gradual deterioration until a complete failure occurs.

OBJECTIVE 6

Explain the components and fittings of a typical pressure vessel.

PRESSURE VESSEL FITTINGS

Pressure vessel components and fittings are illustrated on mechanical drawings, which are part of the process for construction of vessels established under ASME Code Section VIII, Division 1.

Figure 9 illustrates a horizontal separator with all its components and fittings.

This vessel operates at a high pressure and, in effect, consists of two vessels, the upper one being a cyclone separator and the bottom, an accumulator. The flow of gas, to the separator, is controlled though the use of an inlet flow control valve. Once the gas enters the vessel, internal baffle arrangements cause the gas to spin in a circular motion. This action causes the heavier entrained liquids, such as water, to be thrown to the outside and so be removed from the gas stream. The water then drains to the accumulator.

The level transmitter senses the water level, in the accumulator. This level indication is transmitted to the level controller, which operates the level control valve to drain the excess water to sewer. The vessel is also equipped with a level gauge glass, pressure gauge and temperature indicator.

To prevent the possibility of the vessel being over pressured, two pressure relief valves are installed, which are set to relieve to the high pressure (HP) flare.

Figure 9	Horizontal Separator

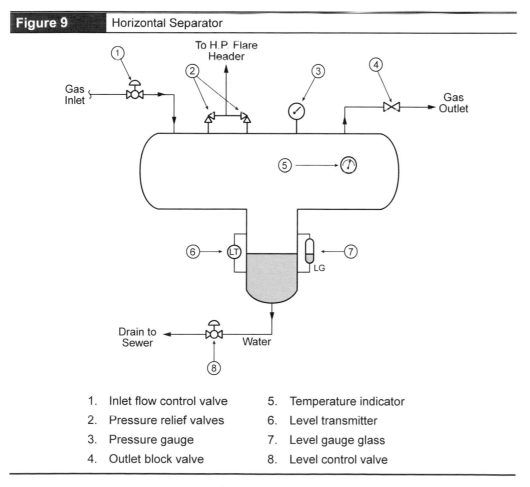

1.	Inlet flow control valve	5.	Temperature indicator
2.	Pressure relief valves	6.	Level transmitter
3.	Pressure gauge	7.	Level gauge glass
4.	Outlet block valve	8.	Level control valve

OBJECTIVE 7

Explain operating and maintenance considerations for the safe operation of pressure vessels, including the appropriate use of hydrostatic and pneumatic testing.

INTRODUCTION

Principal causes of incidents, relating to the operation of pressure vessels, are:

- Poor equipment and/or system design
- Poor maintenance of the equipment
- An unsafe system of work
- Operator error
- Poor training/supervision
- Poor installation
- Inadequate repairs or modifications

OPERATIONS CONSIDERATIONS

The efficient operation of pressure vessels is critical to maintaining system efficiency, reliability and availability. Every operator must be trained to understand and fulfill the responsibility for the successful performance of the equipment and for the safety of all personnel involved. To be prepared for all situations that may arise, an operator must have a complete knowledge of all components, their design, purpose, limitations and relationship to the other components.

The operating personnel should know the operating conditions:

- Know what liquid or gas is being contained in the pressure vessel.
- Know the process conditions, such as the pressure and temperatures.
- Know the safe operating limits of the pressure vessels and any equipment directly linked to, or affected, by them.
- Ensure there is a set of operating instructions for all the vessels and that these instructions contain what to do, in an emergency situation.

MAINTENANCE CONSIDERATIONS

Routine maintenance is the key to maximizing the production and life of pressure vessel(s). A comprehensive program should be in place to complete routine and shutdown maintenance. This program should take into account the system and equipment age, its uses and the environment.

A Quality Control (QC) program should also be in place to complete routine monitoring of the condition of the pressure vessels and their associated piping systems. This would include:

- Vessel and pipe metal thickness
- Signs of wear and corrosion
- Condition of insulation and protective covers, if installed
- Tell tale signs of system problems, for example, a passing safety valve. This could be a indication that either the system is over pressuring or the safety valve is not functioning properly.

Each pressure vessel will have been installed with suitable protective devices, which would cause a shutdown when the pressure, temperature or liquid level exceeds permissive limits. These protective devices must be removed and inspected, on an annual basis, to make sure that:

- They are in a good operating condition
- They will function, as designed, at the correct preset operating condition

When combined with ongoing unit operations and a program of inspection and upgrades, routine maintenance maximizes safety, reliability, availability, efficiency and environmental protection.

PRESSURE TESTING

Regulations require that pressure vessels, built to the American Society of Mechanical Engineers (ASME) Code, be pressure tested when they are completed. This test serves two purposes:

- It verifies that the vessel can withstand the pressure for which it was designed
- There are not any leaks present

Pressure testing is also used on vessels that have been in service, particularly when they could be subjected to corrosion, or cracking. The test verifies that:

- The vessel can still safely withstand the operating pressure with a proven margin of safety
- There are not any cracks which penetrate the vessel wall
- Holes have not developed

Pressure testing is especially useful if, due to the design of the equipment, the inspector does not have adequate access to conduct a visual inspection. Many jurisdiction inspectors, as well as owners, require the organization performing the pressure test to provide a written test procedures. Reviewing and approving these procedures, prior to the test, may avert any potential problems. The following methods are used to test the integrity of pressure vessels:

- Hydrostatic testing
- Pneumatic testing

1. Hydrostatic Testing

ASME, Section VIII, UG-99 gives the "Standard Hydrostatic Test" requirements for Section VIII pressure vessels. The standard hydrostatic test pressure is given as "1.3 times the maximum allowable working pressure".

In a new vessel, all connections such as flanges and couplings must be closed off with blind flanges and plugs. A drain valve should be located at the low point of the vessel to allow the water to be removed after the test. The filling connection must have an isolating valve, and a vent valve is required at the top to allow all air to be expelled.

For testing of in-service vessels, more preparation is required. If the fluid normally handled by the vessel is toxic or flammable, the vessel must be cleaned and purged. The vessel must then be isolated from the rest of the system. Existing valves may be used if they are in good condition; otherwise, piping connections at the vessel should be opened and blind flanges installed. Control line connections to the vessel should be removed and closed off. The procedures listed for the preparation of new vessels should also be performed.

If a vessel is filled with water during normal operation, the hydrostatic test should not pose a problem. However, large vessels that normally contain a gas may not be designed to hold water. In such cases, additional supports may be required for the vessel and the foundation should be inspected to ensure that it will be able to carry the additional weight.

Safety Concerns

Liquids are used for testing because they do not expand significantly when the pressure drops. The theory is that, should a failure occur, only a small harmless flow of water will be released. In practice, because all the air cannot be vented from vessels, some gases are trapped and compressed. Therefore, in the event of a failure, there is still danger to personnel in the vicinity. Blind flanges, whose bolts failed during a hydrostatic test, have been known to travel up to 20 metres, and plugs have left couplings with enough force to kill a person. For these reasons, all nonessential personnel should leave the area when pressure tests are being conducted.

Advantages

Pressure testing, especially using water, is relatively inexpensive and safe. It will identify leaks through cracks and pinholes in the pressure envelope. By demonstrating that the vessel is capable of withstanding 1.3 times the maximum allowable working pressure, a certain degree of confidence in the integrity of the vessel is assured.

2. Pneumatic Testing

Pneumatic testing involves the pressurization of a vessel with a compressible gas, such as air or nitrogen, to determine if any leaks are present. This type of testing is normally used if:

- The interior of the vessel could be damaged by water, as in the case of refractory linings or catalyst beds.
- The vessel design, and support system, does not allow for the additional weight, when it is completely filled with the test water.
- Testing of the vessel, when using water, in freezing temperatures.

Safety Concerns

The primary hazard in pneumatic testing is the amount of energy stored in the compressed fluid during the test. The results would be catastrophic, if a failure should occur. Pneumatic testing should be done with all non-essential personnel removed from the danger zone.

CHAPTER 15 - QUESTIONS

1. Define the term 'pressure vessel'.

2. Describe in your own words the purpose of the ASME Code Section VIII, Division 1.

3. Identify the information required on the nameplate of a pressure vessel constructed per Section VII.

4. What are the five common head designs used on a pressure vessel?

5. a) What is the minimum required dimension for elliptical and circular manholes?

   b) What is the minimum required dimension for a handhole?

6. Explain the following terms, which cause internal stresses and are considered in the design criteria of vessels.
   a) Thermal load
   b) Static load
   c) Seismic load
   d) Cyclic load

7. List the principal causes of incidents in the operation of pressure vessels.

8. Discuss the following methods used to test the integrity of pressure vessels.
   a) Hydrostatic testing
   b) Pneumatic testing
   c) Advantages of each test
   d) Safety concerns associated with each test

ANSWERS: All answers are found within the content of the chapter.